D1236616

Penthouse Uncensored

OTHER BOOKS IN THE SERIES

The Editors of *Penthouse* Magazine Present...

Penthouse Uncensored

WARNER BOOKS

A Time Warner Company

Warner Books, Inc.
1271 Avenue of the Americas
New York, NY 10020

 A Time Warner Company

Printed in the Unites States of America

ISBN: 0-7394-1436-4

CONTENTS

PART I

PART II

PART ONE

Letters to Penthouse III

Women With Women

Wifely Duty

My wife and I were expecting a visit from our good friend. We have had a decent sex life, but we have never experimented with anything at all kinky, and we've had no bisexual experiences.

Our friend arrived and we had much lost time to catch up on. For several days we showed her the sights and we totally let our hair down. One evening we let our hair down to unlimited bliss. My wife, Monica, our friend, Stacy, and I planned to hang around our apartment for a quiet evening of wine and videos. We ate dinner, drank some wine, and started to feel pretty good. The video we watched was an erotic film called *Body Double*. The movie had a lot of sensual dancing and some enticing masturbation scenes. We drank some more wine, and by now we were feeling no pain. The movie released desires within me which I could feel being generated by the girls also.

When the movie ended we could each sense each other's excitement. I was feeling pretty bold, so I put in one of our even more explicit adult tapes. Feeling the embarrassment of an imminent hard-on, I left the girls on the couch, turned off all the lights, and took a place on the floor.

After about thirty minutes of slamming and come shots came an extremely hot lesbian scene. At that time I felt Mother Nature calling and I got up to use the bathroom. Instead of breaking the moment by pausing the video, I thought I'd simply dash in and out of the bathroom in record time. After about five minutes I returned to the living room, but the sight in front of me froze me in my tracks. There, reclined on the couch, were Monica and Stacy locked in an extremely passionate embrace.

Trying not to be detected, I hid around the corner and watched the passion that was unfolding before my eyes. I couldn't believe it! Here were my straight wife and our friend innocently exploring areas which only a woman could know about. I was shocked, but I was also highly aroused.

Monica broke the kiss and moved her pouting mouth to Stacy's neck. She sucked and tongued her sensitive skin as Stacy threw her head back and let out a little gasp. Stacy's full breasts needed some attention, which my wife was willing to give. Monica unbuttoned Stacy's blouse to expose her erect nipples. She gently took a nipple into her mouth and nibbled on it. Judging by her reaction, Stacy obviously has sensitive breasts. She began to grind her pelvis into my wife's thigh, and they realized that they were at the point of no return. They tenderly undressed each other and returned to their private moments.

Stacy took the lead and laid her head on my wife's stomach, sucking and nibbling at her flesh. Stacy slowly descended her way down to my wife's love nest. My wife parted her knees to allow Stacy access to the slick folds and fragrant scent of her special place. My wife squirmed and raised her hips as Stacy's tongue darted in and out of the wet areas. After several minutes of this excitement my wife could no longer hold back. She grabbed Stacy's head and pulled it deeper into her dark caverns. Stacy zeroed in on her throbbing clit. She sucked it hard, which sent my wife into a seizure of orgasms which she had never before experienced.

My wife seemed to drift in and out of consciousness as her hips bucked in the air. Then, after what seemed like hours, my wife collapsed into a euphoric state.

While watching all of this erotic behavior, I noticed that I was unconsciously stroking my rock-hard erection through my pants. I needed some relief immediately, so I pulled my cock out. I was so aroused that within three or four strokes I lost my load on the wall!

As I was cleaning up my mess, Monica came around the corner and said that she and Stacy were going to bed. She also mentioned something about the couch giving Stacy a backache for the past few nights, and asked if I would mind if she slept in the king-size bed with us. Although nothing was mentioned about what had happened, I had no objection! Sensing my wife's shyness and anticipating more sexual activity ahead, I wanted to give them more time alone together, so I stated that I was not yet ready for bed and would stay up to watch some tube.

As the girls went through the charade of getting ready for bed, I inserted a movie in the VCR to indicate that they wouldn't be bothered for a few hours. The girls were in bed as I sat on the couch going through the motions of watching a comedy. I was very sexually excited about what had happened and was thinking about what was now happening.

I drank some more wine and sat with my heart pounding, not paying any attention to the movie. Excitement got the best of me, so I crept into the dark hallway toward the bedroom door, and ever so slowly opened it just a crack. Knowing that the bed was opposite the door, I could get a view without being noticed. The room was dark except for the streetlights peeking in through the venetian blinds. My eyes quickly adjusted and confirmed my suspicion as I stood in the hallway.

Stacy and Monica were fully nude, and were too engrossed in each other to notice my presence. Stacy lay on her back, arms about her shoulders and legs slightly parted. Monica was between Stacy's legs, sensuously kissing an erogenous area behind a gently bent knee. Slight moans could be heard from Stacy as Monica worked her mouth and tongue slowly up the silky flesh of Stacy's inner thighs. An eternity passed as Monica slowly sucked one thigh, then the other, methodically working her way toward her final destiny.

Stacy trembled slightly as my wife made her descent to the moist cleft of love. Monica slowly ran her tongue up one side of Stacy's private gates and down the other. Then Monica wrapped her arms around Stacy's thighs, holding herself in place as she lapped Stacy like a hungry puppy. Stacy's body was now shaking more and more intensely. She opened her legs wider for Monica's wet tongue. I didn't know how long I could stand watching or listening to the slurping sounds of Monica's hot tongue on Stacy's pussy.

Stacy halfheartedly pushed Monica away as if to actually be inviting her in. Her tongue was now deep within Stacy's cunt, and Monica sucked like a wild banshee. Sensing Stacy's mounting climax, Monica pulled her tongue out and sucked on Stacy's excited clitoris with passion. Stacy let out a stifled gasp, grabbed Monica's head and pulled it back into her special place. Stacy held Monica's head and wildly ground her hips against Monica's face as she went through what seemed like one incredible orgasm after another.

After the fervor died I snuck back into the living room for fear of ruining their private moment. I drank more wine, stroked myself off and fell asleep. Late the next morning I was awakened on the couch by two beautiful, smiling faces.

Monica and I have since discussed her bisexual encounter, and she insists that Stacy is not a lesbian. She simply stated that there was a spontaneous attraction felt between them, as well as a certain experimental curiosity that they had to fulfill. Curiosity or not, I'm secretly saving money and vacation time for a tour of Stacy's town!—*Name and address withheld*

FIVE IS MORE THAN ENOUGH

There was only one female bathroom in our barracks. The showers were in one room, with nothing separating them. I couldn't resist looking at the other women in the shower. The way they lathered their bodies, rubbing the soap over their well-muscled arms, legs and asses, never failed to turn me on. I could feel my clit swelling as I watched them. I always imagined what it would be like if we all made love in that steamy, pussy-filled room.

One night when I went in the shower, I noticed that five of the most gorgeous women in the unit were there. The first one, whom I'll call Marie, was tall with long, blond hair. She had the most beautiful hips imaginable. She lifted weights, and her slim, tanned, and toned figure made me instantly horny. Susan was also there. She was tall as well. Her blue eyes looked me up and down as I dropped my towel on the floor and entered the shower. Dawn had short brown hair and a beautiful smile. When I looked at her, her green eyes sparkled. The fourth woman was Pam. She was new in the unit. I couldn't help noticing her wonderful tits. They were large, smooth orbs of sexual splendor. Finally there was Tina, whom I didn't really know that well. She was shy and quiet, with warm brown eyes and a small, voluptuous body.

I turned on the faucet and felt the first hot splash on my size 38C breasts. As I held the soap in my hand and washed my throbbing clit, I noticed that Susan was washing Marie's back. It seemed more like foreplay than anything else. As I watched, I began to imagine it was me washing Marie's back.

As my pussy began to fill with love juice, I closed my eyes and began squeezing my tits. I was suddenly surprised to feel someone's lips on one of them. I opened my eyes to see Dawn sucking on my left nipple. She began rubbing my aching clit with a bar of soap. Then Pam came over to us and began rubbing her hard, soapy body up and down my back. There I was, moaning in sweet ecstasy, sandwiched between two beautiful, passionate women.

I reached down to feel the soft, slippery warmth of Dawn's cunt. It was so hot and juicy that my finger slid deep inside her with ease. She let out a soft, low moan and leaned up against me, arching her tits up into my face, rubbing her pussy against mine. I used my mouth to play with her nipples, sucking and teasing them with my tongue until they were hard.

Pam grabbed the soap from my hand and let it drop to the floor. As I continued to suck Dawn's soft, bronze breasts, Pam slipped her finger into my pussy. I let out a whimper of pleasure and began thrusting my hips back and forth while still sucking Dawn.

We heard Marie's moans of pleasure as Susan began to suck her clit. I began playing with my own clit, but someone grabbed my hand, pushed it away and started opening my pussy lips. I looked down and saw Tina kneeling before me, ready to plunge her long, hot, hard tongue into my muff. I screamed as her lips began playing with my clitoris. I couldn't control myself any longer. I began to feel faint from my own excitement. I sank down to my knees, removing my finger from Dawn's dripping cunt, and pushed Tina down to the floor. Dawn began kissing and licking Tina's face, neck, lips and breasts while I began stroking her stomach and thighs. I put my head between Tina's legs and began tenderly sucking her freely flowing love juice. As I slipped a finger inside her, I was electrified by the feeling of someone's tongue on my own clit. It was Marie, who had by then grown tired of playing only with Susan.

I looked behind me and saw Pam licking Marie's clit, and finger-fucking Pam. By this time Dawn was sitting on Tina's face, rocking her hips back and forth and squeezing her tits. I continued feasting on Tina's tasty hole.

Tina came with a cry, followed almost instantly by Dawn. They fell back, exhausted. I turned my attention to Marie. I grabbed the soap and began lathering her smooth, round tits and rock-hard abdomen. As I leaned over her body, she raised her head to grab my nipple with her lips. I pulled my breasts away and kissed her lips, nibbled her earlobe, then sucked her neck. I slid my tits over hers and began rhythmically moving my body up and down along her muscled torso and throbbing mound. I slid my tongue into her mouth and kissed her deeply. Her excitement from Pam's tongue licking her sopping-wet hole caused her to suck my tongue even harder. Then Pam turned around to face Susan, and the two of them began to caress, stroke and play with each other. Tina, who had by then been revived, was being finger-fucked doggie-style by Dawn.

I covered Marie's body with my own and continued to kiss her. I ran my hands gently up and down her body, circling her breasts and teasing her nipples to keep them erect. We moved our thighs and pussies together, feeling each other's wetness. I couldn't stand it anymore. I turned around and we positioned ourselves in a satisfying 69. I worked her clit with my tongue while I simultaneously inserted my finger between her swollen, red, luscious lips. Stroking them, sliding in and out, making her groan with each inward thrust followed with a sweet, hot flick of my tongue. We began thrusting against each other faster and faster, building up to a hot, sweet climax.

We lay spent on the floor of the shower. I couldn't believe I was surrounded by five beautiful women.

The water suddenly turned cold, rousing us from our sexual reverie. We collected our soap and towels, laughed and promised to get together again for more showers.—*L.D., Dallas, Texas*

SOME LIKE THEM SMALL

I recently returned to college after a five-year absence. I am a very attractive lesbian, and have won several beauty contests in my day. I am now twenty-seven and still very shapely, although I have a bit of a tummy that I'm constantly trying to tighten. My small breasts have remained as soft and firm as ever.

I dropped out of college—I was more interested in making women than good grades. I returned because I wanted a degree to enable me to find a better job.

When I got to my dorm I found I was to live with three other girls—Pam, Samantha and a sweet blonde named Tori. I fell in love with Tori right away. It wasn't just her body and looks—I loved her personality as well. Samantha and Pam were both good-looking too, but Tori was incredible. It only took a couple of days for the attraction between Tori and me to develop.

One day after classes, Tori and I were playing cards on her bed. She was wearing pink shorts and a halter top that did a good job of hiding her nice tits. I was wearing a pair of tight jeans and a thin singlet with no bra underneath. My tits dangled loosely under the flimsy garment. I always dressed that way in the hopes Tori would catch a glimpse of my tits.

As I dealt a hand, I asked her how she managed to keep her stomach so tight. "Lots of sit-ups," she said. She reached over and gently poked my flabbiness. "I'll bet that makes you even more lovable, doesn't it?" she asked, staring dreamily into my eyes. She let her finger slowly trail a path down my tummy.

I reached over and ran my fingers gently over the skimpy fabric covering her breasts. "I love your halter top," I whispered. She took my hand from her chest, kissed it softly, then set it on the bed. She reached behind her back, obviously undoing the top, and said, "If you're going to play with my tits, you might as well go all the way."

For a second I was confused. In a moment she had the top off and dropped it in her lap. Much to my surprise, Tori's breasts were extremely tiny. They looked like two flat cookies dangling off her chest. Her tiny pink nipples were puckered, and looked to be as hard as rocks. "Now you know why you never see me without a bra on," she said. She showed me the thick falsies in the cups of her top. She held each of her breasts and lovingly squeezed them.

"Okay, sweetie, your turn," she said softly.

"You don't know what a relief it is to see that you're tiny too," I said. I slipped my top off, exposing my little tits. "I thought you'd be disappointed when you saw how tiny mine are," I went on.

Her eyes glazed as she reached to touch my tits. "Oh, no, Kelly," she whispered. "I love them, and, oh, do I want to taste them." I leaned back on my elbows as Tori brought her lips to my tits.

Except for the sounds of our sucking, there was absolute silence in the room.

Then Tori rose from the bed and went over to the door to lock it. She looked so sexy as I watched her strut across the room. I loved the way her small tits flopped up and down as she walked.

She stood in front of me for a moment, smiling. She put her hands on my shoulders and eased my face forward into her tiny tits. I took one in my mouth, easily the entire tit, and sucked hard. "Oh, yes! Yes!" she moaned. "Suck them!"

I started to work my way down her tummy to her bushy blond pussy. I slipped my tongue as deep into her as I could. In a moment Tori shifted around so we could tongue each other. Believe me, it was wild!

Afterward we lay there, exhausted, and I looked at her. She was so perfect, with her long legs, her sexy feet, her red-painted toenails. The rest so slim and trim . . . I loved her for sure. As she lay back on her elbows, her tits had disappeared completely, but she was still one very sexy lady.

We have made love several times since that day, and although Pam and Samantha have never actually caught us together, they have a pretty good idea we're lovers.

My relationship with Tori gets better and better with each day, and I think we'll be together for a long time.—*K.B., New York, New York*

PIZZA ARRIVES, SHE DELIVERS

I am a thirty-three-year-old woman and have never married, but I have an active fantasy life that I occasionally get to live out.

Recently, I broke up with a lover and found myself hornier than hell. One evening, facing yet another round of masturbation, I knew I had to feel something human—and not just my dildo—inside my hungry pussy.

Then I remembered Gina, the pretty, young delivery girl from the pizza place down the block. She'd delivered several pizzas to my house and, unbeknownst to her, already played an active role in my fantasies. She was young, about nineteen, and quite attractive. But while I'd undressed her many times with my eyes, I'd never gotten up the courage to engage her in anything but conversation. She was always very friendly with me, but I never encouraged her attentions. This time, however, I was ready for anything, and picked up the phone.

In about twenty minutes there was a knock on the door. I had a plan. I took the phone off the hook and placed it on the table. When I answered the door I asked Gina to come inside. "I'm on the phone," I said, then picked the phone back up and had a few moments of fake conversation. All the while I kept a close watch on Gina. She didn't take her eyes off my body, a good sign. After I hung up, I apologized to Gina for the delay. She remained seated, which made me realize she already knew what I was up to.

"What is it you would like, Gina?"

She looked at me and, with a smile, said, "Well, you owe me eight dollars for this pizza."

"Would you like your tip first?" I teased.

"Sure," she answered, playing it cool.

"Do you have a boyfriend, Gina?" I asked. She said she did. I could see that she was actually a little shy, so I kept talking. "I don't have a boyfriend right now. Gets a bit lonely, you know?" Gina nodded as I took the pizza from her hands and put it on the coffee table. I could almost hear her heart beating. "What would you like as a tip?" I asked her.

"What did you have in mind?"

"I want you to decide," I said into her ear, licking it with the tip of my tongue. "Don't be shy."

"Would you go down on me?" she asked after a moment's consideration. I realized then that little Gina wasn't as shy as I thought.

"Has a woman ever done that to you before?" I asked.

"No," she said with a nervous laugh, "but I've always wanted to see what it's like."

"If you like it, would you eat my pussy?" I asked, straddling her lap slowly and letting my breasts rub against her face.

"I'd love to," she answered.

I was sitting on her lap now and could feel her squirming against my ass. I gave her a long, wet kiss on the lips, then went to work on her neck. She returned my kisses with a young girl's enthusiasm, stroking my body with her hands while grinding against me with her young cunt. I decided to give her a treat. While we kissed, I slipped my hand into my panties and fingered myself to orgasm. I could tell she was incredibly turned on as I brought myself off with a shudder and a sigh. Then I let her lick the cunt juice off my finger. As she practically deep-throated my hand, I realized that my long sex drought was about to end.

I led Gina to the bedroom and slowly undressed her. Then I handed her the phone. "Shouldn't you call your boss and tell him you're going to be late?"

"How late?" she asked.

"Well, you delivered in twenty minutes," I said. "But I'll need an hour."

While she told her boss she had to run an errand, I undressed her. It was fun to hear her voice crack as I ran my tongue up the inside of her thigh. I took the phone from her and laid her back on the bed. Her smooth, naked body was total perfection. I took off my own clothes and began kissing her, starting at her toes and slowly moving my way up to her lips. As our tongues wrestled I rubbed my pussy against hers, giving her little clit a workout unlike anything it had ever known.

Gina gasped as I slid my hand between us. Rolling my hips in a fucking motion, I put one finger in each of our pussies. We were both wet. Gina's nectar was especially hot, and her tongue was darting in and out of my mouth with such intensity. I knew she was in heaven.

"Do you want me to eat your pussy now?" I asked.

"Yes," she said. "I want your tongue in me."

Before eating her out, I rubbed Gina's body with warm baby oil. Her tits were small, but the nipples were swollen and full. I sucked one into my mouth, teasing it with my lips until it was hard. Gina willingly offered me her breasts, letting me suck the right one for a while, then putting the left one in my mouth. She rubbed her own pussy, a quick up-and-down motion that had her quivering. I wanted to make her come before she did it herself, and slid down the bed until my mouth was on her tender cunt lips.

I poked through the wisps of blond hair with my tongue. Her cunt was sweet and hot, and no sooner had I touched the inside of it than Gina came. Instinctively I pulled back, but she took my head firmly in her hands and urged me on. "Oh, suck me!" she cried. "That's it, suck it, suck it!"

I explored every bit of her tight pussy, licking the lips with long strokes and plunging deep inside her with countless thrusts of my tongue. Gina's legs were wrapped around me, her feet pressed tightly against my neck, coaxing me to nibble and suck her delightful cunt. I wiggled her clitoris with my tongue and was richly rewarded as a burst of her tangy cunt juice exploded into my mouth.

I was so deeply engrossed in feasting on the cunt of this lusty creature that I didn't realize we had changed positions until I felt her mouth on my own burning pussy. She nipped at my box, tentatively at first, even a bit awkwardly. "Slowly," I coached her. "Just let your tongue taste every part of my cunt. Feel the softness. Smell it." She was an excellent pupil, and soon she had me with my legs raised high in the air. As she rubbed my willing clit against her tongue, I came in a series of vigorous explosions.

We didn't say much afterward. I held Gina tightly in my arms and watched as she slipped into a nap. Remembering her work commitment, I phoned the pizza parlor and, pretending to be her mother, told them that Gina would be out sick for the rest of the evening. I wasn't even sure if she lived with her mother, but the masquerade must have worked because she didn't get in trouble. Gina and I have had many such rendezvous since. She continues to see her boyfriend, with my blessings. And as for me, well, I seem to be ordering quite a lot of pizza.—*J.K., Little Rock, Arkansas*

COED COMES CLEAN IN SHOWER

I'm a twenty-year-old brunette, five feet six and just over one hundred ten pounds in my birthday suit. I've been told by boyfriends that I have a great figure, especially my set of 40D jugs. However, it wasn't until Jennie, a fellow student at college, noticed my tits that I learned what it meant to feel really sexy.

Jennie and I weren't friends, but we both worked out at the college gym. One afternoon I noticed her intently watching me shower. At first I didn't let on that I saw her staring, but I was interested in what she was thinking. I stayed in the shower a long time, washing myself sensuously and really getting off knowing she was watching my every move.

Intrigued, I asked if she wanted to soap my back. "It's so hard to get some of those spots," I said. She agreed and began spreading the soap all over my back. She was a redhead, with the most magnificent tits I have ever seen. They were larger than mine, probably about a 42D. I'd never had any sexual feelings for women before, but suddenly I felt an overwhelming urge to fill my mouth with those incredible tits.

While Jennie lathered my lower back, I felt her hand go down to my cunt. It was a super feeling to have a woman's hand on my box, and I made no attempt to stop her. I felt as though I were about to lose my virginity all over again. And in a sense, that's exactly what happened. She started to lather up my front, spending a long time soaping the tender areas just beneath my breasts. "You have the prettiest boobs," she whispered in my ear, giving my nipple a playful little pinch.

I was getting hot and was about to get even hotter. Jennie soaped up her tits, then got down on her knees and lathered up my pussy with her big breasts. "Look, no hands!" she joked. I found myself squeezing my legs shut—not in protest, but to trap Jennie's tits near my pussy. After rubbing her nipples against my clitty for a couple of minutes, she stood up and began to finger me. She used one finger at first, then two, pumping them in and out of my soapy, wet cunt. It was better than fucking a big dick, and I twitched each time Jennie wiggled her fingers inside me.

Then Jennie dropped to her knees to suck me. It was an incredible sensation. I'd had plenty of men go down on me in the past, but to have someone so soft, so feminine, licking me to the point of orgasm brought me a release unlike any I'd ever felt. The orgasm Jennie gave me surged through my entire body, leaving me both weak in the knees and so energized I could have had sex for hours.

Suddenly we realized we had company. A few other women had been watching us go at it. I looked up in time to see two of them frigging their clits in response to our lovemaking. What followed was an all-out orgy, with tongues and tits and clits and cunts mixing and matching there on the shower floor. It was an experience none of us is likely to forget.—*Name and address withheld*

A WOMAN'S TOUCH

My very loving husband picks up your magazine every month. I'm hoping that if my husband reads this letter, it will ease my guilt.

My husband works the night shift, so we do all our shopping in the morning before he goes to work. One day while we were on our weekly grocery expedition, I ran into a girl, Louise, who was a friend of mine in college. I hadn't seen her for a few years, so we exchanged numbers and made plans to get together. I found out that she had just arrived in our city a few weeks before. I also found out that she worked a swing shift that ended just as my husband's was starting. It was perfect. I invited her over to the house and we renewed our old friendship.

Toward the end of the following month she invited me to a party she was having at her place. She said it was just going to be a small gathering of some friends and work associates.

It was fun. I met a lot of new people and drank a lot of wine. I hung around after the party broke up, helping to clean up. When that was done Louise and I took our wine into the bedroom to continue the party. She said she had some clothing she couldn't fit into anymore that might look nice on me. I was trying on a few things when suddenly she gave me a very sexy baby-doll outfit to model. I had to be nude if I wanted to see a really proper fit, so I removed my bra and panties and put it on. I didn't think anything was strange when she kept telling me how good it looked on me. But I did feel a little funny when she began to caress my back.

She came to me when I took down the top part of the outfit in order to get out of it. She took me in her arms and kissed me, explaining that for the last year she had been dreaming about having sex with another woman. I could feel the heat of her body through her clothing, and her hands stroking my lower back and hips. Her kiss was loving and tender.

I had never even thought of going to bed with a woman. Also, I was in love with my husband and I felt that my body was his. Nevertheless, I just couldn't push her away. She began to kiss and caress my breasts and push me back across the bed. It was like I was dreaming. I felt as though I was watching somebody else submit and feeling everything that was happening to them. She seemed to know just how to touch me. My body was on fire. I wasn't even aware that she had removed her clothing. Everyone knows that a woman's body is different from a man's. But I just can't believe that any woman can come close to imagining how good one feels pressed against them, unless they've had the experience.

I just lay there, letting her do as she pleased. I can still remember the feel of her breasts as they pressed against my inner legs, her fingertips slowly opening the lips of my vulva, and the shock of her lips and tongue touching my clitoris. I have received oral sex from men before, and I must admit that I have always found it enjoyable. But this was different.

Very quickly, with her fingers and tongue, my friend had me in such an aroused state I would have screamed if she'd stopped. When my orgasm did come, it was powerful. Wave after wave of wonderful release shook my body and mind totally out of any reality. When I did come back, my friend was caressing my lower stomach just above my pubic hair. She was kissing my face and telling me how much she enjoyed making me feel good. Then she whispered that I would have to get up and get dressed if I wanted to be home when my husband got there.

Then I just started to cry. I felt so guilty. I felt the guilt of letting somebody other than my husband be intimate with me. But most of all I felt guilty because I had enjoyed a woman's touch.

I hid what happened to me in the back of my mind. And I swore to myself to never tell my loving husband that I had left the house, let alone that I had cheated on him.

It was about a week before my girlfriend stopped at the house again. Over coffee we talked. She told me that on the night of the party she was very high, yet she couldn't get what had happened out of her mind. She remembered how I looked, what I felt like, and even my scent. She wanted me to let her make love to me again. I told her no. The first and only time was a mistake, and we were not going to do it again. That's when I found out how weak I really am. She kept talking to me, urging me to try it just once more. Finally I gave in.

It was different the second time. The end result was the same, but watching her hands touch me, watching her body press against mine, her lips cover my nipples and tease them hard, all of this seemed to make everything better. I was still an inactive partner, but this time, besides leaving my eyes open longer, I kissed her back. A few times I even let my hands stroke her back or sides. When it was over she lay next to me, touching me to prolong the feeling of my explosive orgasms, and we talked.

She told me she had met a guy she liked the night after the party and had spent three nights in bed with him. She explained that she really loved and got off on being with me. She had always thought that she was gay because she thought there was a chance that she could give up men altogether and be with women only. She thanked me for allowing her to see that she was truly bisexual. She hoped that I would stop thinking that being with her was cheating on my husband. In her way of thinking, I couldn't be cheating if I was letting her give me something that he couldn't— a woman's touch.

It was three nights later when she called and begged me to meet her at her apartment. I honestly thought about not going, but I wanted to find out what she wanted. When I arrived, she handed me a strong drink and stated that we were going to go to bed. She promised this was going to be the last time she would ask me. Before I could say anything, she explained that she wanted me to be active.

"I want you to feel my body, kiss and taste it. I am asking you to do this because I think it will help you and your husband. I find that when my boyfriend makes love to me, knowing how my nipple feels between his lips or how my pussy feels against his tongue, allows me to feel closer to him."

At times I've wondered how a man felt when he was licking my vulva, so what she said made sense. Besides, since I vowed to myself that this was to be the last time I would be with her in a sexual way, I decided I should relax and enjoy myself to the fullest.

In the bedroom we slowly undressed each other. As we lay on the bed holding each other and kissing, I was nervous. My mind kept telling me, "This is a woman." I became calm and relaxed when I started thinking of her as a person made of flesh and blood like any other person.

As our intimate embrace progressed I became totally involved in what I was doing and feeling. I learned how to feel completely comfortable with caressing her body. And when I sucked her nipples, her stomach, and finally worked my way down to her wet pussy, I was extremely hot and excited. Louise seemed to enjoy teaching me to be active. It excited her more.

I think every female should, at least once in her life, have a sexual experience with a close female friend. Maybe I shouldn't have vowed that I would never make love to Louise again.—*Name and address withheld*

Voyeurism

Seek, Watch, and Enjoy

My wife Tina and I have been married for twelve years. To keep our marriage intact, we work very hard to keep our sex life alive and active. Often, we try different fantasies to excite each other. Sometimes we plan "dates" together and sometimes we role-play our fantasies. Fate played a hand in one of our dates and really changed things for us.

Sometimes Tina catches a taxi and meets me after work at a club where we appear to have just met, having an instant attraction to each other that causes us to leave for a night of hot loving. It's a hot "one-night-stand" fantasy.

We've agreed that it's perfectly fine to flirt around a bit and dance with others because the little pangs of jealousy add to the experience. Because she is a knockout and can really dress to kill, Tina usually attracts any number of prospective suitors. It's fun watching her flirt and dance provocatively with other men, and then feel their jealousy when she leaves with me. For that matter, dancing with a few lovely ladies while I'm enjoying Tina's performance doesn't hurt either. Tina says she gets a kick out of watching me.

On this occasion we chose a club we've been to once or twice and agreed to arrive around nine, flirt with others for a couple of hours, meet and "fall in love" around eleven, and leave about twelve.

Plans don't always turn out as expected, though. An emergency came up at work that was going to delay me for an indeterminate amount of time. I tried to call Tina at home and apparently just missed her. I tried to rush through the problem and get out of work earlier, but one thing led to another, and it was now ten. Then I tried to call the club to have her paged a couple of times, but the line was busy. So, by the time I got to the club it was after eleven.

The place was pretty crowded, so I grabbed a seat at the bar and looked around for Tina. Pretty soon I spotted her on the dance floor with a guy who was in his mid-twenties and built pretty well. His hands were roaming all over her during a slow, sexy Lou Rawls song. He really seemed excited by her, and I doubt if he realized that she was easily five years older than him— like I said, Tina is a knockout! She was wearing a new outfit that I'd never seen before; a silk scarf accentuating her neck and a sexy white dress with a bare midriff showing off her flat, tanned tummy. It was cut to reveal much of her ample bosom and tantalizing, strong legs. White polka-dotted heels completed the outfit and really set off her gorgeous ass.

Tina seemed to be enjoying herself too, and looked as if she'd had more to drink than usual. I realized that she had recently lost ten pounds, was probably feeling sexier, and that alcohol would affect her more since she'd been dieting.

Her partner was grinding an obvious hard-on into her pelvis, and she was returning the pressure with undisguised pleasure. He kissed her lightly a couple of times, and I've never felt so jealous in my life. She didn't even see me, although several times they danced very close to where I was sitting.

After dancing awhile, they returned to a table where they were laughing and drinking. All the while, his hands were on her. Tina was pretty responsive too. I could see her hand tracing small circles on his thigh, and she had dropped a shoe to trace his ankle with her toe. I couldn't believe it. The more I watched them, the more excited I became.

Both of us have been *Forum* readers for about three years and are intrigued by the letters, but I never thought I'd be one of the guys who'd want to see his wife make it with another man. In fact, I'd always thought I'd want to break the guy's back if he was fooling around with Tina. Yet, here I was, watching them and getting more turned on than I had been in years. I was extremely aroused by the thought of Tina giving this guy the screw of his young life!

Without really thinking it possible, my mind played out various scenarios for getting them together. The guy certainly seemed interested enough, and Tina was acting much bolder than I'd ever seen her before. I'm fairly sure she has never been unfaithful to me, so this was going to be tricky. I thought about prearranging a meeting with her, joining them and inviting the guy back to our apartment for a nightcap to see where it would lead. But I was pretty sure that, bold or not, Tina couldn't relax enough for a threesome. I concluded that, for the first time at least, Tina would have to take this guy on her own.

With that, the guy got up and went to the men's room, so I took the opportunity to go to their table and ask Tina to dance. She was a little annoyed, feeling like I'd nearly stood her up, but I explained the emergency and how hard I'd tried to call her, and she accepted it. I asked if she'd been having a good time and I swear she actually blushed. I told her that I'd been watching her with her handsome partner for over a half an hour and, although she played it down, I could see she was very turned on.

She told me that she'd probably spent too much time with this guy because it seemed to be leading him on, but she liked him and didn't know how to break it off without hurting him. I remarked that she seemed pretty turned on, and she started to deny it, but realized that I knew better and watched me intently.

I reminded her of a time when, in one of our role fantasies, I had played the role of another man and she had been highly aroused—she said that she remembered it very well. I held her very close during our dance so no one else could hear and told her that if she wanted to take this man home it would be okay.

Tina immediately said that she couldn't. I told her that I could see how aroused this stranger had made her and confessed that it had me turned on too. She continued to protest, but I could feel an involuntary shiver in her, and I could see her nipples go taut against the fabric of her dress as she considered it. I could only imagine how wet she was becoming.

I knew she was getting serious when she asked where I would spend the night if she took him to our apartment. I reassured her, saying that I'd be fine and could probably grab a motel room or something. Really unsure now, Tina repeated that this was fun, but she didn't think that she could go through with it.

Her new friend was returning to their table, so I told her I'd stick around for another hour or so. I suggested that she get to know him a little better and dance some more. If she decided to take him home, she should remove her scarf. I'd take that as a signal to leave them alone. She would get him to drive her home, invite him in for a drink, and see what happened. If, after an hour, she still had the scarf on, I'd come to her table to be introduced as her husband, meeting her after a late appointment, and leave with her. Thus, she could break it off without hurting him. Tina was unsure but very excited as she returned to her new date's table.

I returned to the bar, where it hit me that this was our original fantasy, only with a new player. I watched them and danced with a couple of girls myself, but I was so focused on Tina and this stranger, that I was inattentive to the girls I was dancing with. Some faster numbers came up and Tina was dancing more and more provocatively, giving me a quick wink when our eyes met. Tina seemed to be getting extra turned on knowing that I was watching her. Her partner was so intent on watching her body sway that someone could have hit him with a chair and he wouldn't have known it.

When the hour was up, they were at their table and things seemed pretty intense, but the scarf was still in place, so I began to walk toward them. When I got close, Tina smiled with a far-away look and slipped the scarf from her lovely neck. As I passed her, I gave her a sly pat on the shoulder and was glad to be wearing a jacket to cover my bulging erection. In fact, I thought that people might be able to hear my heart as it pounded when I left the club.

I was left with the task of finding a place to spend the night, fantasizing about Tina and her new lover. I didn't even know his name. I started driving toward a motel near our home when it occurred to me that I could double my pleasure by staying quietly in our guest room and catching some of the action.

I parked a couple of blocks away from our apartment and slipped into our guest room to wait. After about an hour, I was beginning to think they might have gone to his place when I heard them enter our living room. After a long silence during which I presume they shared a long, wet kiss, I heard Tina say, "Would you like a drink, Dale?" She fixed the drinks while he put the stereo on low, and I could hear them laughing and talking between stretches of silence. A couple of times I thought I heard sucking noises. Then I heard some low moans from Tina that I *knew* were real. After a few more moments, I heard Tina making some soft protests, almost like she was trying to convince herself to back off. I could hear Dale talking in soft, reassuring tones, then it got quiet again. Later I heard Tina mumble something about the bedroom.

I was hoping for this, since the mirror in the guest room reflects the bedroom if the doors are left open. If I was careful I could watch the whole thing. I'd never been a Peeping Tom before. This was a night of new experiences. I nearly blew it, but stifled my gasp as they went into the bedroom. Dale, clad only in briefs, was carrying Tina, who was wearing a push-up bra and crotchless panties.

At this point, my jealous feelings were so strong that I wondered if I could bear to watch them and, at the same time, I couldn't take my eyes off them. They were locked in a passionate kiss and nearly fell on the bed. Tina let out what was almost a scream when Dale began to lick her pussy right through the crotchless panties. He sucked her for long minutes as she bucked, moaned, and tossed her head.

Soon she told him that she wanted to taste him too, so she pulled off his briefs and they got into a 69 position. His cock was shorter than mine, but thicker. Tina took him in right to the balls and sucked him for a long time until his body went stiff; I knew he had come. I never saw Tina swallow semen before and didn't really see it this time either, but she must have because she kept on sucking him until he was hard again.

He pushed his cock into her hot mouth until he announced that he couldn't stand it anymore and had to ram it into her wet, pulsing pussy. As he pulled out of her mouth Tina was writhing and saying, "Yes, I want you in me now!" She gasped as he entered her. She kept chanting, "Yes, yes" over and over as their passion mounted. And finally they both came so hard that Dale had to grab the headboard for balance.

After a few minutes of afterglow, I could hear Tina begin to cry softly, and I wondered if this guy had hurt her or if this had been a bad idea. Dale asked what was wrong. She said that he was going to think she was silly, but she had never been with another man in the twelve years that she'd been married and she felt guilty.

He said that he didn't think she was silly at all, that her husband was a lucky man, and he felt almost blessed that she had chosen to be with him tonight. He wiped her tears away with a soft kiss and very slowly began making love to her again. Tina forgot her tears and fears and began to respond with low moans, moving her body.

Their passion built slowly for a while, and soon Tina got on top of Dale and became really demanding. She guided his manhood into her and pumped like a wild woman. I could see tracks of wetness streaming down her thighs as she pumped him and made primal noises low in her throat. When they came, so did I—which was weird, because I hadn't even realized that I'd been masturbating as I watched them.

Dale had come inside her, and she was slick with it when she finally got off him. I remember hoping that she hadn't forgotten her birth control pills. Dale certainly got a better cleanup than I did, because Tina went to the bathroom and returned with a warm washcloth and towel. She washed and dried him tenderly, and they lay quietly holding each other, talking softly for a good half hour.

I must have fallen asleep then, because I woke up to hear Dale leaving and see the sun was coming up. To my surprise, Tina, wearing a soft peach kimono, came into the guest room and bent down to kiss me. I was too startled to move, but I sure kissed back.

She told me that when she started making love the second time she heard something in the guest room and realized that I was there. Instead of being embarrassed or angry at being spied on, she said it really turned her on that I was watching her fuck this man, and she really went wild. She said she wished she had been able to see my face as she washed Dale afterward.

She also said that she had feelings for him. It wasn't love, and she wouldn't let him threaten our relationship, but that she wanted to see him again, perhaps on a regular basis.

I said that it was okay with me and asked how she felt about threesomes. She didn't think she was ready for that, but would keep it in the back of her mind for a while. She said that I should consider developing a safe outside relationship to spice things up, and that she would help me by having more "dates" with me to see what might turn up.

A month or so later, we found a beautiful young girl for me, and about once a month we see our respective lovers. We also continue to role-play and date each other from time to time. I get to eat my cake and have it too. I don't miss the piece that

Dale eats (figuratively and literally). In fact, it has become part of the icing for the rest of the cake. If we desire new lovers after a while, we're open enough to find new ones. We're both happier than ever.—*G.L., Los Angeles, California*

STUDY BUDDIES

When I was a graduate student in college, I spent a lot of time on the fifth floor of the library. It was the top floor of the building, and hardly anybody studied there. I liked the quiet and the privacy.

One day I was deeply absorbed in my studies when a young man sat in the carrel in front of me. I wasn't really aware of his presence until I leaned down to get a pencil from my bookbag, which was on the floor. It was then I noticed a small hand-held mirror pointed directly at my crotch. I was wearing a miniskirt, so he must have gotten a pretty good view. I clamped my knees together and sat up straight in my chair. I was shocked and a little disgusted, but I was also a little intrigued, so I didn't say anything. He sensed that he'd been caught, and left almost immediately. At first I thought I would report him to university security, but as the days went by I began to feel less disgusted and more intrigued. The next week I went back to the fifth floor, half hoping that he would show up.

I hadn't seen his face, only a glimpse of his jeans and T-shirt when he rushed off. Still, I recognized him when he returned. He was sitting in exactly the same carrel and there was an air of expectancy about him. He had his face inside a book, but that was okay; I didn't really want to know what he looked like. I sat down and got busy with my schoolwork.

After a while I glanced down and saw the mirror in his hand. I parted my legs ever so slightly. I was getting aroused as I imagined this stranger looking up my dress. I spread my legs a little farther apart and sat back a little in my chair so he could really get a look. I wondered if he could see my pussy swelling up inside my panties. After a while, I put my hands on my knees and moved my skirt up, very slowly. I didn't want to scare him off. I pushed it up to my upper thighs and sat there, just letting him look.

The next day I went back to the fifth floor. This time I was prepared. I wore a short black skirt, stockings, garters, and no panties. But when I got to my carrel, he wasn't there. I sat down to read, but all I could think about was the mysterious young man with the mirror. I could feel the elastic of the garters stretched against my thighs. I was already getting wet, thinking about how I would look to him, my wet box framed in his little mirror.

Finally he arrived. I stared at my book, pretending not to notice him. I knew that this anonymity was part of our game. When he had his mirror out, I spread my legs and heard him gasp. I could feel my pussy opening up like petals on a flower as he gazed. I hitched up my skirt and sat on my hands, propping myself forward. I wondered what would happen if somebody else came up to the fifth floor, but this thought only excited me more.

The next day I wore the same outfit. He was there when I arrived. I made a big show of unpacking my bookbag, opening up my books, arranging my notebooks and pencils, all the while making him wait for me. When I sat down, I lifted my skirt all the way up so my bare ass was on the hard chair. I was already leaving a wet spot where I sat.

After a few moments I realized he was no longer using a mirror. Instead he was kneeling on the floor, his face still hidden under the carrel, looking directly at my wet, excited snatch. I spread my knees and waited. Everything was quiet. Then I heard him whisper, "Close your eyes." I closed them. Then he said, "Touch yourself." I rubbed my clit and put my fingers up my snatch. I could almost feel his breath on my pussy, which made me even more excited than my hands. Just before I was about to come, he gently moved my hands away. I gripped the chair, agonizing, moving my ass on the seat, trying to come. I waited and waited, breathing hard as he looked at my juicy box. Finally I felt his mouth on my pussy. His tongue darted expertly over my clit, his hands holding my legs apart, his lips working over my lips until I came. My whole body shuddered violently with pleasure.

I never saw him after that. I went back to the fifth floor time and time again, but he never returned. Still, I always sat in the same carrel—and I never wore any underwear, just in case.—*J.V., Atlanta, Georgia*

THREE'S COMPANY AFTER THE HONEYMOON

Connie and I were married this year. The most exciting thing in the world to me is to cause her to have a stimulating, mindblowing, earthshaking orgasm. One night, after watching an X-rated video, we went to bed and started talking about our fantasies. Connie told me that her favorite fantasy was to have two men in bed with her at the same time. I then revealed to her that one of my fantasies was to see her in bed with another man, watching her get a huge cock put inside her beautiful little snatch. We laughed and talked about it a little longer.

Later, we spoke more about this, and I told her that if we really wanted to, I could set this up. I told her about an old friend of mine, Michael.

Michael has been married for ten years now and has a family. The good thing about him is that he has a huge cock. We continued to talk and decided that if we could find a way to set this up we would go ahead and try. I found it hard to believe that this was a fantasy of mine because I'm probably the most jealous person in the world—with good cause. My wife is five feet eleven inches, with blond hair, blue eyes, big beautiful breasts and the greatest body.

When I went to see Michael, I showed him a photo of Connie. He commented that Connie had a nice set of tits and that she looked like a model. I knew then that this was going to be easy. In virtually no time, Michael and I had everything set up.

It took place on a Saturday. Connie and I went to dinner and had a few drinks. When we got home I had a big bottle of wine chilled. I told Connie that this was going to be a night to remember. Connie had taken off her dress and was wearing her matching black silk bra and panties with her black garter belt and black stockings. She also had on a black silk robe that barely reached the bottom of her very sexy ass. We turned out all the lights in the house and lit some candles. I had made sure to plan this evening very carefully so it would flow perfectly.

We continued to drink wine. The more we drank, the more we talked about sex—our desires and fantasies. Just knowing what was in store for us gave me the biggest, hottest hard-on that I've ever experienced. It was obvious that Connie was getting hot too. As she spoke of her fantasy of making it with two guys, she would occasionally reach down to touch her moist panties.

It was about nine that evening when the doorbell rang; Michael was right on time. Connie asked me to see who it was. I looked to see, acting as though I was not expecting anyone, and yelled out, "It's Michael!"

Connie started to put her dress back on, but I was able to convince her not to put any more clothes on, but to just have fun teasing Michael. She was very agreeable to this. When Michael came in, I went to get him a drink and I watched Connie go into the living room to greet him. She was wearing just her slinky, silky lingerie. Michael's hard-on sprang up almost immediately. Michael's cock is rather large, and I noticed that Connie could hardly take her eyes off his gigantic bulge.

We sat down and talked, mainly about sex. Somehow the subject of cock size came up and Connie said, "Let's have a contest. Whoever has the largest cock gets to remove my panties and show me just what good fucking feels like!" She said that the second-place winner was to watch and wait his turn. At this point we were all excited, because it was obvious that Michael's large cock was going to be the winner. Off to the bedroom we went.

Connie took off her robe, then Michael helped remove her panties. When they got in bed, Connie started to suck Michael off. Her hands looked very small as she grasped his cock. She was dripping hot as Michael slowly moved his fingers in and out of her pussy. Then Connie pulled Michael on top of her and between her legs. My heart was pounding with excitement. Connie reached down and guided Michael's huge cock up to her wet pussy. Her face winced with pleasure as Michael slowly introduced himself to her. After his full penetration was complete, their bodies moved together with a very fluid motion.

I came just watching them copulate. They continued screwing for about thirty-five minutes. I went to the end of the bed and enjoyed every in-and-out stroke of Michael's cock. Connie moaned almost every time he went in! All of a sudden, Connie's body started to quiver and become very rigid, as did Michael's. I was able to watch them both have the biggest orgasms that I've ever seen in my entire life. They jerked and moaned, and as Michael came inside Connie's pussy, I could see that not only did his cock fill her up, but his hot creamy juices flowed outside her pussy. While he moved in and out, I could see his come oozing from her pussy.

All the excitement caused me to get stiff again, and I wanted to get some of the action. I moved in close so that Connie could give me some head. Michael was so hot that he never lost his hard-on, so he continued to grind his big cock in and out of Connie's tight little pussy. I never knew that my wife was so talented. She handled the two of us very well. Within about fifteen minutes we all came again.

I think we were so excited having this threesome for the first time that it caused us all to have multiple orgasms. I wouldn't suggest this arrangement to someone with heart problems. But

Connie and I just can't wait to experience it again!—*T.L., Bangor, Maine*

STARRY, STARRY NIGHT

It was nearly dusk, a starry night, and the Jacuzzi was steaming as Al and I sat enjoying our wine. Al went inside and poured me another glass. Then he said he was going out for a while, but that I should sit back and enjoy myself.

I kicked back, enjoying the night and the wine. When I looked around me, everything was dark except for a faint red glow coming from our bedroom window just across the deck. Then there was another soft glow and another. Our bedroom was filled with shadows and colors reflecting off the wall. I looked up to the window and saw a shadow moving about. It seemed that Al was undressing, but all I could make out were shadows reflecting against the mirrors and walls in the bedroom. It was even more mysterious because of the steam coming up from the Jacuzzi.

I briefly considered going inside to join him but decided to sit back and enjoy the show. He was very clever about it all. Every once in a while he seemed to glance my way, but he never stopped his act.

He was undressed now and on all fours, on the bed. Then he was on his knees, on the bed. Soon he was holding his cock in his hand. Then he turned ever so slightly, and everything changed—kind of. Now I could see him stroking his shaft, but I could also see another shadow that looked just like him, his shadow on the wall.

Now the entire wall was a shadow of Al stroking himself for me. I could see his head tilt back, his hand on his shaft, stroking slowly. It must have felt very good to him. Especially since he knew I was watching.

His cock was all I could see now. He has the biggest tool I've ever seen. It filled the entire wall. It appeared to be four feet long, and his hand was slowly working its way up and down his long dick. He began stroking faster—his ass jiggling and his mouth open. He was stroking faster and faster until streams of juice was all I could see.—*J.A., Phoenix, Arizona*

THE ORAL EXAM

I never thought I would qualify for a "My letter was printed in *Forum*" T-shirt, since after several years of almost perfect wedded bliss, I was convinced my marriage would remain monogamous forever. Then the most incredible thing happened on the last evening of our vacation in Puerto Rico.

I was sitting at the beach bar of the vacation condo where we were staying, sipping rum and Cokes while my wife waded in the clear waters of San Juan. Ellen was engaged in conversation with two men and a very attractive young woman. This woman stood out more than my equally lovely wife, because each gentle wave revealed her beautifully formed, naked breasts.

I was content to stare at her until the two men came to the bar and joined a third man seated beside me. They must have all been new arrivals, as I had not seen them before. One was a fair redheaded young man, one was dark with curly hair, and the third was a quiet muscular man.

Red and Curly were very excited and spoke animatedly. Their voices grew louder, and I could hear part of their conversation. Pointing to the women in the water, they told the third man, whom they called Phil, of their good fortune in running into a girl they had known in school. When they claimed she had given the most exquisite blowjobs to a great many of the senior class males, my interest in her was piqued. I have always considered my wife unsurpassed in that category and am naturally interested in anyone who can possibly compete with her talents.

Red and Curly delighted in telling Phil of the woman's escapades, including the time they witnessed her suck off six men at a friend's bachelor party while her girlfriend fucked the bride-groom. Curly said that although she worshiped cock, and they had often enjoyed her hand jobs and oral ministrations, they knew of no one who had fucked her. Now that she had promised to meet them later, they were hopeful they would "get it all." They were anxious to go buy a couple of bottles and get set up in their room.

Phil was invited to join them in apartment B-10 after they got things going. They felt sure the girl wouldn't object once the party got started. But Red cautioned Phil not to come in too early. "Look in first and make sure things are well under way be-fore you attempt to join us." He added, "Don't blow it!" and the three left, laughing at the pun.

The sun was setting when Ellen joined me, and we moved to a nearby table. We had drinks and sandwiches while watching the beautiful sunset. Even though I made no mention of the con-versation I overheard at the bar, it was foremost in my mind.

Later, when I invited Ellen to go for a long walk on the beach, she told me she wanted to shower and do some last-minute shop-ping. She went back to our room, and I went walking alone.

San Juan has a seven-mile stretch of beautiful, sandy beach. I walked until it got dark, then I turned around and headed for apartment B-10. I had a stiff cock just thinking of the action that might be going on there.

I approached the apartment patio, and could hear the drone of the air conditioners and music as I tried to conceal myself be-hind the giant leaves of the tropical plants. The sliding glass doors heading in from the patio were closed, but the drapes had been left open. As I moved to a better position, I could see clearly into the studio. The redhaired man stood with a drink in his hand in front of the couch talking to my wife. *What was she doing there?*

Curly walked into view and served Red and Ellen new drinks. Then he sat on the couch beside Ellen. They talked, laughed and drank. Both men wore only bathing suits, and my wife had changed into a pair of shorts and a halter. As they talked, Curly nonchalantly rested his hand on Ellen's thigh. She did not protest. After a few minutes, Curly must have hit paydirt. Ellen's facial expression changed; she closed her eyes, licked her lips and parted her thighs. He had worked his hand to her pantyless crotch.

As if on cue, Red's bathing suit dropped to the floor and he stepped forward. Ellen opened her eyes and her mouth, and engulfed Red's semi-erect cock.

My jaw dropped open. I was suddenly struck by the revelation that Ellen was the girl they had been talking about! She had been sucking dick all those years before I met her, and loving it!

Ellen took Curly's rod out of his trunks and stroked it while she sucked on Red's fully erect cock. She stopped momentarily, took Curly's pre-come, coated Red's shaft with it, and resumed licking and sucking. Curly stood up beside Red, letting his trunks slip off, and Ellen alternated between them. She licked the sensitive underside of their balls while she pumped both cocks, desperately trying to make them spurt the cream she loves so much. When Red's first burst hit the floor, he immediately received Ellen's full attention as she sucked his cockhead in her mouth, trying to squeeze out every last drop.

Someone moved outside. I stepped back and hid. It was Phil. He walked to the patio and stood by the window, looking into the room and blocking my view. He stood there rubbing his crotch through his shorts, inspired by the action inside. After a few minutes, he walked out of sight and around to the front. I moved back to where I could see what was going on inside.

They had moved to the bed. Ellen lay naked on her back, sucking off Curly as he knelt by her head. Red lay on his belly, his head between her legs, eating pussy. Ellen worked frantically, trying to coax the cream from Curly's cock.

Phil walked into the room. He had stripped, and stood there watching them. Ellen didn't notice him until he changed places with Red. Curly ejaculated as Ellen looked up, trying to figure out who belonged to the extra body. Caught off-guard, she tried to catch as much come as she could in her mouth. Then she rubbed the jet of cream that had hit her breasts into her body and licked her fingers. She said something and smiled.

Phil climbed on her and started fucking her hard and fast. Ellen closed her eyes and Curly put his soft cock back in her mouth. He stroked her head softly while he watched Phil pump her.

Red said something and Phil, without pulling out, rolled over so that Ellen was on top of him. With her breasts flattened against his chest, they glued their mouths together and continued fucking.

Red was stroking Ellen's back and buttocks. He bent down and started kissing and licking her ass cheeks. She parted her legs and ground her pelvis into Phil.

Red then knelt between her legs and started jerking himself off with his cock between Ellen's cheeks. Ellen writhed between the two men. Her head began moving from side to side and her eyes were closed tightly. Red held Ellen's hips and started thrusting.

Red's body stiffened. Then he collapsed on top of Ellen, drained of energy. They were all motionless. Finally, the forgotten Curly moved Red aside, and as soon as Ellen rolled off Phil, Curly mounted her, fucking furiously. Phil and Red left the bed and watched them from the couch. Curly didn't last very long. He lay still as Ellen got out from under him. When she got up and started dressing, I cut out.

I rushed to our room, stripped, and climbed into bed. Confused thoughts reeled in my head. It seemed forever before Ellen arrived. When I heard her enter the room, I feigned sleep.

She came to the bed immediately and removed her clothes. Breathing heavily, she bent over me and kissed me on the mouth. Ellen tasted of liquor and semen. Her body smelled of sex. My erection grew as she peeled back the sheets and took my cock in her mouth. Then she straddled my head and pressed her sopping pussy against my face. She rubbed her cunt harder against my mouth until I stuck my tongue into her wet pussy. As soon as I did that, Ellen came violently, soaking my face with juices. I started coming so much it hurt. My balls emptied gobs of cream into her mouth. She kept sucking long after I was empty.

She got up from our 69 position, swung around, and sat on my semi-erect cock. It slid easily into her slippery pussy and grew hard as she moved against it. Hundreds of sexual thoughts assaulted my mind. I couldn't believe how insatiable she had become.

We haven't discussed that night, and I don't know if Ellen has any idea what I witnessed. Twice since our return from Puerto Rico, Ellen has come home late after "going out with her girlfriends." She is still very horny when she gets home, and comes straight to bed. It's obvious to me she's been freshly fucked, but it turns her on when we have sex like this more than at any other time.—S.R., Portland, Oregon

Swapping

Double Jackpot

On a vacation trip to Las Vegas—a first for my wife—we both encountered an experience that I wish to share with your readers.

I have a beautiful wife, as I am often told. She is a tall blonde with a dark tan. Everywhere we go, men look at her. For the past three years of our ten-year marriage we had been fantasizing about a threesome. While in Vegas, we were in a casino, playing the dollar slots, when my wife and I both hit jackpots, one right after the other. My wife was still jumping up and down when a young couple next to us hit a jackpot too.

In no time at all, the four of us were fast friends. I invited them to join my wife Lynn and me for a drink. We ended up spending the rest of the evening together—gaming, dancing, and having dinner. During those four hours that we spent together, I had become aware of Tim's interest in my wife, who, though in her mid-fifties, gives the appearance of being much younger.

In my opinion, Tim's wife Carole was quite a knockout herself, a very tall, athletic-looking blonde with tits that would make most men look twice. Her legs were long and well-shaped, and she wore a very short skirt. Tim and Lynn danced together many times and, as they returned to the table, I noticed the growing bulge in his pants. I knew that Lynn was well aware of the effect she was having on him by the sexy flush on her face. I was not aware that Carole had noticed her husband's hard-on until she mentioned it to me during one of our dances.

She danced very close to me, and I didn't know if she meant anything by it or if it was just her style. Then she whispered in my ear about the effect my wife was having on her husband, and I said, "What the hell! We're in Vegas. Let them have their fun and so will we."

She pulled closer to me, practically riding my thigh. For the next hour I danced with Carole at her request, and my wife danced with Tim. Carole got to where she would move her pussy up and down over my engorged and aching cock, without saying a word. She was moaning and gasping in my ear. It was Tim who suggested that we do a little casino hopping. The women wanted an hour to freshen up and change clothes, so we went to our rooms. While I was changing, Lynn mentioned that she had noticed my hard-on and had seen Carole rubbing herself all over me. I told her that I had seen the effect she and Tim were having on each other. There was a moment of silence, then Lynn said that she supposed it was true. She asked if I was upset, and I said no. We reassured each other of our love and agreed that this was what we had been fantasizing about for so long. We decided to see where this encounter was leading.

Lynn put on a white dress that came to just above her knees, white heels, black stockings, and a black garter belt. Her sexy look turned me on so much that I nearly canceled our meeting with Carole and Tim.

While riding down in the elevator, Lynn raised her dress to smooth out her stockings. To my surprise, she wasn't wearing any panties! When she saw my reaction, she said that she wanted to keep Tim busy so I could make some time with Carole.

We met them at the bar, and my eyes almost popped out of their sockets at the sight of Carole in a short white miniskirt, black high heels, and a very revealing blouse. In my embarrassment I turned my attention to Tim, and found him staring at Lynn.

Tim proposed that we have a contest while we gambled. He suggested that we switch partners and see which couple could win the most money in three hours or less.

We all agreed and started with a drink. Carole came to sit with me and Lynn went over to Tim. We decided the couple winning the most money would be treated to a steak breakfast by the losing couple. As Carole slid into the booth beside me, her skirt slid up, giving me a beautiful view of her crotch. For a few seconds I just stared with my mouth open. She wasn't wearing panties either!

Within the next few hours, Carole and I had accumulated about three hundred and fifty dollars in winnings from the slot machines. They were the most frustrating two hours I'd ever spent. While playing the one-armed bandits, Carole would sit next to me on her stool and open her legs wide in front of me, exposing her well-trimmed cunt. Other times she would drop her coins and bend over to retrieve them, giving me an excellent view of her prize possessions.

When we were no longer winning, she suggested that we stop gambling for a while and save what we had if we wanted to win the contest. I agreed.

There was an hour yet to go, so she suggested that we go to their room to rest. She had the only key, so we wouldn't have to worry about Tim walking in on us. On our way there, all kinds of thoughts went through my mind. I wondered if she was just teasing me or if she really wanted to seduce me. I wanted her, but I couldn't make the first move. As it turned out, I didn't have to.

We walked toward the parking lot, and she pointed to an RV parked in the lot. "That's it," she said. She said that it was cheaper and more comfortable than staying in hotels. Once inside, she excused herself to change.

When Carole returned, I couldn't believe my eyes. She was wearing a lace teddy just long enough to cover her pubic hair. Her large tits were visible through the lace; her large nipples stuck out in points, indicating that she, too, was quite turned on. She came up to embrace me and whispered that she wanted me. Without another word, we started kissing.

I sucked on her sloping breasts, alternating from one to the other, while she pulled my hand down to her pussy. I rubbed her clit and she spread her legs, giving me better access to her steaming pussy. We continued to kiss and fondle each other while she removed my shirt and I dropped my pants to my ankles.

Her mouth descended to my cock as I let go of my hold on her pussy. I leaned against the wall, enjoying the effects of her skilled mouth on my dick. It was so intensely enjoyable that I lost myself in the sensations I was experiencing through my balls and cock. I had never been given head so well.

I finally pulled away and carried Carole to the bedroom. Within seconds of placing her on the bed I was sucking her pussy clean. She was fucking my mouth and screaming to have my big, fat cock inside her. I spread her legs and guided the head of my cock into her pussy while she reached out with both hands to spread her swollen cunt lips.

I worked my cock gently into her tight pussy. I felt her hands come around to cup my buttocks as I thrust into her. It seemed to take just a few seconds of stroking before she came. I was amazed at her sexual prowess. She was a demanding lover; her pussy muscles grasped and drained my cock.

We rested for a while, then cleaned up and prepared to meet our spouses at the casino. Walking there, Carole gave my hand a squeeze and told me that I was the best fuck she'd ever had. We met Tim and Lynn at the specified time. They had broken even, so we were the winners and were treated to a steak breakfast. I could tell from Lynn's expression that she, too, had hit the jackpot.—*E.M., Flagstaff, Arizona*

HOTTER THAN A PISTOL

Our neighborhood had a Fourth of July party that was a real blowout. After the fireworks had all been set off and the kids were asleep, the adults had a fireworks display all their own.

My husband and I and three couples in the neighborhood had been barbecuing and drinking all day, and we decided to go for a midnight swim. Everything was normal until the most conservative woman in the group suggested we all skinny-dip. The rest of us were shocked but not put off by her suggestion. (Luckily the pool we were in has a deck with a privacy fence built all around it.) We took off our suits, and there was some playful kissing and petting among all of us. Having a size 40D chest, I was receiving quite a bit of attention from the men. I'm not shy in the least, so I was enjoying it and getting very hot!

My husband was also getting heated up by the lady who lives across the street. They were in their own corner of the pool, kissing and stroking each other all over. My husband had often teased me about how much he'd like to make Donna scream in ecstasy, and it looked like he was going to get his chance. I noticed others beginning to pair off and realized I was going to get to make a fantasy of my own come true.

My husband works nights, and when I'm horny at night, I get myself off to thoughts of the man who lives nearby. He's tall, bearded, slightly balding, and has a great body. I've always been turned on by Clarence, and there he was, waiting for me.

I was hot already and getting hotter by the minute just thinking about being with him. Clarence's kisses were burning a path like wildfire over my lips, face, and neck. Clarence sucked and fondled my tits and nipples until they were so hard I thought they would explode. My knees were shaking, my legs were like rubber, and I felt my whole body erupt with an orgasm. I had never gotten off from a man just sucking on my tits, and it was pure heaven. Clarence told me he had just begun to please me. He lifted me out of the pool so that I was sitting on the edge of the deck. Still in the pool, he began kissing my inner thighs and finger-fucking me. I was quivering with excitement, anticipating the moment when he would finally put his lips on my completely shaven pussy.

Finally his tongue began teasing my clit. I came instantly all over his face. Clarence murmured something about how a wet pussy turned him on and he had never seen a wetter pussy than mine. He buried his face in my pussy and ate me like a starving man would a steak dinner. It seemed to last for hours, and I'm surprised my screams didn't wake the rest of the neighborhood. I'm a very sexual person, but I finally had to beg for mercy and ask him to quit using his tongue on me. By now my head was spinning, my ears were ringing, and I felt as though my teeth were all on edge. Yet all I could think about was having his dick inside of me. I slid back in the pool, ready for him, but when I reached down for his dick, I was surprised to find it only semi-erect. Clarence admitted rather sheepishly that he had come while eating my pussy. I didn't think I could get any hotter, but that did it—the *thought* of a man being that turned on by pleasing me.

He might have thought we were done, but there was no way I wasn't going to fuck him. I took a big breath and started sucking Clarence underwater. This was no easy feat, but the way his cock felt in my mouth was keeping my juices flowing. I came up for air once and went back under, taking all of him in my mouth. I could feel his dick getting hard in my throat. Finally the need for air made me come back up to the surface. Before I had time to catch my breath, Clarence had grabbed me to him, and I felt his shaft penetrating me. We were facing each other, my arms around his neck and my legs wrapped tightly around his waist. Each stroke of his cock made my whole body shake with a new orgasm.

Clarence's fucking was excellent. He'd use short, light strokes, then faster, harder ones. Then he stopped for a moment and had me turn around so I was holding on to the edge of the pool. He began to enter me from behind, but only put the head of his dick inside of me. No matter how I squirmed and wiggled, I couldn't get more of him in me. Clarence told me that if I wanted all of his dick I would have to ask nicely. I was quivering with excitement. I would have promised him the moon if he had rammed his whole cock into me. I said *please*, told him I would do *anything* he wanted. Finally, after what seemed like an eternity, he plunged deep inside me. I had the most fantastic orgasm of my life. He kept driving his dick deeper and deeper. All the while I'm screaming and moaning like Jane of the Jungle. We were bumping and grinding so much, the pool must have looked like it had a whirlpool in it. I could tell by his breathing and the tautness of his body that Clarence was ready to come. He let out a moan as I felt his come filling my pussy. I was in heaven! He pulled out of me, and we were gasping, hanging on to the side of the pool.

When we turned around to see how the others were doing, we found them all looking at us. Clarence and I broke out laughing. He pulled me to him and said, "That was great!" The other women were getting out of the pool, but I was too tired to move. I didn't realize I was on the brink of another fantasy.

The men were teasing me about how they felt left out because Clarence had gotten the wildest fuck of the party. I said jokingly that I could fix that by doing all of them at once. They all laughed and dared me, so I said if they could get it up again, we'd go for it.

The five of us got out of the pool and I was amazed that all four men had hard-ons already, so it looked like I had to do my part. At this point I was ready for anything. I had one man lay flat on his back on the deck. I found a bottle of suntan lotion we had all been using and squeezed a liberal amount on his dick. Then I straddled him with my back toward his face. I was so loose from drinking and all the good sex that I had no trouble sliding him right into my cunt.

After he was in me, I leaned back so my head was resting on

his shoulders. He told me he didn't know what I had planned, but he liked it already, and I had better hurry because he was ready to come. I motioned to the man who lives next door to put his dick in my hand. He got on his knees and slid his cock into my waiting fist. Then Clarence sat on me between my tits and shoulders, and I started sucking him. My husband was gracious enough to let all of these men have the prime spots, since he gets whatever he wants *whenever* he wants at home.

The three of them were all pumping their dicks in me, and when I looked up, my husband was standing next to me stroking himself, and from the look of his cock, he was going to come any minute.

The man I was on top of came first, and while I was enjoying the feel of his hot load in my pussy, Clarence started filling my mouth with his come. I was greedily sucking him dry when my husband's jism hit my breast and the man in my hand exploded. I had the combined strength of four orgasms rolled into one eruption through my body. We all lay together totally spent.

Sometime during all the fun the other women had gotten dressed inside. We got dressed and received a very cool reception when we got in the house. Since then the women in the neighborhood never stop by for coffee anymore—but their husbands sure do!—*Name and address withheld upon request*

DOIN' THE CLUB SCENE

It all started one Friday night when my wife Lisa and I were watching a porno movie that we had bought. I had always wanted to watch my wife with someone else, but I had never told her until then. I waited until I noticed that she was excited. I was playing with her cunt, and I mentioned to her that I wanted to see her sucking some guy's cock. I also told her that I had fantasized about her going down on another female. As I told her this her pussy got very wet. She confessed to me that she had always wanted to eat pussy, but was afraid to let me know because I might think she was strange. The more we talked about it, the hornier we got.

We decided to go out that night and try out at least one of our fantasies. I hurriedly took a shower and dressed; my wife locked herself in the bathroom to get ready. When she came out she was wearing a see-through blouse, no bra, and a short skirt just covering the cheeks of her ass. Underneath she wore black stockings and high-heel shoes. She had also shaved her cunt to surprise whomever we would get together with that night.

We got in our car and started to drive to Philadelphia. We had never done this before, so we didn't know where to go to meet people that would be interested in partying.

It was late. We went to a bar on State Street and ordered drinks. I went to play some music and check out the crowd. My wife sat down, facing the bar with her legs partly open to give anyone who cared to look a view of her hot and juicy cunt. We didn't see anyone we were interested in making it with.

We waited for an hour to see if anyone interesting would walk in. Finally, we went walking around, and I enjoyed watching other men look at my wife's tits. That made me very excited.

We started to go home, when we stopped at a newsstand. We picked up a swingers' magazine and saw an ad for a club not too far from where we were. We went to check it out.

After paying the admission, we walked in. Much to our surprise, everyone there was completely nude, and people were making love all over the place. One couple saw us walking around and they came over to explain to us that everyone was there to have fun but that nobody would be forced to participate if they didn't want to. Earl was tall, black, and hung like a horse; Jessica was very attractive, with big tits and a very bushy cunt. We decided to party with them. They were very nice, and we headed to a private room.

I asked Earl and Jessica to party with my wife first, because I wanted to watch her making it with them. Jessica started kissing my wife on the lips, and I thought I noticed a little tongue action. Jessica went right down to my wife's clean-shaven cunt, and Lisa was coming like there was no tomorrow.

Earl then went over to my wife and put his cock near her face. She reached with both her hands for it. She took his balls and stuffed them in her mouth. She licked his pecker to the head and then stuffed in as much as she could, which wasn't much. My cock was now getting ready to come. I tried to hold back, but then Earl shot his load in my wife's mouth. Some of it dripped from the corner of her mouth as she screamed with excitement. Jessica said Lisa's come tasted sweet, then lay down and asked me to eat her very hot and juicy pussy. I did, and it was sweet. The smell was like a rainy morning, very clean.

After we had come we rested for a little bit. Then I noticed that Earl's cock was starting to get hard again. My wife stuffed it in her mouth to help it get harder. I just loved it when I saw it in her mouth, but now I wanted to watch him ram it in her hot love-hole. My wife positioned herself on all fours to allow him to go in deeper. He first inserted just the head of it to open the way for the rest of it. I was watching this, and my prick started jerking from the excitement. I was surprised that she was able to take it all. She started to scream for him to fuck her hard, and he did. He just kept ramming it in and out for a long time before he shot his second load.

He then moved aside, and my wife asked me to lie down. She hovered over my face just high enough so that I could watch Earl's juices drip down to my mouth. I tasted his come and I shot my load from the excitement.

We thanked Earl and Jessica, exchanged phone numbers, and left to meet someone else.—*Name and address withheld*

EVERY BUDDY'S HAPPY

I've written to you before about how my husband wanted me to sexually tease a friend whom he met a few months ago and plays golf with almost every Saturday. My husband Mick even invited Wally along on a four-day vacation, where he asked me to prick-tease Wally and show as much of my body as I could.

Even though I told Mick he was crazy, I agreed to fulfill his fantasy if he'd never ask me to do anything like this again. Well, like I wrote before, it all ended up with Wally screwing me silly on all four days of our vacation.

My husband Mick never knew that Wally's huge tool kept me coming for four days. Three weeks had gone by since I last saw Wally. Mick has been telling me since we got home from our vacation what a turn-on our vacation had been. He even asked me if I was tempted to let Wally make love to me. I told him I went far enough with his fantasy and reminded him that he'd promised he'd drop the subject.

I have to admit our sex life has improved one hundred percent. Mick always seems horny since our vacation. But for some reason the last week Mick hasn't been interested in sex. I was really getting horny, so before Mick got home from work I dressed as sexily as I could, wearing a miniskirt with no panties underneath. Even though my breasts are too large to go braless, I left my bra in the dresser.

I heard Mick's car drive up, and my pussy was getting wet already. When the door opened I was in shock. Wally walked in with Mick. My husband said, "I hope it's okay. I invited Wally over for supper." When Mick saw how I was dressed, his eyes lit up. As he walked by me he said, "I love you." Mick said he was going down to the rec room to make us all a drink.

Wally didn't waste any time. Standing behind me, he held me close, with both of his hands rubbing my breasts while he was kissing my neck. Wally asked, "How did you know I was coming over?"

I told Wally I didn't know he was coming and pulled away from him. Wally's dick was hard and pressing into my ass cheeks as his hands lifted my skirt and his fingers softly stroked my pussy. Wally said, "Don't lie to me. Your pussy is soaking wet already."

I told Wally his hands felt so good, but I wasn't going to cheat on Mick ever again. We heard Mick coming up the stairs, so I quickly pulled away from Wally, pulling my skirt down.

After finishing his drink, Mick went out in the yard and put three steaks on the grill. I stood next to the couch by the bay window, watching Mick work on the grill and knowing Wally wouldn't dare try anything with me in clear view of Mick.

Wally lay down on the couch. Then I heard something and looked at Wally. He was unzipping his pants and taking out his huge tool. My breathing was getting heavier as he stroked his nine-inch prick, moaning, "You can't leave me like this." God, I wanted him deep inside, remembering how good it felt to be stretched to the limit. I told him to put his prick back in his pants and wait until tomorrow—when Mick went to work, I'd let him do anything he wanted. Wally asked me if I'd suck him until he shot his load if he waited until tomorrow. I promised him I would try and admitted that I wanted him as bad as he wanted me.

I almost died on the spot when I heard my husband Mick scream, "You damn cheat!" I couldn't turn around and face Mick— I felt my whole world coming to an end. Mick said, "I thought you loved me more than this."

I started to cry as I turned to Mick and told him that I did love him, and begged him to please forgive me. He just walked away.

I ran into the bedroom and lay on the bed, crying and trying to forget the whole day. Mick came into the bedroom and told me he was going to show me what happens to cheating wives. Mick reached down and ripped open my blouse. "Look," he said, "your nipples are still hard from looking at Wally's hard dick." Mick lowered his mouth and started sucking my tits. Suddenly I felt the bed move on the other side of me, and when I opened my eyes Wally was kneeling on the bed next to me, completely naked.

Wally started sucking one of my tits as Mick did the other. Oh God, it felt so good! I held both their heads to my heaving breasts.

Mick got off the bed and removed all of his clothes. As I looked over at him, he smiled. His dick was standing straight and hard. Mick unhooked my skirt and pulled it off, laying down next to me. Wally said to Mick, "It looks good enough to eat."

Mick admitted that he had never tried licking me. "Let me show you," Wally answered.

Wally spread my legs and licked all around my pussy, never touching it. I grabbed Mick's hard dick and lifted my legs. With the other hand I pushed Wally's head so his wonderful tongue was licking and sucking my pussy. With his tongue buried in me, I started to come. My orgasm left me completely drained. Wally lay next to me and, as our lips met, Mick was kneeling between my spread legs rubbing his hard dick against my wet pussy. After a while I pleaded with Mick to stick his dick in me.

In one thrust Mick was in me, pumping as fast as he could. It felt better than ever before, but I could tell by Mick's moaning he was going to come after only about ten strokes. I yelled, "Oh Mick, honey, not yet!" but I could feel his hot come shooting as he slowed down.

Wally was now holding his dick close to my mouth. He told me if I sucked him a little he'd put out the fire between my legs. I opened my mouth and had his huge tool working in and out of my bobbing mouth as I stroked the rest of his dick with both hands. Wally stopped me and spread my legs. As he was about to fill me with his big tool, Mick said, "Wally, I think you're too big for Beth. You'd better stop." I only moaned as I wrapped both legs around Wally's back and with one hand inserted the head of his tool in my pussy. Wally pushed, and in a couple of strokes, I could feel his balls against my ass.

Wally kept slowly pumping me, and it felt like he had his whole arm in me instead of his dick. I lost count of how many times I came, but after about fifteen minutes his pace quickened and then he started moaning, "I better pull out—I'm almost ready to come." I pulled Wally down so his hairy chest was against my breasts. I tightened my legs around his back and told him to fill me with his hot come. I could feel him coming as I had one last complete orgasm.

We all got out of bed and dressed before Wally left for home. Mick asked me if I was going to see Wally again. I told him never without him along. Mick kissed me and told me how much he loved me, and suggested that I plan something exciting for next Saturday after their golf game. I can hardly wait.—*B.L., Memphis, Tennessee*

FANTASIES IN BLACK AND WHITE

For quite some time, my husband Teddy and I have been good friends with a woman named Pam who swings with us occasionally. Pam had a black lover whom she saw on and off, and she always told us how he turned her on. This guy had entered her life again, and she was smiling from ear to ear. Pam knew that Teddy's birthday was coming up and that we were interested in meeting her lover, so she suggested that the four of us get together to celebrate the occasion. We agreed.

Pam and Greg showed up that Saturday night at the appointed time. We had some drinks and got to know one another. All the time I felt a nervous twitter inside. I was aching for this black man to take me in hand. We finally got down to some action.

Teddy, who's well built and good-looking, took Pam to our bedroom. Pam is dark-haired, petite, and attractive, and I knew that Teddy was attracted to her. Greg and I went to the family room where the couch unfolds into a bed with a king-size mattress. We took off our clothes quickly; I was eager to try this guy out. Greg reached out and took my tits in his hands. I backed up into him and felt his huge cock pressing against me. Reaching around, I took it in my hand. It was heavy and thick like a big warm sausage. My knees went weak and my mouth watered.

I turned slightly and our mouths met, his tongue swallowing mine. We moved to the mattress, where I sat down, intending to suck his cock into my mouth, then lean back and let him plunge it into me, but he had other ideas. He scooted me back on the bed and laid me down. I reached for his cock and he pushed me back. "Don't move yet," he told me.

He started at my feet, licking and sucking my toes and blowing on my skin until chills ran up and down my body. He worked slowly, inching his way to my knees, then my thighs.

I was panting and quivering, wanting him badly. I reached for him, begging him to fuck me, and he smiled, turned me over on my stomach and resumed his licking. When I was thoroughly soaked from my own sweat and his saliva, he let me turn around. Only then did he start to play with my pussy. Oh, how I needed relief! He was so slow and languid.

He put two fingers in me, sliding them back and forth while his thumb grazed my clit. I couldn't stand it. I wanted his cock inside me. Finally he straddled my chest and allowed me to take his big cock and stroke it.

He was uncircumcised! I took him into my mouth and tasted his salty meat. I licked and sucked him while I ground my ass into the mattress, trying to give some attention to my aching cunt. I pulled his foreskin back and ran my tongue around the head before plunging as much of his cock as I could down my throat. I cupped his balls and tongued them, getting hotter by the second.

He was ready to fuck. He crawled down my body, dragging his cock over me as he went. I lifted my knees and he entered me slowly, stretching my dripping cunt to capacity. I couldn't believe how big his cock felt inside me. He thrust slowly in and out, teasing me. Finally he started to pump faster. I never wanted him to stop. He looked down at me with his dark eyes, taking everything I had to give, and I spread my legs wider, returning every thrust.

I could hear sounds from the bedroom, which told me that Teddy was well into fucking Pam. This made me hotter. Suddenly Greg pulled his cock out of me and sank his head between my legs, teasing my clit with his tongue. Shoving two meaty fingers up my cunt, he licked and sucked my clitoris until I came.

He wanted more, so we rearranged ourselves once again. I got up on my hands and knees, and he entered me from behind. He started slowly and built up quickly to his jackhammer pace. My tits were moving so fast they slapped my chest as he moved inside me. He worked his arms around me, under my knees, so that I was wrapped tightly as his fucking machine hit high gear. I tried to hang on and enjoy the ride.

Greg was near orgasm. His balls, which had been slapping my ass with every stroke, were drawing up, and I could feel his huge black cock growing even bigger inside me. He took my hips in his hands and really slammed into me. Then I felt the spurt of his fiery come as he pounded his cream inside me. I felt it overflow and stream down my legs along with the river of sweat we had created.

Pam and Teddy had come out of the bedroom and were walking over to the mattress as we slowly uncoupled. Teddy took one look at Greg's huge cock and knew how well I had been fucked. I was soaking wet. My hair was plastered to my head and all my makeup had melted away. I'd never been fucked so hard for so long, and I loved every stroke.

That evening with Greg gave Teddy and me so much more fantasy material than we imagined it would. Thinking about it never fails to make us hot.—N.D., Cleveland, Ohio

GAL FRIDAY DELIVERS

Linda, a beautiful full-figured brunette of about forty, is my boss but she is also my friend. Her business requires her to travel to various cities about four times a year to attend conventions. Her husband, Don, knows that she regards these trips as vacations from marital fidelity and that she usually shares her bed with Bob, her well-hung twenty-eight-year-old executive assistant.

What Don may not know, but Linda has confided to me, is that after a night of getting reacquainted with Bob's super-thick cock and his exquisite lovemaking technique, she usually becomes more adventurous, and may spend the final night or two in some other man's bed. Occasionally she and Bob get together with one or more other men. One time last year, for instance, Linda spent a night with Bob and three strangers they met at their hotel. She began the evening by sucking one man's cock, and by the time she had swallowed the last one's come, the first man was hard again. That gave all four tremendous staying power, and Linda said it was probably the best sex of her life. The next several hours were just one orgasm after another, as these four muscular young studs took their pleasure of her again and again until everyone was tired out and totally satisfied.

The only problem Linda has is that, when she gets home, she is usually rather tired from lack of sleep (and sometimes a little sore as well). But Don is hot and horny from several days of deprivation (and imagining his darling wife moaning with pleasure as she offers her moist cunt to the ardent thrusts of her gorgeous young co-worker).

The situation has caused trouble between them at times, so before Linda's last trip out of town she suggested that I might be able to keep her husband satisfied while she was away. I was flattered and very willing, since I have a soft spot for Don. Also, I was divorced two years ago, and with no regular boyfriend (only a date or a weekend now and then with a couple of married men I know), I haven't been getting as much sex as I need. I was also apprehensive, since I am not nearly as good-looking as Linda. I'm sort of mousy blond and I have put on a few pounds I shouldn't have since my marriage broke up. But the next day Linda told me it was all arranged, and said with a wink that Don was looking forward to it.

Linda left on Thursday, and that evening Don picked me up to take me out to dinner. I was wearing my nicest dress, with garter belt and new stockings. I wasn't wearing any underwear and, at the right time, I was going to show Don what was going to be all his the next couple of nights. He gave me a warm greeting kiss, and even held my hand while we were waiting for the food. During our conversation, his voice was smooth and seductive but mine was nervous and husky, and I kept blushing every time he gave me one of those looks that said, "I know you are all mine tonight."

Over the coffee he finally said, "You know, I've wanted your body for a long time. I can hardly wait to get my mouth on your pussy." All I could reply was, "It's all yours whenever you want it. For your sake, I'm not wearing anything under this dress," and I managed very quickly and discreetly to pull up my skirt so he could catch a glimpse of my brown bush and the pink lips between it. It was only a few minutes before we were naked on Don and Linda's bed, with Don's head buried between my thighs. He was literally worshiping my ass and cunt, and he brought me to climax until I was literally begging for his cock and telling him that I wanted him to fuck me long and hard, again and again. Soon I was kissing my juice off his handsome face as the purple knob of his long prick nudged its way between my moist inner lips.

Then, with a quick thrust, Don was deep into me, and, for the first time in my life, I felt the tip of a man's cock caressing my cervix. We both came right away, but I wanted to keep Don hard, and so I started talking to him about what Linda was probably getting right then from Bob, describing it in detail and suiting my actions to my words. As I guessed it would, this got Don very excited, and soon he was banging away at me. He was out of control, gasping sometimes my name and sometimes Linda's. I just lay there getting the fuck of my life, moaning and begging him to give me all he had.

I spent the next three days with him at their house, getting fucked whenever I wanted it, which was quite often. In between times, Don ate me, and I could always get him hard by sucking his cock. I also learned to love the taste of Don's jism, which is silky sweet, not bitter like my ex-husband's. Linda was very impressed by how contented her husband was on her return, and after comparing notes, we found out that I had been fucked more times during her trip than she had—though she had welcomed a different man into her body each of the three nights and found them all delightful. Don and Linda now describe their extramarital joys to each other while they fuck, and they say their marriage is better than ever.

All three of us decided to make Don's screwing me a regular part of Linda's frequent business-with-pleasure trips. Don and Linda are still strictly faithful to each other when they are in the same town, but just an hour ago I saw Linda off at the plane for San Francisco. Linda's cute husband has just come in as I've been writing this, and my dress is already half off. God, I am horny! I promise you that when I go to the corner to mail this, the lips of my cunt will be dripping with delicious love milk Don loves to pump deep into my belly.—*N.R., Utica, New York*

Crossdressing

How He Became a
Bearded Transvestite

I am writing to let the whole world know of my life as a panty fanatic. It started rather innocently. My wife and I were on a ski trip and I had forgotten to bring my long underwear. She handed me a pair of her panty hose and told me to use them until we could get to the shops. She always wore them under her jeans in cold weather and swore they kept her warm, so I figured, why not?

When we returned to our room that night she had me take off my ski bibs but leave on the panty hose. Something about the tightness—the way the nylon mashed down my pubic hair, cock, and balls—turned her on. She fussed over me all night, smoothing her hands down my thighs to feel the silky nylon. Then she gave me the most sensuous blowjob of my life. I figured that it was worth wearing panty hose in exchange for all the attention she was giving me, so I wore them for the remainder of the week. On our last night there she asked me if I had enjoyed all the sex we'd had that week. I responded that it had been the best week of our marriage. Then she asked for a special favor; she wanted me to wear a nightgown and panties over the panty hose, just for one night.

I balked at the idea, but she kept going on about it until I consented. I warned her never to tell anyone about it or I'd never do it again. She assured me that that would be the last time she'd mention it. Also, I'd been wanting to grow a beard for some time, but she had been against the idea. She now added that if I did this one thing for her—wearing the lingerie—she wouldn't mind if I grew a beard. The sex we had that night topped any we'd had before, including our honeymoon.

After we returned from our ski trip, she didn't bring the issue up again. After six weeks my beard had grown in and I felt more macho than I had in all my life. On Valentine's Day, we exchanged gifts. When I opened mine I was flabbergasted. She had bought me a dozen pairs of panty hose, some slips, girdles, a dress, and a pair of high heels. I was stunned.

"What the hell is all this? I'm not wearing this stuff."

She said that if I would wear what she wanted, she'd make it worth my while. She pulled out some glossy photos of me in a nightgown and nylons, taken while I was asleep on our ski trip. I grabbed the pictures and ripped them up, but she just laughed and said she had many more copies. She said that she could tell how much it turned me on to wear lingerie—she just wanted to help me be the man I wanted to be.

She asked me to go put on the panties, bra, girdle, slip, and heels and she'd put on the sexy teddy I had bought her. We wore the same outfits every night for a week, and I had to admit that it *did* make me very horny. She took some more pictures of me in female clothes. With my full beard, there could be no doubt that I was a man. That's what turned her on.

Her next step was to throw out all of my male underwear while I was asleep. Now I was left with only bras, panty hose, slips, and panties in my dresser drawers. I would have no choice but to wear panties and panty hose twenty-four hours a day. Then she made me a deal: I would wear feminine underwear beneath my suits when I went to work all that week and, if I could truthfully say that I didn't enjoy it, she would never bother me about it again.

Although I agreed to her terms, when it came down to actually doing it, I have to admit that I cheated a little. I wore the bra to work but took it off when I got there. Then I put it back on before I came home, so she would think I'd worn it. But since she had disposed of all my masculine underpants, there was no way to get around wearing the panties unless I wanted to go without beneath my suits, which was hardly practical.

When the week was up, I went back to wearing my male attire, but I didn't like it. I missed the soft caress of nylon beneath my pants when I sat down. I missed the sensual feel of panty hose rubbing against the material of my trousers when I walked. After two weeks of traditional men's underwear, I was ready to go back to wearing women's attire. I had to admit my wife was right: I preferred it.

Now I wear women's clothes all the time when I'm not at work. The more I get into the female role, the more my relationship with my wife is changing. She has gone back to work and is making so much money that I could quit work if I wanted to and spend all my time tending to the house. I already do all of the cleaning, wearing an apron over my frilly dresses. The other day, after vacuuming, I found my wife talking to the Avon lady in the living room. Forgetting that my beard looked a little strange with my June Cleaver dress and apron, I came in and sat with them. At first, the Avon lady stared at me. But, professional saleslady that she was, she soon got over her shock. Before very long, she was showing me lipsticks, makeup, and nail polishes.

I don't usually wear a skirt or dress outside. When I do, it is a special occasion. If people stare, I just say hello to them. I guess they think I am some kind of a freak, but I have to please myself. As for now, I must go. My wife saw a miniskirt in a store that she thinks would look good on me. I'm looking forward to trying it on in the men's dressing room.—*K.I., Chicago, Illinois*

MAY I HELP YOU?

As a professional in a large company, I wear an expensive suit every day to work. I have been crossdressing for many years and prefer the feel of women's underwear. A silky bra and panties feel elegant underneath my tailored suits. One evening after work I was walking through a quiet shopping mall when I noticed a sale sign in the window of an exclusive clothing store. The shopkeeper directed me to several racks of "athletic fit" suits, then left to answer a phone call. As she was the only one in the store, I signaled to her that I wanted to try on a light gray suit, and she pointed to the dressing rooms.

On my way back I passed a rack of women's suits, and saw one made from the same material as the one I had chosen. I selected a size that seemed right and proceeded back to change. The men's suit fit fine, so I tried on the women's one. It had a very flattering waistline and a short skirt. As I stood before the triple mirror admiring how well the outfit looked, my eye caught the saleswoman watching me from behind. She didn't act alarmed at all, but being a true professional, walked up and suggested that I try a colored blouse and scarf instead of my white shirt and tie. I took off the coat, tie, and shirt, revealing the lacy bra I'd worn to work. She returned with a pink silk blouse and a paisley scarf, tying it in an attractive manner around my neck. Her hands slid over my bra as she fastened the buttons up the back of the blouse. I was getting more turned on by the second, and could feel my rock-hard cock pulsate against my silky panties under the short skirt.

She took a step back, then suggested that I needed some shoes to complete the outfit. I told her my size and she brought back several boxes of black pumps. Handing me a package of black, thigh-high nylons, she explained how to pull them up without getting a run. She knelt before me as I sat on a bench, watching my panty-enclosed cock. I trembled a little as I slid the sexy nylons up my thighs, their dark color hiding my leg hair. She pulled a shoe from each box and we decided on a medium-height heel with a pretty bow and thin heel strap. She gently stroked my ankles while slipping the shoes onto my feet and fastening the straps. I stood between her and the mirrors to model the entire outfit. The shoes were a comfortable height, and I didn't wobble at all while walking or turning around. Still kneeling on the carpet, she said I looked great, and her hand stroked up the inside of my nylon-clad legs!

I couldn't believe what happened next! Reaching her hands up my legs, she lowered my come-stained panties and wrapped her luscious lips around my throbbing cock. Her hand continued to stroke my thighs while her mouth gave me the blowjob of the decade. It didn't take long before I exploded in great bursts of come, which she swallowed without missing a drop.

Then it was her turn. I knelt between her legs as she sat on the edge of the bench. Raising her skirt, I discovered that she didn't wear panties, but she had on the same type nylons that she'd given to me! My tongue nearly burned as I dove into her incredibly hot and juicy cunt. She cried out for me to lick harder and faster, until her legs wrapped around my neck and she came in violent spasms. My cock was rigid again, so I rolled her over on the bench. Spreading her legs, I plunged my cock into her flaming pussy. The sight of the two of us in women's clothes was reflected in the mirrors, bringing us both to new levels of excitement. She unbuttoned her blouse and begged me to grab her tits. I held her boobs tightly while slamming into her from behind. She bucked and grunted wildly, coming several more times before my jism streamed into her box. We collapsed onto the bench, drained by the awesome experience.

Afterward, I asked her if she was worried about other customers walking in on us, and she assured me that she had locked the door before waiting on me. I did purchase the men's suit, and she threw in the whole women's outfit at half price since it was "used." I'm on her new mailing list, and can't wait for the next sale!—*G.H., St. Paul, Minnesota*

GIVING HEAD TO A SALESMAN

Although my wife has never cared for the fact that I like to wear women's clothes, I'm still able to indulge my fetish regularly. My job requires me to travel a lot, and when I'm on the road, away from my family, I really get dolled up.

My last trip to Atlanta was one of my best experiences. At six in the evening, when I returned to my hotel, I started my routine of showering and shaving my legs as well as my face. It had been a while since I had had the chance to go out in drag, so I was looking forward to the evening. I decided to wear a basic white bra and panties with a full black slip and black panty hose. I took my time doing my nails and putting on my makeup. (This is one of the most sensual aspects of the entire ritual.) I had recently bought a bright red, *faux* leather skirt, and I pulled it up below a frilly white blouse. When I topped myself off with a shoulder-length blond wig, I was truly gorgeous.

I stood in front of the mirror and straightened everything out one more time, then stepped into my red spike heels and gave myself another spray of perfume. Throwing a few things into my purse, I headed for my car and sped off toward one of the "liberated" bars I know in the area.

The place wasn't far away, and once I was there, it didn't take long for me to start a conversation with some other transvestites. After a while, a rather large, muscular guy sat down at our table and joined in the conversation. It wasn't long before he moved next to me and asked me to dance. I don't consider myself gay or even bi, but I like the idea of playing the female role to the hilt, so I got up to dance with the guy. I figured that as long as the music was fast, I was okay. But when the deejay switched to something slow and the guy pulled me toward him, I found myself in a completely new situation. I was a bit taken aback by this, but soon I felt compelled to lean in closer to him. He whispered in my ear that this night he'd make sure I was all the woman I could be. I put my arms around his neck and told him that if he treated me like a lady, I was all his.

A song or two later we sat down. Our bodies were touching along one side, and I placed my hand on his thigh, quickly finding an erection growing in his pants. I could feel my own cock sliding around in all the nylon under my skirt, and I was afraid that it too would soon be bulging. I told him it was time to leave, and we headed for the door.

When we got back to my hotel, it felt good to kick off my heels. I had to take a leak, and that gave me a chance to fix my lipstick and make myself ladylike again. When I came out of the bathroom, he was already on the bed, loosening his belt. I climbed onto the bed and whispered into his ear, "Leave the rest to me."

I unbuttoned his shirt and started kissing his chest, running my tongue over his nipples and down around his belly button. His hips were pushing upward, and with my left hand I slowly unzipped his pants and freed his enormous cock. Cupping his hairy balls in one hand, I lightly stroked his masterpiece with the other. All this time, my kisses inched down his body. Finally I wrapped my lips around his oozing head and gently squeezed and tugged at it. He kept pushing it farther into my mouth and I had no choice but to run my lips up and down the length of his shaft. I was in heaven as I gobbled and slurped as much of his dick into my mouth as I could take. His butt was bouncing up and down on the bed, and when I started pumping the base of his cock in tandem with the tongue-lashing I was giving the head, he started to come. Great spurts of jism started streaming into my mouth. Inexperienced as I was, most of it dribbled down my chin and splashed onto his tight, hairy tummy. I don't know what had gotten into me, but the sight of his pulsing, flaring cockhead made me glad I hadn't held back.

He lay there exhausted and I fell back onto the floor. After a minute he was crawling toward me, his hands inching up under my skirt. I got kind of nervous, and in my semideep voice said, "Not tonight, sweetie. It's that time of the month."

"Don't be stupid," he told me. "I know you're a guy. Now, let me at that tool. I want to return the favor."

While he pulled my panties down around my ankles, I unzipped my skirt, completely exposing my already excited dong. In no time, he had his lips pistoning from the head to the base, and his tongue was simply incredible. Bucking my pelvis into his head, I warned him that I was about to spew. He just moaned, taking an ass cheek in each hand, pulling my prick even deeper into his hungry mouth. Just as I felt I was about to come, he started gently massaging my balls. I let loose with the warmest, creamiest ejaculation I have ever had, and my experienced new friend expertly swallowed it all.—*Name and address withheld*

A Special Kind of Girl

After five years of living with the same woman I found myself back in circulation again. Tired of having my sexual exploitation limited to the company of my right and left hands, I decided to check out the nightlife in town and see if I might get lucky. But after spending the evening dancing with a number of black-clad, self-absorbed lovelies, I was heading home alone without even a phone number.

I decided to stop at a hip, late-night cafe for a bite to eat. As I walked to the table I spotted a raven-haired beauty. She was wearing an incredibly tight black leather skirt with long seamed stockings. Her legs ended in a pair of "fuck me" stilettos. I could see the garter straps against her thighs. She looked like a "wild thing" from a heavy-metal video.

I looked up and realized she had caught me drooling over her. I quickly averted my eyes and found my way to my table. Almost before I was seated, there she was with both hands on my table, showing off her lovely cleavage. With a smoky voice she said, "The coffee is much better at my place. Want a taste?"

I was dumbfounded but able to blurt out, "Sure." Then we

were on our way out, heading down the street to her flat. I followed her up the stairs, enjoying the view of her lovely backside. My heart was pounding and I could feel my cock start to swell as we reached her door.

Just as I was aware that my bulge was more than obvious, she dropped her keys, bent over and pushed her perfect ass right into my crotch. As she ground that lovely leather-bound package against my straining cock, I thought my zipper would burst open. I could feel my stiff member bounding in time with my heartbeat.

Once she got the door open she spun around and pulled me inside, kicking the door shut. She pulled me close and went straight for my neck, licking and kissing as she savagely ripped off my pants. She nearly tore my shirt off as her mouth traced down my neck to my nipples. She bit and sucked, slowly working her way down my torso to my pulsing cock. She hungrily devoured me, licking and sucking from the purple tip down the shaft to my balls, juggling them with her tongue. This babe loved to suck cock. This was by far the best head I had ever received.

When I thought I would scream from the erotic overload, she started to pump the length of my shaft hard and fast. I could feel my balls pull tight and I knew I was far over the edge. She moaned with every spurt, keeping her greedy mouth glued to my shaft. Suddenly she stood up and mashed her mouth against mine. Our tongues danced in a river of my sweet, sour, and salty semen. She whipped off her lacy top, and I spread our mouthful over her neck, down to her perfect breasts. Semen was everywhere, running down her flat belly faster than my tongue. I ran my hand down her hip, found the zipper to her skirt, and pulled it down.

As I worked her zipper down, she stiffened. Just as I was about to pull her skirt free, she jumped back. I stood up with my cock hard again, wondering if I had hit the wrong erogenous button. I watched as her skirt fell away, revealing her beautiful body clothed in garters, stockings, stilettos, and lacy G-string. I was in for a surprise, though: a huge hard-on poked out of the top.

I was stunned, and she could see it. She took one step back and said, "I guess the night's over."

Well, I'm very open-minded, but I've never been attracted to men. In a split second, however, I responded, "I hope not."

She grabbed my hand and said, "Right this way, then." She led me to the bedroom, where she lay back on the bed and slowly pulled off her G-string panties. The huge cock she had so well concealed was free. I lay down next to her and started giving her the same treatment she had given me. I started at her neck, moving down to her breast and down her stomach to the first and only cock (other than my own) that I had ever touched. With a bit of guidance I started to run my tongue all over it. I took the head between my lips and circled my tongue around it.

I was just doing what I knew I liked having done to me. I experimented, taking the full length down my throat, sucking and licking her balls. I have to admit I was enjoying myself. Then, just as she had, I started stroking her huge tool hard and fast. Her ass lifted off the bed as she groaned, "Oh yes." I felt her ball sack tighten and I really started going at it. She pushed her tool deep into my mouth and blasted a huge load of hot semen. I thought I was going to gag. As I pulled away another load shot past my face.

I went up to her mouth and shared her spunk with her as our tongues wrestled. By morning we had sucked each other off twice more. I left weak-kneed.

I never saw her again and didn't really want to, but I had had the opportunity to try something different. I was glad I didn't stay home alone that night.—*B.G., Miami, Ohio*

GIRLS, GIRLS, GIRLS

I'd like to share a wonderful experience that I had a while ago. I am a twenty-eight-year-old heterosexual male, about five feet eight inches tall and slim, living with a beautiful twenty-six-year-old woman named Julia. Julia has a boyfriend named Adam.

One evening Julia and I were reading *Forum* together. A few stories about crossdressing excited both of us. That night Julia encouraged me to try her clothes on.

On my birthday, Julia and her friend Leslie had a surprise for me. First they gave me a nice, hot bubble bath, and shaved my legs and underarms as close as they could. Then they sat me down in front of Julia's dresser and began to apply makeup: base, eyeliner, mascara, eye shadow, lipstick (red), even long fingernails with red nail polish.

After makeup was done we went to Julia's room and I began opening my birthday gifts. There was everything I needed to be a woman: black stockings, high heels, a tight black dress, a long brunette wig, and a pair of silicone breasts. After I put everything on, it was time for me to take a look at myself in the mirror. I just couldn't believe my eyes, I looked so beautiful and sexy.

Next we all went to the living room. Julia and Leslie showed me how to walk, talk, and act like a woman. We practiced for a couple of hours, drinking wine the whole time.

I was getting pretty horny and having a great time. "Let's go dancing," Julia suggested. I was so drunk that I let them talk me into it.

On the way to the nightclub the girls taught me a few things about how to talk to guys when they ask you to dance. They even gave me a name: Tabitha.

At the club a few guys asked me to dance, but this one guy—about six feet tall, dark and handsome—stuck with me. During one slow dance I could feel his hard cock rubbing against me. It really turned me on. Then, before I knew it, he slipped his tongue into my mouth and French-kissed me. I had never kissed another guy before, but I admit it was great.

Julia, Leslie and I went home and we talked about how much

fun we had had. Julia and Leslie kept telling me I should have brought the guy home so we all could have made love to him.

The next Saturday, Julia said that she had another surprise for me. I told her that I wouldn't go out this time. She assured me that wouldn't happen. We went through the whole procedure again. Once again I looked sexy.

After we got dressed up, the doorbell rang. Adam, Julia's boyfriend, walked in. He didn't recognize me at first, but someone had told him about the games that we play. We sat around, watched X-rated videos, and drank more wine. Adam was sitting in the middle of the couch with Julia and me on each side. We all were getting pretty horny. Adam and Julia were kissing, then Adam put one hand on my leg and started to rub it up and down. Then he turned and kissed me while Julia was unbuttoning his shirt.

Julia and I started to kiss Adam's muscular chest and she led me down to his crotch. I unzipped him and pulled out his half-hard cock. "Go ahead, put it in your mouth," Julia told me as she pushed my head down on his cock. The skin was soft on his cock as I started to suck on it. I had a bit of a hard time putting it in my mouth at first, but soon I got the hang of it and really enjoyed it.

Then Julia and I started passing his cock back and forth between us. His cock was hard and nine inches long. Julia showed me how to deep-throat Adam's cock. Before I knew it I was putting all of his hard cock in my mouth. All of a sudden he shot his steaming load into my mouth. It seemed like he came forever.

Then Julia grabbed me by the chin and started kissing and licking the rest of Adam's come off my mouth. Adam's cock was still hard, so Julia pulled down her panties and sat on his cock with her back to Adam. She asked me to lick her pussy and Adam's cock while he was fucking her.

Next Julia asked me to fuck her while we both sucked on

Adam's cock, and before long Adam filled our mouths with his come and I filled Julia's pussy with my come.

After that wonderful night, Julia, Leslie, and Tabitha play our game now and then. All three of us play the game at least once a month, then we all make love together. We are the best three girlfriends that there could be.——*P.T., Kansas City, Missouri*

PANTIE PALS

With each new issue of *Forum*, I look forward to getting turned on. I especially like the letters about crossdressing and men sucking cock. I found myself fantasizing about doing both. Finally, I tried it.

I went down to a women's clothing store and headed straight for the lingerie. I told the saleswoman I was shopping for a girl-friend. There were so many things to choose from that I almost couldn't decide what I wanted. I finally bought some nylon panties because of their soft, shimmery, smooth feeling.

I now have some red string bikini panties that let my cock stick out above the waist when I have a hard-on; some black hip-huggers that fit nice and hold my cock down so it strains at its confines; a G-string that lets me rub my bare ass and my pantie-covered cock at the same time; and two pairs that are cut really high on the leg with a high waist. I've worn them all and jacked off many times.

I decided one day to suck a cock. I went to the local adult video store and went to the video booths in back. I wasn't leaving until I had a hard cock explode down my throat. I was so hot! I began watching the movie (a she-male flick with a lot of hard cock in panties!) and stroking my pantie-enclosed cock. I was at full erection when I heard the door next to me shut and the sound of a zipper going down. My heart began beating faster as I made my move.

I tapped lightly on the door and heard a whispered "Yes?"

"I can help you out with that if you let me in," I replied.

The door opened and I quickly entered. Inside was a cute young guy, about twenty years old. He looked really nervous, so I took charge. I got him to relax, then slowly slid his jeans down. He had a smooth, hairless body and a nice, stiffening bulge in his bikini briefs. I pulled them down and gently squeezed and stroked his cock. He had about six inches when he was completely hard. The shaft was so smooth I had to lick it. I ran my tongue up his cock and heard him suck in a breath.

I stepped back and very slowly pulled my slacks down. His eyes widened and he let out a moan as he saw my hard-on completely covered by my panties. He reached down and began rubbing my balls through my panties. I went down on him and his breath quickened.

He started jacking me off through my flimsy panties. A few large drops of pre-come oozed out. By the light of the video monitor, I could see my cock perfectly through the wet material. He told me my cock felt so good through my panties that he wanted to wear some and rub our stiff poles together through them. I said, "Then let's go to my place and we can!" He agreed, and we quickly left for my apartment.

He got undressed as I selected a pair of light-blue panties for him. He pulled them on and began stroking himself. He got on my bed and begged me to dry-hump him. I kissed him deeply as our rock-hard members rubbed together. I pulled back, went down and kissed his cock through the nylon material. I slid them down and positioned myself so my cock was up near his head. I hoped he would start to suck mine.

I started swirling my tongue around his cockhead, covering it with saliva. I tried to remember all I had seen in porn movies and put it to use. I must have done well. He told me I sucked cock better than his girlfriend. I immediately went at him more intensely, deep-throating his young love-rod.

I was overjoyed when he grasped my cock and started licking and sucking. He was doing all right for a beginner.

I felt the quick spasms of his orgasm. I gave him a final deep-throat and sucked hard all the way to the soft head of his cock.

He came in four quick spurts. I caught it and let it go down my throat. I continued flicking my tongue around the head of his half-hard cock.

I neared climax and shot a giant load into his mouth and onto his chest. I licked it off, rolled it around on my tongue, and swallowed it. He still held most of my load in his mouth as I kissed him deeply, causing him to swallow it.

He thanked me for a wonderful time and asked if he could shower. I told him to go ahead. I quickly grabbed my camera and rushed to the shower with him. I told him to leave his panties on as he showered. His cock, as well as mine, sprang back to attention at the idea.

We took a roll of photos and made plans for our next few encounters. He wants to let his girlfriend in on our secret and have an all-night threesome. She rubs her panties on his cock now, so I guess you could say she's headed in the right direction.—*Name and address withheld*

WHAT A BARGAIN

I am twenty-four years old, stand five feet seven inches tall, and weigh about a hundred and thirty pounds. Ever since my early teens I've had a desire to crossdress, and for several years now I've occasionally gone out wearing heels and hose. One afternoon I decided to try something new. I went to the mall wearing my denim miniskirt, garter belt, nylons, and high heels—and no panties!

I had a raging hard-on (or at least as big as my little pony will get) as I pulled the denim mini over my red and black lace garter belt and black, sheer nylons. With this I wore a light blue cotton top with spaghetti shoulder straps, a small-cupped strapless bra (stuffed, of course), a touch of makeup, and my favorite black high-heel slip-on sandals.

When I arrived at the mall, I quickly made my way to the outside entrance of a women's shoe store. The place was empty with the exception of a middle-aged woman who was simply browsing and two salesgirls talking behind the register. I walked over to one of the displays of shoes, and as I passed the register, I could hear the two girls giggling, one of them saying, "It's a guy."

With my back to them, I picked up an ankle-strap sandal and was looking at it when one of the girls approached me and asked if she could help me. I showed her the shoe and told her my size. As she looked me up and down, she smiled, said, "Sure," and strode off. When she returned I was standing near the seats, but I was afraid to sit down—I was worried that she might see my little penis. But the shoes looked great, and I just had to try them on.

When I sat down, I noticed that my stockings were exposed almost to the garters. I tried tugging at my skirt, but the salesgirl told me not to worry. She said she'd caught hundreds of inadvertent peeks at women's privates. "It's part of the job," she assured me.

About this time the other salesgirl walked over and sat in the chair to my left, saying that my shoes looked good. The first girl, still kneeling in front of me, suggested that I walk to see how they felt. I uncrossed my legs, stood up, tugged at my skirt, and walked to the mirror. When I returned to my seat and sat down, I forgot to check my skirt, which promptly rode up my legs, exposing not only the tops of my stockings, but also the head of my prick!

Before I got a chance to pull my skirt down and apologize, each of the girls grabbed a side of the mini and pulled it up around my waist. At first I thought they were just trying to embarrass me, but when the girl kneeling on the floor leaned toward me and wrapped her lips around the head of my prick, I wasn't embarrassed at all—I was in heaven!

"What about customers?" I asked.

"We locked the door just after that old lady left," the girl to my left assured me as she unbuttoned her blouse and brought the rosy nipple of a small but pert little tit to my mouth.

I had one girl hobnobbing my modest little dick while I paid tongue service to another willing nymph. These girls couldn't have been more than seniors in high school, but they'd obviously had more sexual experience than I'd ever even dreamed about.

Just when I felt like I was going to shoot, Salesgirl Number One slurped away from my dick and, grabbing my ankles, pulled me to the floor. I said good-bye to my pink little mammary friends, but was soon greeted by an ever more palatable protrusion. When Salesgirl Number Two stood over me and lifted up her skirt, I saw that she wasn't wearing any panties either. Nestled at the apex of an inverted triangle of fine, brunette pubic hair was a sweet little vaginal gash, surpassed in beauty only by the throbbing clit that, exposed by the salesgirl's knowing fingers, was rapidly descending upon my mouth.

I lapped at that little tiger as if I hadn't eaten in a week, and soon the girl was gyrating madly above me, grinding her patch against my nose.

The other girl had continued her blowjob, and soon my dick had grown to around five or six inches, a record for me. Just as the girl on my face was about to come, she yelled over her shoulder, "You got him ready, Alicia?"

"I think that's as big as it's going to get, Anne."

Again the sweets were snatched from my mouth, and again I didn't mind. Anne inched her butt down toward my dick, leaving a trail of warm, wet jism, and gently descended upon my rod. Oh, ecstasy. How many times had I beaten off in the past year, dreaming of this moment. I started pushing up my pelvis, and Anne met my every thrust. Sweetly, warmly she slid up and down on my cock, occasionally rocking from side to side, making sure to stimulate the entire surface of my dick.

When I was ready to come, Anne sensed it and leaned back, placing her hands on my knees. This really stimulated the head of my penis, but it prohibited me from coming just yet. She humped me in this position a couple of times, and when she finally lunged forward, I let loose with at least five good spurts of love cream.

Sweat was beading on her little titties, and Alicia, who'd been masturbating while watching us, lowered her mouth to lick those little orbs, swinging her ass and luscious blond pussy onto my face.

It wasn't till I got home an hour later that I realized I was wearing a brand-new pair of shoes.—*Name and address withheld*

S&M

Wife Does the Driving

I am dressed like the little slut I am. My hair is primped and teased. My lips are painted my favorite shade of pink, my eyes are shaded with just the right amount of blue and red, and my lashes are coated with mascara. My chest is covered by a frilly, lacy red bra. Around my waist is a matching red garter belt that holds up my red fishnet stocking. Oh yes, I almost forgot about my red crotchless panties, from which my hard and dripping cock protrudes. That's right, I'm a man, and I'm about to get fucked. And, believe me, I'm going to enjoy it.

Denise stands before me. Her lips, painted bright red for this occasion, are locked in a smile that tells me she is looking forward to using me like the slut I am. Her breasts glisten in the soft glow of candlelight that bathes the room. Her pink nipples stand straight up at attention; I know this is a sure sign that she is hot. My eyes move from her tits and across her flat tummy to her waist. Her shaven pussy is hidden from my view, not by panties or any other garment, but by a strap-on dildo. It looks just like a real cock—flesh-colored and veined, about six inches long and half as wide. My heartbeat quickens as I realize that this plastic penis will soon be buried to the hilt in my virgin ass. But for now Denise has other ideas about where to put it.

"Well, my little slut," she whispers, "if you want this cock, you're going to have to prove that you love it." She pushes me to my knees, my lips now inches from her makeshift cock. "Tonight you are going to be my little cocksucker, aren't you?" she asks. When she receives no answer from me, she asks again. This time I answer, "Yes, Denise. Tonight I'll suck your cock. Tonight and any night you want me to." Her hand moves to the back of my head. My mouth opens wide as I take the head of the dildo in my mouth. My lips close and then I take them away so I can admire my lipstick print on the wonderful shaft. "You had better do a good job of sucking my cock," Denise tells me. "The wetter you get it, the easier it will slide up that virgin ass of yours. Besides," she continues, "if you do not suck me the way I want you to, I may not fuck that pretty little ass of yours. You wouldn't want that."

"No, I wouldn't," I whisper. "I want you to fuck my ass, and I'll do whatever you want. Just please tell me you'll fuck me." Her only response is, "Suck it," and that's just what I did. My lips closed around the plastic penis, and I sucked it into my eager mouth. Her hands gripped the back of my head as she pushed the cock deeper into my mouth. My tongue eagerly licked the shaft as she plunged it in and out of my mouth. It was hitting the back of my throat, causing me to gag with each thrust. She just laughed about that as she fucked my face, all the while telling me what a good little cocksucker I was. After what seemed like hours of using my mouth, she finally pulled the cock out. "Now," she said, "I want you to tell me where you want me to put this dick."

"I want you to put it in my ass, Denise," I whispered.

"What?" she asked. "I really can't hear you, but I'm sure you didn't say please."

"Please," I cried. "Please, Denise, fuck my ass. Shove that cock deep inside me. Please fuck me, please."

"That's better, you little slut. Now I can hear you," she hissed. "Now I know you want it, and I'm going to give it to you. Turn around and stick that sweet little ass in the air," she said. "I want your cheeks spread wide."

I quickly did as she said. Resting my face on the floor, I used my hands to spread my cheeks wide. I had been waiting a long time for this, and when she finally did break my cherry ass, I wanted her to be as deep inside me as possible. "That's a good little slut," she whispered. "Spread them cheeks wide, because I'm going to fuck you good."

She knelt behind me, and I felt the tip of that cock pressing against my hole. It was slick from my saliva, and my ass gave little resistance as the head slid inside. It hurt but excited me at the same time. Slowly she inched her way inside me, my asshole expanding as it was filled with the cock. I was squirming with delight when I felt her thighs slap against my ass. I was completely filled, her cock buried in my ass, and I was loving it. "Fuck me, Denise," I was screaming without even realizing it. "Stick that cock inside me. Fuck me like the little slut that I am."

"You love it, you little slut, don't you?" she cried.

"Yes, I love it. My ass is yours. Do what you want with me," I whimpered. "Just please don't stop." She raped my ass until she was tired of it, plunging in and out of my anus with wild abandon. When she tired, I would drive my ass backwards on her cock. I just couldn't get enough. I had her lie on the floor and I lowered myself onto her cock. Then I rode it the way I had seen her ride mine so many times before. Finally, with her behind me, again fucking my ass very gently and slowly, she took my cock in her hand and jerked me off. When I came, she caught every drop in her hand. She then brought it to my lips and I sucked my come from her hand. My story ends here, with a cock up my ass and come in my mouth. Just like the little slut that I am.—*M.D., Trenton, New Jersey*

THE WHIPPING CANE

It pays not to keep your secrets locked in. Although I was brought up in a country where in most homes it is still commonplace to find a whipping cane, I'd never experienced it myself during my entire childhood. Nevertheless, somehow I became obsessed with whipping canes and the things that can be done with them.

I was twenty-six when, in a weak moment I revealed to Charleen, my new girlfriend, then just recently visiting from England, the fantasies I'd had since adolescence about girls with canes and switches and about getting spanked by them. I said this to her mostly to explore the possibility of her one day being willing to play those games. Charleen's first reaction was, "You are crazy!"

For two weeks she avoided me and I feared it was all over between us. Then finally she phoned and asked me to meet her at a summer pool party at Cathy's house. Cathy was her English friend. I had never met her before.

It was at a condo on the far north side of Detroit on a hot summer day. Charleen was not there, and I, being quiet and unsuspecting, had not found it strange that only Cathy, the twenty-three-year-old, short-haired, blond and statuesque nymph from England was there, with her much younger roommate Maryellen. Both were in their swimsuits. They insisted that I, too, put my trunks on and join them at the pool to wait for Charleen. Little did I know. I was still buttoning up my fly when, without knocking, they were in the room saying that I must join them for a drink first.

The bar was in the rec room that was below the ground level. My heart jolted when I noticed a three-foot-long, thin, supple switch of ringed, jointed bamboo ominously shining on top of a black leather-covered hassock in the middle of the brightly sunlit room. The switch was curved at one end into a handle. I was startled. "Will you take it off yourself," said Cathy point-blank, "or do we do it for you?"

Blood froze in my veins when she took that switch, and I think that my toes curled when she flexed it testily to her side. She was the type who most likely threw the discus over two hundred feet, and to relax spent an hour or more on the vaulting horse. I stood transfixed, then stupefied by embarrassment when Maryellen pulled my trunks down and off. Before I knew it I was across that hassock myself, tied to it by the hands and feet.

Charleen had told them about my fantasies and I was there to be rid of them. I was there to get a licking that would ensure I wouldn't sit for a day, Cathy had announced as she turned the stereo on high. I confess to pleading and crying out in pain like a child, but to no avail. Cathy had whipped me until I couldn't sit, not for one day, but for three.

Charleen had never mentioned anything on our next date, and I was too embarrassed to bring it up. It was a month later that she told me she'd made another appointment for me with Cathy, being absolutely inexorable about it. I was to either keep the appointment or lose her.

I'm not sure which was worse: the embarrassment of facing Cathy and Maryellen again, undressing before them, or seeing that flexing switch and knowing what was coming next. Cathy's announcement drilled me into the floor. "You'll be getting lickings from me once a month until you're completely cured of your freak fantasies, and it is I who will decide when that is."

I had ten sessions with Cathy's switch, across the hassock in the rec room, even though my fantasies had really been dead after the second, if not already after the first. I had tried to put this across to her time after time. Still, I had to keep on returning until she finally was convinced that it was so.

That was more than ten years ago. Charleen and I have been married for over nine, and I must say very happily. Our sex life is great and Cathy never talks about our early sessions, although her switch has hung for all these years on the inside of the closet door in our bedroom, visibly bowed now.——*Name and address withheld by request*

Take My Wife, Hard

For Christmas, my wife Allie bought me an expensive toy, a camcorder. Little did she know that she would be my prime subject. I now have several hours of her on video: in suits, tight skirts, teddies, garter belts, and stockings, and of course, in the raw. I had a big and daring video planned, but I needed her approval. Finally, after much begging and persuasion—and a promise from me that I would never ask her to do such a thing again—she agreed to be in the video I'd proposed.

Through a friend of mine who manages an adult book store, I was able to get two guys who would treat my wife to some rough sex while I operated the camera. John and Max were very big, very strong men. They said they'd be careful, but guaranteed to give Allie a workout none of us would ever forget.

On the appointed night, Allie and I waited nervously for them to arrive. As I readied the camera, Allie put on a white blouse, a red knee-length skirt, and high heels. Allie may be forty-three, but she has the figure of a beauty pageant contestant. She's small on top, with a firm, round bottom and legs you could look at all day long.

I heard the doorbell and let in John and Max. They introduced themselves to Allie and we chatted a bit. John was tall and on the skinny side. Max, who was black, was built like a pro football player. He was over six feet tall and must have weighed two hundred twenty pounds, all of it solid muscle. His chest and shoulders were massive. As I gave them my instructions and told them what I expected, I could tell Max's mind was elsewhere. As he sat across from Allie, who had her legs crossed, he was getting a good look under her skirt. Well, I thought, he'll be seeing a lot more of her soon.

I turned on the camera and we got down to business. John, Max, and Allie went into the bedroom. When I gave the signal, the men carried her into the living room, holding her tightly by the arms. I'd told Allie to put up a bit of a struggle, for effect. At one point, she jerked her arm so furiously that she freed herself from Max's tremendous grip. I could tell it was going to be a great video.

John grabbed Allie from behind, pinning her arms to her side. Max quickly took her by the legs. They carried her to the couch and threw her onto her back. She attempted to get up, but she was like a fly in a spiderweb. I focused on John. With just one hand, he held Allie's hands securely over her head. With his free hand he started to unbutton her blouse, then simply tore it away. He unsnapped the small clasp at the front of her bra. It sprang open to reveal her pert tits, the enormous brown nipples swollen with excitement.

Max, at the other end, had worked her skirt up above her stockings. I zoomed in for a close-up of her creamy, bare thighs. Max rested his body over her ankles. That gave him the freedom to do what he wanted with his hands. And right now, each hand was busy caressing and fondling Allie's thighs, slowly working their way under her skirt.

A quick movement caught my eye: John was still holding Allie, but now he began to unbuckle his belt with one hand. Unzipping his fly, he was able to wiggle out of his pants. Allie's eyes were on the bulge in his underwear. My wife didn't have to wait long to see the big six John was packing. Kicking his briefs aside, John threw a leg over Allie. In a kneeling position he straddled her chest, his cock just inches from her mouth. He pinned her wrists to the couch, and gently slapped her across the face a few times with his hard cock.

Allie tried to get his cock in her mouth, but he teased her and would never let it past her lips. Finally she turned away, but John reached down and turned her head to face him. Just then, she gave out a short sigh of pleasure. I knew at that point that

Max was up to something, so I tilted the camera in his direction.

Max had removed Allie's panties, bent her legs at the knees, and lowered his mouth to her juicy cunt. I could smell its sweetness all the way across the room. I watched with a hard-on as Max tongued my wife silly. He kept her legs spread wide apart with his strong hands. When he pulled away for a moment, her pink slit was visible within the thick, jet-black hair that shrouded her pussy. Then Max's tongue disappeared again in the hot folds of Allie's cunt.

I couldn't keep up with the action. John already had his swollen cock in Allie's mouth. His strokes were hard, fast, and sure. Each time he withdrew his wet tool, I watched with excitement as it slammed back into her mouth. I could tell she was doing everything possible to please him with her mouth and tongue.

Max's head was bobbing up and down. I knew Allie was getting a good tongue fucking. I saw her abdomen begin to jerk as her hips rose off the couch to meet his busy mouth. Suddenly her hips shot forward, and the muscles of her belly quivered with orgasm. I know from experience that as soon as Allie comes, she needs to rest a few minutes—she has told me the pleasure is so intense it is almost painful if she continues on. But this time, although she tried closing her legs and pushing him away, Max would not let up. His head continued to bob, and Allie had no choice but to endure the passionate thrusts of his demanding tongue.

Now it was John who was beginning to spasm. He threw his head back and filled my wife's mouth with come. She swallowed deeply each time he pumped out a little more juice. When he was totally drained, he pulled his dick out of her mouth. She tried to talk, but he silenced her and told her to stroke his dick with her hands. He was hard again in a few minutes and, pushing Max away, sank his long bone into Allie's cunt.

As John fucked Allie's pussy, Max took his turn in her mouth. His black, uncircumcised cock was a sight to behold. Thick and heavily veined, it glistened with Allie's saliva as she sucked it feverishly. I pulled the camera back to get them all in frame just in time to catch their orgasms on tape. They all came within seconds of each other. John emptied his load in Allie's cunt, Max's rocketed straight down her throat, and Allie herself alternately screamed and giggled with the most powerful orgasm I've ever seen her experience.

The big surprise was that after the men left, Allie said she wouldn't mind doing it all over again. Perhaps I can convince her to work the camera while I go at it with a pair of sexy women.— *D.M., Madison, Wisconsin*

How to Handle Pressure

I love reading letters about women who are slaves, since I have been one myself for the past two years.

I am a twenty-six-year-old female. I am also a high school teacher. The pressure of my job caused me to lose many friends and divorce my husband. I asked my friend Clara, who is twenty-five years old, and a teacher at my school, how she handles the pressure. She told me to come home with her the following Friday. She told me that I must not tell anyone about what I would see nor what would be done, and I had to do anything I was told to do.

When we got to Clara's house we went into the master bedroom, where I was told by Clara to strip down to my bra and panties. Clara did the same. Then we headed for the basement, where we waited for Clara's husband, Jason, to come home from work. I asked Clara what was going to happen, but she told me not to ask any questions. When Jason finally arrived, he told Clara to remove her panties and bra and lay across the pool table. Then he pulled out a long strap from the closet and gave her twenty-five whacks with it as I watched. Her ass was turning crimson red as she cried out, twisting and jerking under each blow.

When he was finished with Clara, Jason turned to me and told me to remove my panties and bra, which I did. Then I lay down across his knee and he gave me fifteen whacks. In my case he used his open hand, since it was my first spanking. He told me that as the weeks went by, I would get spanked in the same manner Clara did. After the spanking, Jason took our bras and panties with him upstairs and told us that they would not be returned until we stopped crying.

After a couple of months of this treatment I was invited to live with Clara and Jason. I eventually told them that I would, but not until I had mulled the idea over in my mind for a couple of weeks. I decided that the idea excited me. That's how I became Jason and Clara's personal slave.

The relationship dictates that I obey all the rules they set up for me. I must not speak unless I am spoken to first. I must address Jason as "sir" or "master," and Clara as "mistress" when we are at home. Before I go to work on Mondays, Jason uses a studded strap on me so that I can't sit down properly for two whole days. He also bought a special bra for me. This bra is made with metal wire, so if my tits become hard the wire juts into my nipples. It can become very painful. I must wear panties that have the day of the week printed on them. If I wear the wrong panties I am given a quick, hard spanking, and I am not allowed to wear any panties for the rest of the day.

Since I am not allowed to have any pubic hair, I must keep my legs and pussy clean-shaven at all times. Jason can check my pussy at any time, so I make sure I'm prepared.

Jason likes me to keep a dildo up my pussy while I work. During my lunch break Clara and I go into the staff restroom. I lift up my skirt so that she can check to make sure the dildo is still in place. She is allowed to remove it and fondle me if she wants to, and most times she does.

After our workday I must take a shower with Clara. Jason orders me to masturbate as Clara feels my tits. Then I must masturbate Clara. The only sex I am allowed to have is with Clara or other women. When I have sex with another woman, Jason and Clara watch. When Jason and Clara are having sex, I must watch. During these times I masturbate, and then I must eat Clara's pussy. After she is satisfied I am tied spread-eagle to the bed. Clara straps on a dildo and enters my pussy. When she is finished I am turned over on my stomach. She places a pillow underneath me to prop my ass up in the air. Then she slowly enters my asshole, thrusting back and forth until I cry out in both pain and pleasure.

Often Jason rents adult movies. I must watch them with him and masturbate openly for Clara and Jason. After the movie, Jason duplicates with me what was done to the woman in the movie.

Clara made up a game that I play with her. She makes me dress up like a little girl while she pretends to be my mother. She tells me I am a bad little girl and she must spank me to make me mind my manners. I lay down across her knees as she lifts up my skirt and pulls my panties down. Then she promptly gives me a spanking with a hairbrush. As she is whacking me I must cry out, "Please, Mommy, I'll be a good girl!" After I am disciplined, Clara takes off her dress and panties, and orders me to stop crying and eat her pussy. If I break any of her rules I get punished. And when I get punished by Clara, she gives me a bare-bottom spanking with a hard, wooden paddle.

When I get punished by Jason he takes me into the basement, where I am tied up, wrists together, and hooked to a chain that is hanging from the ceiling. He puts clothespins on my tits and pussy. Then he takes a whip to my ass. Afterward he removes the clothespins from my pussy and gives me ten whacks with a wooden ruler.

Even though I am a slave to Jason and Clara, it is clear that I am able to leave at any time. But I choose to stay.—*Y.T., Seattle, Washington*

BETTER THAN GOOD

My girlfriend Sophie recently moved to another state for a few months to take a job. I miss her a great deal, but our reunions on weekends have been spectacular.

First let me tell you about Sophie. She's five-feet-four, weighs about one hundred pounds, has long jet-black hair, and is in terrific shape (she used to be a gymnast). But the thing I love most about Sophie is her imagination. She's willing to try anything, and our sex life has become increasingly wild and exciting. In the course of this, I discovered that she likes to be overpowered and "forced" to have sex.

On her most recent trip back here, I picked her up at the airport on Friday evening, but instead of rushing her back to my apartment, as she expected, I took her to dinner. We both knew what was coming, and as we sat, eating and talking, I knew she was getting wet with anticipation.

When we finally arrived at the apartment, I was very formal and stern with her as I sat her on the couch. "Sophie," I said, "you've been gone for three weeks and you've neglected my cock. You know you'll have to be punished for that."

"No, please don't," she pouted. "I've been good."

"Good? I lie here at night aching for you, and you say you've been good? Now pull down your pants and climb across my lap. You're going to be spanked." I grabbed her by the wrist and pulled her across me.

With one hand, I reached under her and unbuttoned her pants, which I quickly yanked down to expose her lovely, tiny bottom. I ran my hand over the soft skin for a moment. Then, holding her by the nape of the neck with one hand, with the other hand I slapped her bottom, first softly, then with more force, until her pale white cheeks turned pink and she began to moan.

I paused for a moment to remove her pants completely. "Spread your legs," I told her.

She obeyed, and I ran my hand up her thigh to feel her pussy. She was soaking wet. "This excites you, doesn't it?" I said.

"Mmmm," she moaned. I released her neck and used that hand to continue her spanking as I gently stroked her clit with my other hand. Her legs parted even more. She was squirming now and making the little noises she makes, the noises that always get me hard.

"Okay, baby," I said, stroking her. "You're very wet. You need to come. Go ahead, babe. Give it to me. Come hard."

It didn't take long. Her pent-up sexual energy needed some release. She went stiff for an instant and then her entire body began to quiver. With a long, agonizing moan, she pushed her cunt onto my hand and came, soaking my fingers with her juices.

I let her recover for a few seconds while I removed my clothes and the rest of hers. I sat back on the couch and told her to kneel in front of me. She did so, meekly. "Now take my cock between your lips," I said. "I want to come in your mouth."

"No! I . . ." But before she could complete her protest, I grabbed her by the hair and forced my cock into her mouth.

Sophie loves to give head, and once she had the taste of it, her natural inclinations took over. I sat back and enjoyed it—the way she licked, sucked, and flicked her tongue back and forth on the underside of my rod. She took me almost to the peak, then looked up at me, into my eyes, and slid my rock-hard tool slowly all the way down her throat. That finished me. I had wanted her for weeks. Grabbing her hair with both hands, I fucked her mouth until my come exploded down her throat.

I lifted her head and looked into her face. Her eyes were glazed. "I know you're still very wet," I said. "I'm not done with you." And with that, I lifted her into my arms and carried her into the bedroom, where I laid her on the bed.

She was limp. I had tied a set of handcuffs to the bed with a length of rope, and I now fastened the cuffs around her wrists. Her eyes opened very wide.

"What are you going to do?" she asked.

"I've missed you," I said. "And now you're mine. Turn over."

She hesitated. "You're not going to spank me, are you?" she asked.

"Yes.

"Please don't."

I flipped her over, slid my legs under her, and began spanking her still-pink bottom, harder this time, until she squirmed and cried out and begged me to stop. I put my hand between her legs and felt her pussy. She was even wetter than before. "You need to come some more, don't you, babe?" I asked. She didn't answer.

I turned her on her back and spread her legs. Sophie's cunt was glistening with her juices. I teased her a bit by running my tongue up her thighs to her dripping pussy and licking the lips of her snatch, but stopping just short of her aching clit.

She moaned pitifully. "Please . . ." she begged. "Please . . ."

Abruptly, I slid two fingers into her cunt and flicked my tongue furiously back and forth over her hard clit. She came instantly. Her pussy contracted around my fingers and she called out my name. She was twisting and wriggling and fighting me until, again, her whole body trembled and she drenched my hand and the bed with her come.

This time I gave her no rest. The taste of her juices had reinvigorated me, and I climbed atop her and slid my cock into her soft, wet hole. I'd never felt anything like it. She was still coming, and the muscles of her cunt were contracting spasmodically around my stiff rod.

I lifted her legs over my shoulders for deeper penetration and fucked her hard and slow, plunging all the way into her and sliding almost all the way out, savoring her grasping, tight snatch.

She was just making noises now, unable to speak complete words. Her long black hair lay tousled about her head. I'd never seen her more beautiful.

I buried my cock in her and rested for a moment, then I kissed her. "If I release your hands, will you do as you're told?"

"I'll do anything you want," she said. I reached for the key on the bedside table and removed the handcuffs. I slid my cock out of her.

"Turn over," I said. "I want you on your hands and knees." She did so. "Now reach between your legs and play with yourself," I told her. "I want to see how you make yourself come."

She needed no further encouragement. Starting slowly at first, she stroked her clit, occasionally slipping two fingers into her pussy to wet them. She was moaning now and rotating her bottom, inviting me to enter her. She was putting on a show for me.

I took the jar of Vaseline from the bedside table and applied some along the length of my rod, then slid two greased fingers between the cheeks of her lovely bottom and, ever so gently, into her ass. I held them there for a moment as she continued to finger her clit. She was breathing very quickly. She was in a frenzy of anticipation.

I removed my fingers and placed the head of my cock against her asshole. I was in a frenzy myself, but I knew I had to take it slowly so as not to hurt her.

I rubbed it up and down over the tightest of her holes, then pushed firmly until the head popped into her ass. She groaned.

"It hurts a bit," she said.

"Do you want me to stop?"

After a pause, she answered, "No." She continued to play with her clit, more furiously now, as I gradually buried my cock all the way into her ass. I held it there as she brought herself closer and closer to orgasm.

Finally, I reached around and replaced her fingers with my own, and that did it. She came. She came hard, in a screaming, squirming, moaning fit of pleasure. It was all I could do to hold her down as the orgasm swept through her body.

"Now fuck me," she begged. "Please fuck me. Please. Hard. Shoot it in my ass."

I lay on top of her, flattening her on the bed, still holding her down and slamming my pole into her until I couldn't hold it any-more.

With one last plunge, I buried my cock deep in her ass as she wiggled her bottom and sucked my come into her hot little hole. I was shaking. It seemed to take forever. It seemed to come from the base of my spine.

I lay there on her for a minute, exhausted, before easing my rod from her bottom. I turned her over and kissed her. "I'm crazy about you," I told her.

She smiled, a coquettish, little-girl sort of smile. "I still think I'm a good girl," she said coyly.

"No, you're not," I replied. "You're better."—*M.D., Boston, Michigan*

UNDER BAD INFLUENCE

I am a white male, five-foot-ten, one hundred sixty-five pounds, and I love to be spanked. As long as I can remember, I have fantasized about and enjoyed erotic spankings. My girlfriend enjoys this aspect of sex very much.

Besides enjoying this, she finds that it's a good way to discipline me when I am a bad boy. After our relationship was a year old, I had to tell her my feelings about being spanked. To my surprise, she gladly said she would give disciplining me a try. I was more than ready to get started then and there, but she said the time wasn't right. She said that she wanted to wait until she had a good reason to punish me.

Two days later, while we were out on a date, we got into an argument, and I said something mean that I readily apologized for. Then she said that she didn't accept my apology. She ordered me to turn off the highway onto a deserted dirt road she knew about. Once we were in a suitably deserted spot, she ordered me out of the car and around to the back. She proceeded to undo my thick leather belt and free it from my pant loops. Then she ordered me to turn around. She unbuttoned and unzipped my jeans and pulled them and my shorts to my ankles. She told me to bend over, place my hands on the trunk lid, and to stay that way until she said different.

Using a force that I had not known she possessed, my girlfriend slapped my behind so hard that an "Ouch!" escaped me. She placed each stinging stroke from the top to the bottom of my ass cheeks. I was at the point of crying when the twentieth and final stroke fell. Then, after ordering me to stand and face her, she pulled me close and said all was forgiven. With my raging hard-on pressing against her dress, I asked, "May I please be made to cry from another spanking?"

She replied that if that was what I wanted I should resume the position. She stepped to a nearby tree and tore off a switch roughly three feet in length. I started to cry after the first hard stroke, but she continued with the switch for seven more stinging strokes.

Finally, she removed her panties and crawled on the trunk. She said, "Make love to me."

And I did—like I never had before. Using all the sexual energy I had built up, we went hard and fast like two horny teenagers.—*J.R., San Francisco, California*

Oral Sex

Float Downstream

Until a couple of weeks ago, probably like the majority of your readers, I had never had a sexual experience that deserved special notice. But a very special and unusual experience came my way recently aboard my ski boat after the annual river raft race.

I had invited two girls to come along with me in my boat to watch the day's events and to catch some sun. At the last moment, Karen had to cancel because of a sick relative.

Fortunately, though, Toni said she would still like to go. After leaving the dock, Toni and I had a swell time taking in all the sights, sipping cold beer and soaking up the rays.

Toni wore a sexy black string bikini that left very little to the imagination. After we'd jumped overboard to cool off, I could see the outline of her nipples through the material. This was a real turn-on, because I had often thought of making it with her and caressing those sexy breasts.

When the raft race was over, Toni and I decided to take a cruise down the river to get away from the wakes thrown up by all the other boats. After we'd gone several miles, Toni asked if Rich, a friend of ours, really skied naked. I laughed, told her it was true, and asked Toni if she wouldn't like to give it a try. I couldn't believe my ears when she said it sounded like fun.

My delight turned to disappointment, however, when I remembered that I had left the skis and other accessories at home to give us more room in the boat. I offered to find a secluded spot so we could take a dip in the buff, which, I assured Toni, was almost as much fun. She said she would give it a try if I agreed to turn around while she slipped out of her suit and jumped into the water. I gave her my promise and looked the other way until I heard her splash into the river; then I dropped my cutoffs and leapt overboard to join her.

We splashed and played for a while, and I "accidentally" brushed up against her breasts a couple of times. When Toni said she was ready to get out of the water and dry off, I climbed into the boat and helped her over the side. To my amazement, she then laid herself back on the seat, naked. I sat at her feet and she began to playfully massage my stiffening cock with her feet. It was a turn-on to see her painted toes playing with my cock.

I moved up beside her, touched her breast, and kissed her gently on the lips. I moved my hand slowly down her stomach and stopped at her navel before moving lower to her silky mound. Toni gave me no sign of objection, so I slipped my hand between her thighs and began to caress her pussy lips. Soon I had a finger inside her rapidly moistening cunt. Her juices really began to flow when I touched her clitoris.

I began to position myself so I could fuck her, but Toni said she didn't have any contraceptives and that she feared getting pregnant. After I promised to pull out when I began to come, she leaned back on the boat seat, drew her knees toward her chest, and spread her legs for me. Her nipples were standing at attention and droplets of water still clung to her blond pubic hair. Her outer lips were spread flowerlike to either side of her swollen, red cunt.

Together we guided my cock into it. What an amazing experience it was to see my cock being slowly swallowed by her pussy. I pulled out almost to the tip of my cock and then penetrated her again. When her warm, tight pussy was well lubricated, I pistoned in and out with a steady rhythm. Toni's brown eyes were closed, and she had a smile on her lips. I hoped I could bring her to orgasm before I had to pull out.

When the time came, with great reluctance I withdrew my pulsing cock just as the first drops of sperm began to spurt out. My gooey, hot wad landed on Toni's inner thighs and stomach. Toni sat up and took my drooling cock in her hand and worked the shaft up and down, letting my come dribble over her fingers. She leaned forward, took the head of my cock in her mouth, ran her tongue and lips over it, and licked off every drop of sperm.

When Toni had licked me clean, I reached down to touch her damp pussy. She leaned back down and pulled her knees up, letting her legs rest on my shoulders. I thrust my tongue into her cunt and tickled her clitoris until her breathing grew heavy and her stomach muscles tightened. A quiet, muffled cry escaped from her lips as she climaxed.

After Toni's orgasm we both just leaned on each other, exhausted. While we cleaned ourselves up in the water, she told me that this was the first time she had experienced oral sex. I asked if she had enjoyed it. Of course she said yes—adding that she had never climaxed before except when she'd masturbated at home with a brush handle.

Dusk was falling when we dressed and began the seven- or eight-mile trip back upriver. Toni and I have since become very good friends, but we'll have to say good-bye at the end of summer, when she leaves for college. We'll make the most of the weeks remaining and look forward to our college vacations.— *Name and address withheld by request*

TABLES TURNED, WITH A VENGEANCE

Last year I attended a southern university where I was a cheerleader for the football and basketball teams. I've always been considered quite attractive. I have a deep suntan and a flawless complexion, and although my breasts are not huge, they are ample for my small, well-proportioned body (34-24-32). I've never had any trouble getting guys to notice me, and I must admit that I've had fun prick-teasing since coming to college.

I try to wear the shortest cutoff jeans that I can without being tacky and I always wear shirts that button down the front, leaving the top four buttons undone when possible. And, of course, I always go braless. It's fun to see how distracted the jocks get when talking to me.

Although I tease a lot, I haven't had many sexual encounters because I've always been particular. I'll only go out with a guy who is well-built, well-hung, and, more important, cute as hell! I've had a few guys of this type to myself already, but I grew tired of them after a few weeks and told them to scram. This semester, though, I learned a lesson.

I was in my first class, a biology lab, when in walked this guy whose appearance left me breathless. He was about five feet ten and blond as hell, with a deep tan that complemented his hair. He had on a pair of light blue cutoffs that were oh-so-very short. You could even see the outline of his balls. He wore his shirt out over his pants and left it open all down the front. This, I might add, always turns me on. I asked the girl next to me who he was. She said that his name was Paul and he was a member of the swim team.

A few days later I bumped into him in class. He looked at me and gave me a smile. I nearly melted away and said something stupid. I couldn't quite put my finger on what made this guy so sexy. His smile seemed to say, "If you're a good girl, I might let you suck me off someday."

I was more than ready. During our next class period together, my lust intensified. He came into class late, as usual. I figured he came in late so everyone would look at him. He sat down next to me and said, "Boy, it's hot as hell out there."

Although his cutoffs fit very tightly everywhere, they were a little loose around his narrow waist, leaving the whole female population eager to slip a hand down there. The combination of his large, well-developed chest, small waist, tight ass, cute smile, and a few droplets of sweat here and there made him unbearably sexy. I told him that I was a cheerleader, which seemed to impress him. I leaned forward a few times as we spoke, exposing a little more of my body than he expected, and that impressed him even more. I asked him if we could get together sometime, glancing down at his crotch and then looking him in the eye with a sexy smile. He said he'd think about it. I couldn't believe it.

He walked out of class with several other studs, his tight ass swaying. His crotch was stuffed to the point of bursting the seams of his cutoffs. As for me, my pussy was soaking wet.

Well, that night he called me up. One of the guys on the swim team was having a party, he said, and I could come if I wished. I asked him if he was inviting me. He said he already had a date, but I could go to the party with them. His date wouldn't mind, he said. It sounded strange, but I agreed. He told me to wear a bathing suit. Well, I had a nice-fitting suit, but I wanted to show this stud that I could be uninhibited and sexy, so I went out and bought a tiny string bikini that blended almost perfectly with my tan. It was a rich deep brown. You could hardly tell where the suit began and my bronzed body left off.

About an inch of my ass crack was visible above the top of the suit. I thought I'd have to shave around my pussy to wear it, but I decided that if some of my pubes showed, it would only be more sexy. The top wouldn't have covered two golf balls, let alone my size-34 boobs.

The chick he was taking to the party was blond like him, well-tanned, and built beautifully. She hung all over him and didn't mind other girls at the party doing the same. I felt a little out of place. There was Paul, in a very small bikini bathing suit, playing around with several girls at poolside. All these beautiful girls in string bikinis were hanging all over him, eager to get into his pants, and you could see that he didn't even have a hard-on. He was very well-hung to be sure. You could see the outline of his prick and nuts, but he never got hard. Occasionally he'd flash that smile at me and drive me wild, but I was getting ready to give up on him when he said that he and Sally were ready to leave and wanted to know if I wanted to go with them. He was treating me badly, but I still had one thing on my mind: sucking him off.

"Listen," he said, with Sally standing right next to him, "we're going to my place to fuck around. Do you want to come?"

"What about Sally?" I asked.

"We just met yesterday," he said (and she laughed). "If you're not coming, I'll go inside and get one of those other chicks."

"Okay," I said, thinking to myself how lucky I was, and I put on my blouse. Before leaving, Paul put on his cutoffs. He didn't wear a shirt, though, and I was beginning to fantasize in the car en route to his place.

Sally tried to put me at ease. As we walked to the apartment she told me, "Listen, he is one of the most popular hunks on campus. He spends half the day in the sun and the other half in the sack, getting laid. It takes a lot to satisfy him. He won't sleep with just one chick at a time. He insists on two."

When we entered his apartment, he lay back on the bed. Sally was still wearing her bikini, so he simply pulled the strings and let it fall away. When he touched me, I thought I'd go wild. He unbuttoned the front of my shirt and said, "Your tits are just the right size." He told me to strip while he watched. While I did as he said, Sally was rubbing her hands all over his body. I looked at his crotch, which appeared stiff but not really hard. He brought out some suntan lotion and told us to oil him down. Sally and I enjoyed that, oiling him down in his cutoffs while we both were nude. Finally he said that we could strip him.

We unbuttoned and unzipped the front of his shorts, just as I had done so many times in my imagination. Out popped the most beautiful dick I've ever seen. It was tanned and rooted in a tangle of blond hair. I wondered how he'd ever got a suntanned dick.

He told Sally to sit on his face because he'd been wanting to eat her all night long. Then he looked at me with that special smile and said, "Laura, go ahead and do whatever you like."

His cock tasted sweeter than any I'd ever sucked before. As I put his big dick in my mouth, it started to grow. I pulled the foreskin back to maximize his pleasure. I saw his pole grow to eight inches while I slurped away. He told Sally to dismount because he wanted to watch me suck him off. He looked at me between his legs with a big smile on his face. "Do you like what you're doing?" he asked. I slurped a big yes. "If you do a good job," he said, "I may let you do it again sometime, but I'm afraid there's a long waiting list."

I couldn't believe this. What really drove me wild with desire was that he wasn't teasing. It was true. All the chicks wanted to suck him off. "Sally, give Laura a hand," he commanded. Sally quickly began tonguing the base of his dick while I worked over the tip.

Wanting to really turn him on, I stared him straight in the eye while blowing him. "Stud," I whispered to him. He could see the pleasure in my face. "Please come," I pleaded as I lapped away. He had a big grin on his face as he lay back and savored the experience. Paul definitely enjoyed sex; it just took him a little longer to get worked up because he had so much of it. He came in big squirts. I lapped up his come and swished it around in my mouth like vintage wine. He liked that.

"Give me a few more minutes, babe, and round two will begin. Sit on my face while you're waiting. And Sally," he said, "why not get behind Laura and help me massage her tits." After a few minutes Paul said that he was getting hard again and wanted to fuck.

"Listen, Laura, you get under me. I want you to massage my balls and eat me while I fuck Sally. But take it easy massaging my balls. I had a rough day at practice today." So Sally and Paul went at it doggie-style while I crawled under. It looked neat to see Paul's dick sliding in and out of Sally's blond snatch.

I told Paul to stick just the head of his prick into Sally's pussy so I could get more tongue on the situation. He liked the idea and said that it felt fine that way. When he came, I got out from under and grabbed him around the waist. His ass looked so neat. There were no bathing suit marks to spoil his suntan. I massaged his buns until I couldn't stand it anymore. I was crazy with lust. So was Sally. But he fell asleep while she and I were trying to suck him off. He was tired. He'd had a rough day.

The next day, I waited for him at class. He came in late, as usual. He looked at me with his if-you're-lucky-you-can-suck-me smile and winked like I've see him do with so many other chicks. I asked if I could help him after class and he told me that while he really had enjoyed my company the other night, he had already invited some "help" over to his apartment. He said that he might call me in the future if he thinks of it.—*L.K., Baton Rouge, Louisiana*

HAPPY ENDING WITH OLDER MAN

I am a twenty-six-year-old Canadian reader of your magazine. I first came across *Penthouse Forum* about seven years ago, when I was in the middle of a very bad marriage to an abusive drunk. We never made love; he just fucked me and I never got any pleasure from it.

I remember reading your magazine at the time, and being struck by the fact that the men and women who wrote to you told of loving, sexual experiences wherein both of the adults involved enjoyed and took pleasure from the experience. I used to fantasize about some of the letters, not so much because I was titillated by the sex, but because of the respect and love shown between the partners, even during casual encounters.

Eventually I got out of the marriage and moved to this province.

I landed the job I have now about three years ago. I am one of four secretaries in one department of a large organization in my city. It was at this office where the incident that I want to relate to you happened.

I had been on the job for only eight months. Since I had the least seniority, I ended up with the late lunch hour. I had few friends and, thanks to my husband, I did not trust men in my age group. As a consequence, I spent a lot of lonely hours in the empty lunch room.

One of my co-workers was a man named Darryl. He was fifty-three years old, a very polite and quiet man, who reminded me of a gray elf. He was not handsome, but he had a lovely smile. He started to visit me in the lunch room. His visits gradually became longer until, by the time my first year at the office was up, we were spending nearly the whole lunch hour together. I grew to love his smile, and I asked him out to dinner. On our first date, walking back to the car, I took his hand, but it was four more dates before I was able to convince him to come up to my apartment. We had been to a concert of classical music that evening and Darryl was still humming a melody from the performance when, on impulse, I took his hands and kissed him. He studied me intently for a few moments before kissing me back.

I led him into my bedroom. I could feel myself getting aroused, even though I had never had a reason to want a man before. At the time, I didn't know what Darryl thought of me, but I was trying to get his clothes off, and moaning and pressing hungrily against him. He slowed my movements and undid my blouse. I felt his beard go down my chest, and he drew one of my nipples into his mouth. It felt incredible. He massaged my breasts, sucking on one nipple, then the other. Then he gently kissed my stomach before straightening and removing my clothes. I remember he looked at me quietly through all this. I only found out later that he had been amazed that so young a woman would want him.

I felt his mouth against the hair on my pussy. His tongue went right between my pussy lips and licked straight up to my clit. After he did this, he lifted his head. I smiled at him, but I think I was trembling too. Anyway, reassured by my smile, he returned to my pussy and licked me with long, deep strokes, each one ending on my clit. I held the back of his head, panting. I felt him gently nibble on my clit, and his hands came under my ass to pull me hard against his mouth. I came wildly, bucking and tensing against his mouth.

Darryl came back up quickly and gently pushed the head of his penis between my pussy lips. I pulled my legs up, grabbed his ass, and pulled the rest of his very hard penis inside of me. He thrust hard a few times, then his penis went rigid. He buried his face in my neck, moaned slightly, and his penis throbbed as he came.

After a rest in his arms, while he kissed me over and over, I took his hand and put it on my pussy. His penis was soft but he kissed me deeply and rubbed my pussy and breasts until I climaxed again. Then we fell asleep.

In the morning, before he was awake, I took his penis in my mouth and sucked it until it was hard. That woke him up and we made love beautifully, though we were nearly late for work.

We've been together now for two years and have lived together a year and a half. It hasn't always been easy. Because of the difference in our ages, some people tend to stare and some make rude comments. Darryl does not discuss his personal life at work, and although the whole staff knows by now, I don't discuss it either, in deference to Darryl. We find a lot of joy in each other.

I have written to you because your letters reflect a wide range of couples and because I want to shout my happiness to someone. I just want to say a few things, I guess in answer to questions that people have rudely asked me and that I would not answer. But if I did respond to these questions, the following is what I would say.

Yes, my bad marriage probably did turn me in the direction of an older man, but we have stayed together because we make each other happy. Since I have had such pleasure with him, I find him beautiful, and he seems to think I am beautiful too. And in answer to that one very rude question, Darryl does not need to be "jump-started." We make love a lot, and I'm beginning to tease him by saying that he really is a dirty old man. There are very few times when he does not get a hard-on. At those times, his tongue is ever able and ready, and it is just as satisfying. Though I have never asked him to go down on me (especially since I know what a devil of a time he has getting my pussy smell out of his beard), he seems to enjoy doing it.—*Name and address withheld*

TAKIN' IT TO THE MATS

I've enjoyed wrestling ever since I first watched it on TV as a kid. In high school I made the wrestling team and I went on to be a pretty fair wrestler in college. Today I continue to wrestle as one way of keeping in shape. I work out at a fancy health club, mainly to show off my physique to attractive women.

Donna is into bodybuilding and has a first-class physique. The idea of wrestling her has fed more than one of my sexual fantasies, but I was reluctant to suggest anything to her. One day, however, she bragged that she had once pinned a guy bigger than me. I laughed, but she told me that she used to horse around with her brother, who was also a collegiate wrestler, and had pinned him several times. I could feel my masculinity being challenged, so I asked her if she thought she could pin me.

We went to my town house, where I have a room with wrestling mats. We agreed that we would wrestle two out of three falls pro-style, nothing dangerous. We excused ourselves to get into our wrestling gear. I put on my skimpiest Speedo briefs and nothing else, but I wasn't prepared for Donna's suit: a flesh-colored bikini with rawhide fringe. As far as I was concerned it was the most erotic swimsuit I had ever seen.

We quickly got into some holds, and I was surprised by how easily she held her own. I knew that I had to watch out for her thighs if I was to win this match. I converted her body-scissors into a leg lock that eventually set up a figure four pin.

We started the second fall more slowly than the first, as we both now had mutual respect for each other. I was able to get a standing arm lock on her and force her down to the mat. I got another good look at her body as she tried to get out of the hold. After a lot of struggling she was able to roll up over me and secure a head lock. My head was scissored between her legs, with her cunt right in my face.

I could feel her gyrating thighs and buttocks as I tried to escape. Suddenly she tensed up and moaned. I realized that she was trying to get off on my face! I massaged her thighs and kissed her cunt through her bikini. It didn't take long for her to reach a shuddering orgasm, and I almost passed out from the pressure on my head, but it was worth it.

Donna was all smiles and said she wanted to return the favor. She untied the knot on the strings of my Speedo briefs and proceeded to pull them off. They were already stained with precome, and my penis was as erect as I can ever remember it being. She gently pulled me down on my back and lifted my legs so that I knew she wanted me to put a figure four head scissors on her. She then eagerly engulfed my cock with her hungry mouth. Getting head while having Donna in this hold was more than I could handle, and I came quickly.

After licking up every drop of come, Donna whimpered that I was the winner, but that she wanted a rematch. I have lost count of how many matches we have had since that first one. We've even come up with some holds where we can both get off simultaneously. Right now we're looking to find another couple who would like to do some tag team wrestling.—*J.H., Toronto, Canada*

SCHOOL DAZE

I am a first-year graduate student at a major university in Southern California and I have read *Penthouse Forum* since my first year of college. I find it a great prelude to masturbating (an activity I enjoy whether or not my sex life is active). I have always wished for a personal experience worthy of being in *Forum* but, until recently, all I could do was dream.

After four years of roommates, I was finally afforded the luxury of living on campus in single-student housing. I live in a coed apartment building full of other single graduate students. Each of us has our own cozy nest. It's a great situation, because everyone you meet is almost surely available. I had already been able to grab a couple quick fucks, which came from being in the right place at the right time. But these never really provided excitement past the several minutes they lasted. It wasn't until I met Lorraine that I had the experience of a lifetime.

I had met Lorraine previously in the hallway and on the elevator, and once or twice I had seen her on campus. She was a voluptuous woman of Mexican-Italian descent with dark hair, dark skin and smoky black eyes. When she walked, I couldn't take my eyes off her. She knew how to dress to show off her assets perfectly. She was the kind of woman a man always dreams about.

One Friday night, broke (as usual), I was watching a video in my room when I heard a knock at the door. I opened it to find Lorraine and her cleavage standing in the hallway. For what seemed like hours I stared at her high cut black leather miniskirt and skintight tank top until I was finally looking at her beautiful face. Before I could speak she invited me to her apartment for a late dinner.

Quickly realizing I wasn't dreaming, I said, "Sure."

"Okay," she said, "see you in ten or fifteen minutes at my place." When I closed the door I remembered Lorraine lived around the corner and must have seen the light in my window from hers. I fantasized what having her would be like while I made myself presentable.

In about fifteen minutes I arrived at her apartment to find that dinner was ready to be eaten. There was only small talk and short glances at each other during dinner, which was a great Spanish meal she had made herself. Not getting my hopes up, I was prepared to leave after we were finished eating so as not to overextend my welcome. I was glad when she gestured me to the couch and moved to turn on the TV.

As she turned from the TV, she immediately pulled her top up to expose her large (braless) breasts. They seemed to defy gravity. She then straddled my lap and placed a large, round nipple in my mouth. I licked and sucked as she caressed my face with her enormous tits. She stood again to lift her skirt. She wasn't wearing panties. Her glistening labia seemed to beckon my tongue. She stood on the couch above me and grabbed the back of my head, thrusting my face into her wet pussy. She let out a loud groan as I massaged her clitoris, sucking up ounces of love juice in the process. My twitching tongue quickly brought her to a moaning, spasmodic orgasm.

In two seconds she was on her knees, tearing into my pants to pull out my already hard cock. She lovingly teased the long shaft with her tongue before she immersed my dick in her wet mouth. She wrapped one hand around my organ and stroked as she sucked. As I began thrusting into orgasm, she moved her head back and jerked me off so I could watch as my come blasted into her mouth.

With both of us in a state of total satisfaction, we removed all of our clothes and lay in the middle of the floor. We caressed each other until I got hard again, and we made love by the light of the TV. This happened a couple more times before we finally slept.

Lorraine and I aren't dating but continue to have similar nighttime rendezvous, which are the highlight of my life. I wish college had always been like this.—*L.G., Los Angeles, California*

SPUNKY GAL

I am a thirty-five-year-old airline stewardess. I am also a divorcée and a natural redhead. I have a 34C-24-31 figure that carries about one hundred and ten pounds. I have strived to maintain my figure, especially since my divorce. I am divorced because I just can't seem to keep my hands off men.

In fact, I have a part-time job as a bachelor-party performer. I crave hot dicks and fat, juicy balls. I personally entertain parties of up to nine or ten men. If a party has more than ten men I simply need another girl. I can think of nothing better than handling nine or ten hard dicks and enjoying the fruits of their nuts. I particularly enjoy sucking a guy off, and then pulling his bone out and aiming his come-shooter at my chest, just so I can watch him bust his nut. I love the feeling of hot, white sperm slithering down my neck and over my tits—the more the better.

Early this summer I was handling a bachelor party, giving hand-jobs and blowjobs to my heart's content. I had already taken five men when a gigantically hung guy dropped his fleshy log (some ten inches) against my face as I knelt before him.

Not only was his hard dick ten inches and engorged by the thickest, bluest veins I've ever seen, but he had a pair of enormous nuts. His balls were the size of duck eggs, clearly the largest nuts I'd ever seen, and that is saying something.

I stood, fascinated and turned on by the potential of this good-looking, thirty-year-old guy's tool. He was about six feet tall and a solid two hundred pounds. I licked his heavy equipment, tonguing his big come-hole as he oozed a rich flow of sticky pre-come. I tongued deep into his cockhead, slurping on his sticky, clear fluid. I began to suck his knob, letting my saliva pour down his shaft. I stroked his meat with one hand, smearing my hot saliva over his hard rod while I continued to suck his knob. With my other hand, I fondled and squeezed his massive balls as they hung low in his hairy nut-sack. I squeezed each nut, luxuriating in the feel of such long, juicy balls.

Suddenly I felt his nuts swell and begin to rise in his bag as his huge, vein-fed meat began to shake. The big dick throbbed in rhythm to his pulse—it was racing. I pushed my mouth down over his fat cockhead just as the sticky, clear oozing began to turn whitish. I swallowed the swelling head as it spit a ribbon of thick spunk down my throat. The glob blasted down my throat as if it were shot from a cannon. The sight of such a long cock shaking so forcefully mesmerized me. I stared in awe as his cock jerked and thrust between my open lips. Wad after gooey wad leaped from his hose as he busted his nuts in me. The overflow leaked out of my mouth and ran down my chin. Jism was slithering down both sides of my neck, over my tits and pooling in my cleavage. I'd seen hundreds of guys get their nuts drained, but this guy just kept coming. After he finally emptied his copious load, I stared at my chest in sheer amazement. My tits had jism oozing all over them and comesicles dripping from my hard, pink nipples.

The guy had come as much as the first five guys all put together. I smeared his heavy seed all over my stomach, chest and arms, giving myself a sperm coat.

The party sort of broke up then as I jammed in my new orgasmic blanket. After fifteen or twenty minutes I went to clean up. When I returned, only Splash, as I called the guy with the big nuts, was left to entertain. Splash gave me another load of nearly the same amount before he left.

I guess I wrote this because I thought I had seen the best of the comers, but found that there is always a better man out there.—E.C., New York, New York

TRAFFIC JAM COMES TO A HEAD

My fiancé Mick and I had a long weekend planned, driving up to Hollywood for a couple of days of sightseeing, dancing, and partying. We got a late start leaving San Diego, however, and the freeways were crowded. As the traffic crawled, Mick told me how he couldn't wait to get to the hotel and screw me silly. He is a large man, six feet two inches tall, with blond hair, beautiful blue eyes and a sexual appetite that just won't quit.

Not long after his bold statement, the radio said there was an accident a few miles ahead on the freeway we were traveling. Traffic was soon at a standstill. It was getting dark, and I was getting horny thinking about the evening that was still ahead of us. I figured Mick had the same thoughts, because it didn't take long for the bulge in his crotch to catch my eye. I could tell from the look in his eyes that we weren't going to wait until we reached the hotel.

I reached over and unzipped his shorts, released his hard cock, and began to stroke it, firmly squeezing his dick and playing with his balls. I was really starting to get off on the idea of giving him head in the middle of traffic. He tilted the steering wheel a little to give me some room, and I eagerly took his hot cock into my mouth. I slid my tongue up and down. He couldn't help but let out a little moan and tighten his grip on the wheel. I leaned a little farther and sucked on his balls—first one, then the other. He was having a hard time concentrating on the road, but this was only the beginning.

Mick was really enjoying himself, but I knew that if I didn't slow down a bit he was going to come before long and not enjoy it the way he could have. I stopped to grab a bottle of baby oil from my overnight bag. I poured a generous amount over his throbbing cock and watched it slide down to his tight balls. I grasped his hot dick in my hand and slowly started pumping it.

I bent over his lap and started once more to suck on his now glistening, oily balls. His breathing was getting shallow and the windows were starting to fog over. He was getting close to or-gasm and his balls were starting to tighten up even more. I quickly moved my mouth up to his pulsing cock, getting ready to catch all of his sweet come. I squeezed his balls slightly and that was all it took. He leaned his head back, moaned, and gave me what I had been working so hard for. His love milk jetted out in warm spurts and I quickly caught what I could in my mouth.

Now, whenever I hear about a traffic jam on the radio, I get a grin on my face. Next time, Mick tells me, I get to do all the driving. I can't wait.—*K. V., San Diego, California*

Exhibitionism

The Summer of Love Revisited

This is a story about my adventures with Diva, a girl who loved cock and loved to show off her body.

My late teens and early twenties just happened to take place during the late seventies and early eighties—before AIDS, yet after sex and porn laws were relaxed in this country. It was a good time to be young, hung, and horny. It really did not matter which gender wanted me, as long as the outline of my eight-inch dick and tight ass in my too-tight jeans made them hot. Adult cinemas were my playground. And Diva would become my swing set.

In the summer between my freshman and sophomore years in college, I worked in the mailroom of a major corporation in San Francisco's financial district, side-by-side with the other sons and daughters of the company's management. That's where I met Diva.

At a first glance, Diva resembled every mother's ideal of a "good girl." Shy, pretty, and polite, this eighteen-year-old dressed in the conservative business styles of the day and carried herself with quiet grace and manners of old money.

The first chink in her armor came with dirty jokes. Imagine my surprise when Diva came up to me one day and whispered a filthy joke about sailors and whores. The next pleasant surprise came when we mutually discovered the other smoked pot. We became fast friends.

During the day, we'd sneak off and get high, telling each other our sexual exploits and fantasies. She especially liked hearing me tell of some stranger in a dark theater deep-throating my dick. Sometimes when we'd go back to the mailroom, Diva would rush off to the women's room, coming back flushed and sweaty. I knew she was getting herself off. And she knew I knew.

Diva made going to work a lot of fun. I began to imagine fucking her while fucking other girls; imagining that I was her while getting fucked by other men. One day at work she pulled a reel of eight-millimeter film from her purse, saying it belonged to her big brother. Her voice got quiet and shaky as she told me she wanted to see it with me. As I looked at the tiny frames of people fucking, we agreed to meet at one of the vacant apartments owned by her aunt.

Clearly she had prepared for the rendezvous. By the time I had arrived she had changed into a tight, thin T-shirt and short, cutoff jeans. The jeans were so short as to show she wore no panties, split up the sides nearly to the belt line. Her nipples stood against the thin T-shirt. I had no idea her conservative work clothes had concealed such a perfect body.

The vacant apartment was almost a public place, with a huge ceiling-to-floor picture window facing the many windows of the apartment building across the street. She turned the projector to a blank wall and we watched a red-haired woman suck off two men at once, come splashing in her face.

I kissed Diva for the first time. Her hot, wet mouth kissed me back hard. As I cupped her tits in my hands, she oriented herself to face the picture window. While she watched the film of the redheaded woman, now getting eaten out as she sucked, Diva rubbed the growing bulge in my jeans. I unzipped my pants while Diva pulled off her T-shirt. Her nipples were as hard as my dick. She looked at me with those big green eyes, her hands feeling her large tits. Her hands took my dick and slowly stroked the length of my shaft.

She took it slow from there, keeping my hands out of her

pants. We touched each other while watching the redheaded woman make it with about a dozen different partners. Diva kept glancing out the picture window. Suddenly, she sat upright and started pulling off her pants. She looked me right in the eye and said, "I want to fuck you. I want your come." She ordered me to take off all my clothes. Sitting on the carpet with her legs spread, she massaged her tits, still glancing out the window. As I took off the rest of my clothes, I saw what she was looking at. Across the street, a man stood at his window, dick in hand, jacking off and looking at us. Into her dripping wet cunt went one, then two fingers. She was hot and soft and very, very, wet. With one hand she gripped my dick; with the other she made little circles on her clit.

"You like showing yourself off. You like when men see your pussy," I said, taking some of her pussy juice on my fingers and giving it to her to lick. She moaned and sucked my fingers like a dick.

"I've dreamed of this for years," she said, pushing me to the carpet. Diva straddled me facing the window. As I guided my prick into her honeyed hole, she kept murmuring, "Fuck me hard, fuck me hard." She came in seconds, flushed and shuddering. We kissed wetly. Then she started again slowly, rising and falling on my rock-hard shaft. I loved the way her tits bounced. I loved her hoarse breathing. She was doing a dance on my dick and grinning from ear to ear. I wanted it to last forever, but shot my load into her pussy. Before I got the chance to pull out, she stopped me and put my fingers on her clit. I got her off again, all while she stared longingly out the window.

The next morning at work, we acted as if nothing had happened. Near the end of the day, I told her we'd go do something after work, something she'd really like. In a short breath of whisper she said, "You're making me wet already." Her pretty face, framed in the shag hairstyle of the day, showed nothing of the hot, horny desire that lurked within. She did not even ask where we were going.

She said almost nothing during the taxi ride to the adult theater that evening. I think she almost didn't get out of the taxi,
not so much because of the theater, but because of the seedy district it was in. It was not a place for good girls like Diva.

She was dressed appropriately for both the business world and
the cold, foggy San Francisco summers—a monster-size purse,
heavy sweater, a long wool skirt, and panty hose. I hoped the
dirty old man at the ticket counter would not ask her for proof
of age, and he didn't.

It was dark and warm in the three-quarters empty theater.
The air smelled of popcorn and come. Diva held me tight as we
made our way to the balcony, where I chose seats under one of
the few working house lights in the place. We watched the film
as our eyes adjusted to the darkness. On the screen a girl about
Diva's age and build was getting a huge dildo shoved in and out
of her pussy by a small-breasted blonde. Diva's eyes wandered
around the balcony. Some of the men watched the movie, some
watched her.

I told her, "I chose this theater because it runs a lot of lesbian
flicks—all the men in here love to see wet cunts."

"Maybe you'd like them to see my cunt," she said, rubbing my
cock through my jeans.

"Yes," I said. "If you're good, perhaps I'll let some of them
fuck you." She just moaned and kissed me wet and hard. Her
hands undid my belt and zipper. As she reached into my pants
to take my dick, she made eye contact with a man jacking off a
few seats away. Diva bent down to lick the tip of my cock while
she continued to look at the man. He got harder and started to
jack off faster. Diva moaned softly, licking my hard dick, squirming in her seat. I felt her shudder with pleasure as the man shot
his load into the air.

Meanwhile, several men had moved closer to us. It almost
seemed there was enough light to read by and everyone in the
balcony could see us. We kissed some more, my hand up her
heavy skirt feeling her hot wetness through her panty hose. I put

my hand up her sweater, but she wore a slip and one of those evil bras that snaps in the back. "Go to the ladies room and take off everything under your clothes," I whispered.

"I'll go take off everything under my clothes after I suck you off," she said, in a voice loud enough that the moviegoers nearby could hear. As I lay back watching her head go up and down on my dick I knew I was going to come quickly. Her mouth was hot and slick on my shaft. She'd go down quickly, taking all of me down her throat, then up slowly. A good-looking man sat down beside Diva and pulled a hard dick out of his pants. As he jacked off, he stroked Diva's leg. She spread her legs. With his hand up Diva's dress, the man came, shooting come into the air. I came in her mouth. When I came, she moved her mouth to the tip of my dick, letting her mouth fill with come. Then she shifted to face me, letting come spill down her chin as she licked her lips. She kissed me with a salty, come-filled mouth.

"I'll be right back to get you hard again," she said, leaving for the ladies' room. I zipped myself up and watched the flick for a while. It was a good one, with three lesbians tongue-teasing a fourth, who was spread-eagled on a bed. Time passed and I began to wonder if Diva had gotten cold feet and left. Then she appeared at the top of the stairs. For some reason, I first noticed her purse, bulging larger than ever. Then I realized why her purse was so large—it contained her sweater and skirt. Diva wore only her shoes and her tan slip. The slip started with spaghetti straps and cleavage, outlined her fine curves, and ended well above her knees. As she walked to our seats, her tits jiggled in the silky slip, showing clearly the outlines of her hard nipples. I had an almost instant hard-on. She sat down prim and proper, folding her hands on her lap. Her eyes were glued to the screen. I put an arm around her shoulder and gave her a peck on the cheek. She started undoing my pants.

"Not so fast this time," I whispered. "I'm going to make you beg for it." I ran the tips of my fingers teasingly along the insides of her thighs, stopping inches short of her pussy. She spread her legs slightly and rubbed my dick through my jeans.

"I'm so fucking wet," she whispered. I cupped her tits in my hands and could see her nipples pressing against the slip. Her breathing was rough.

"Show them some ass," I whispered. She crossed her legs and leaned into my lap, playfully rubbing my crotch with her face. She also pulled back her slip, showing off her legs all the way to her ass. Those men to her right could undoubtedly see up her slip.

By now, most of the population of the balcony had moved nearby. One man directly in front of us had turned around and was watching us. She had dropped one of her shoulder straps and I pulled away the slip to expose one of her round, firm tits. As we kissed, I gently pulled on her nipple with one hand, slipping the other between her legs. True to her word, she was sopping wet. She moaned as I took that wetness with my fingers and moved in a circular motion around her clit. Breathing rough, she watched the men watching her, most of them with dicks in their hands. The man in front of us intently looked up between Diva's fine legs as I fingered her. She ordered me to take off my shirt, as she took my pants down to my knees. As I took off my shirt she dropped the other side of her slip and massaged both tits with her hands. She lifted herself up on the arm of the seat, spread her legs wider, putting one foot up on the seat in front of us. The man there ran his hand along her leg. Diva motioned to a man a couple of seats away. With half-closed eyes, she raised her hips in a rotating motion, spreading her cunt lips with her fingers. With such an unambiguous invitation from such a ripe, young girl, the man came over to fuck her. She guided his dick into her hole, then reached over and put her arms around me.

We were locked in a deep kiss as the man rammed his dick in and out of her. Her breathing became short and rapid, and they both came.

The man withdrew and she moved off the arm of the seat.

Embracing me, she said, "I'm not nearly finished." I reached between her wet thighs and gently fingered her come-laden cunt.

"I want you to eat my pussy. I want you to eat it now," she
said in a loud and panting voice. I got down on my knees and
grabbed her ankles. I put her feet on adjoining seats, spreading
her legs wide. She put her arms across the seat backs and arched
her back, shoving her pussy toward my face.

A man went to the seat beside us, jacking off and sucking on
one of her tits. Diva arched her back even more, leaning her
head over the back of the seat. I pulled my fingers from her pussy
and she told me not to stop. But I motioned toward the man beside us, and Diva got the idea. She stood. Her slip fell to the
floor, revealing a graceful naked body glistening with come. Diva
walked around the other side of the man and began sucking him
off. Her fine ass was not only stuck up in the air, but it was also
in the aisle. An older man dropped his pants and ran his dick between the cheeks of her ass, into her cunt. The man she was
sucking and the man behind her came almost at the same time.
I joined her in the aisle. Holding my dick with both hands, she
kissed me with a come-filled mouth. I lay in the aisle and she
lowered herself down on my dick. As we fucked, I fingered her
clit.

She was the image of lust, dancing on my dick, her tits bouncing up and down, her eyes looking for a dick. Men came and offered Diva their dicks, from which she sucked their come. She
came at least twice. I must have nearly passed out when I finally
came, because I remember looking up and seeing Diva beaming
at me afterward. Diva let a couple more men fuck her before
we left. And then she gave the taxi driver a show as we caressed
in the back of the cab.

I sometimes wonder what she's doing these days. The last time
I saw her was that September right before her parents shipped
her off to school in Europe. Still, that was one summer I'll never
forget.—*Name and address withheld by request*

POP TART—JUST ADD WATER

Although I am a fairly conservative woman in my twenties, I had one experience that stripped me (literally) of all my inhibitions.

Recently, my husband and I took a road trip from New York to North Carolina. We had planned on driving straight through, but as the hours piled up, we found ourselves in need of a rest. We stopped at a small motel, and as we registered, the clerk gave us two free passes to a local bar. He had been planning on going to see the wet T-shirt concert that night, but was forced to work. Although we were tired, we decided that a little dancing might be fun.

On the way there, my husband chided me about entering the contest. But I adamantly refused, being modest and conservative, as I have already said.

Once at the bar, we danced continually. Even though he had a few beers, I drank only sodas so that I could drive back. The music was great, and it didn't take me long to get into some wild dancing. I don't know what it was about the place—maybe it was the mood of the crowd, or maybe it was the anonymity of being so far from home, but suddenly I found myself up on the stage with a bucket of water about to be thrown at me. I took it full force, with great pleasure.

Although my measurements aren't outstanding—36-30-34— they are suggestive of my firm breasts and tight behind. My best features are my sexy eyes and smile, but my long, dark-blond hair and large nipples are nothing to be scoffed at.

When it came time to show off all of my attributes, I wiggled and gyrated my hips under my tight cotton miniskirt, and I ran my hands slowly down my chest to enhance my protruding nipples. I bounced them as well as I could, making sure I got as close as possible to every man's eager eyes.

I had snipped the neck of my T-shirt with the pair of small sewing scissors that I keep in my purse, and when the music reached its peak, I reached for my collar and ripped my shirt halfway to my belly. What hoots and hollers that brought! I leaned over, showing just enough cleavage to get every man in the house rock hard.

Since my time was up, I turned and wiggled my fanny until I got back to my spot. Fortunately, I was the last contestant, so no one else could show me up.

Even though some of the other girls had far larger breasts than me, when they called "contestant number five" the house went wild, and I was announced the winner.

Responding to the calls for an encore, I repeated my act with a little variation. Through the din and smoke, I caught my husband's eye and he winked. He immediately started shouting, "Take it off! Take it off!" and soon the rest of the crowd had taken up the chant.

They began waving money, and the announcer asked if I would do it for ten dollars. I said no. The crowd yelled even louder, and the announcer asked if I would do it for twenty-five dollars. I said no. The crowd roared, and the announcer asked if I would do it for fifty dollars. I ripped my shirt some more and nodded my approval.

I thought the walls would fall in at the clamor. As soon as the announcer had collected enough money, I really got down to business. Dancing to the music, I inched my skirt up little by little until I was almost showing my panties.

Stopping there, I peeled my T-shirt down a little, baring my shoulders: first the left, then the right. Running the tips of my fingers down the cleavage between my breasts as I turned my back, I could hear the crowd moan with anticipation. From the back, all they could see was a wet T-shirt being peeled off. When I whipped around to give them the complete view, I thought I was going to die of excitement. My nipples were hard, and my groin was burning hot with energy of the moment.

Next, teasing my skirt up and down, I turned around again to give everyone a prime view of my smooth behind. I bent over and slid down my skirt, then paraded around the stage in my high-cut, red lace panties.

Realizing that I had gone far enough, I took my bow, collected my money, and retired to the ladies' room, where I got dressed and reconciled with my husband.—*T.A., Buffalo, New York*

TRUCK STOP

One night my husband and I decided to have some fun while we were out driving around. I stretched out on the seat with my head on my husband's lap and my legs spread wide apart. I was wearing a sundress with nothing underneath but smooth skin.

Whenever my husband passed a truck he would turn on the inside light and start rubbing my tits. It was so exciting knowing the truckers and other passersby were able to see this. Sometimes he would even rub my hot cunt. Since I was naked under the sundress, he had easy access. I got so horny from this I slipped his cock out of his pants and started sucking it. The truck drivers who witnessed this honked horns, flashed headlights, and tried like hell to get up beside us for a good look. We carried on this way for about an hour, so we were both really hot and horny by the time we got home.

When we got into the house my husband gave me a long, hot kiss. Then he told me to go down to the local truck stop and let the truckers see me with my skimpy dress. He also told me to take some condoms in case someone asked for some of my hot, juicy cunt. Flushed with excitement, I rushed out of the house. You would not believe how horny I was.

I reached the parking lot of the truck stop. I sat in my car and watched the rugged men walking in and out. I noticed a handsome black guy who looked to be in his late twenties getting into the cab of one of the trucks. I'd never made it with a black man, though I'd wanted to for quite some time. I decided that night would be the night I finally did. I started getting wet just imagining his cock sliding in and out of me.

He pulled out onto the road, and I followed him. After driving about two or three miles, I got his attention on the CB and asked him where he was heading. He told me, and then asked where I was going. "Just out cruising," I said. "Nowhere in particular."

After some light conversation he asked me to come up beside him so he could get a good look at me because, according to him, I "sure sounded good."

I did what he asked, giving him only a quick glimpse. Then I pulled behind him and flashed my lights to let him know I was there. Almost as if on cue he pulled off the road, asking me over the CB to do the same. I was so hot I didn't have to give it a second thought.

I hopped up into his cab, and we talked. He was extremely good-looking, with thick arms and a massive chest. He looked me up and down as we spoke, and I couldn't help blushing because I knew the flimsy blouse I had on did little to conceal my tits. He asked why I was out cruising alone, and I told him I was bored and had nothing else to do.

I knew we were eventually going to end up in the sleeper and I was finally going to fulfill a longtime fantasy of mine. He asked me why I picked him to start flirting with out of all the other truckers. I explained to him how I had watched him come out of the truck stop, and that I thought he was really cute. I told him I had wanted to make it with a black man for as long as I could remember. He said he was glad that I had chosen him.

We got into the sleeper, and he started kissing me roughly and passionately. I felt his hard cock poking me in the stomach through his pants. He started rubbing it back and forth against me. I had heard so much about black men and their dicks that I was dying to see his cock. I unzipped him. He started fingering my hot, wet cunt and rubbing my tits. I got so caught up with the pleasure he was giving me that I had to stop going for his cock. My whole body writhed and shook as his expert fingers manipulated my moist womanhood, gently bringing me to orgasm.

He pulled his pants down and started pushing my face toward his cock. I stopped him, though, and teased him by slowly kissing my way down his stomach, licking, and nibbling at his soft skin. When I finally reached his hard, black cock I let out a gasp. It had to have been at least nine inches long. I tried, but could only fit about half of it into my mouth. The rest of the shaft I rubbed with both hands.

I sucked him until I tasted the first salty drops of pre-come. I knew I would have to stop soon because I wanted to feel him inside of my wet, throbbing cunt before he exploded. I got on top and fucked him till I came. We stopped long enough to get the rest of our clothing off. Then we sucked and played with each other some more.

He got on top and started kissing my neck. Then he slid his cock into me again, and we fucked so hard the whole truck shook. We came together. He must have shot a gallon of come into my hot, wet cunt by the time we finished. It was hot and sticky running down my legs.

Anyway, I was in a hurry to get back home. I knew my husband would be waiting for me. He met me at the door and we went straight to the bedroom, where I told him all about what I had done. My husband had wanted me to do a black man for some time, and he was so happy that I was finally able to.

We started kissing. It was only minutes before I had my lips rising and falling on his ruddy shaft. Then he started fucking me slowly, and told me to describe to him exactly what I had done with the black man in the cab of the truck.

It felt so good I could hardly get the words out between the grunts and moans. My cunt was still dripping come from the trucker. I grinned, thinking any minute it would be shot full of my husband's juice as well.

I don't think I stopped coming until the next morning. I came so many times my pussy was sore the next day. It was a night neither of us will ever forget. The trucker had told me before I left that he hoped to see me again. He doesn't know it, but I have seen him twice since then, both times from a distance. Maybe one day we will get together again, and maybe this time my husband can watch and join in.—*Name and address withheld by request*

FANTASY ISLAND

Denise, my wife, is a tall, twenty-eight-year-old blonde with a gorgeous, well-proportioned figure. She has nice, firm breasts with nipples like large grapes. We are very happily married and enjoy a fantastic sex life together.

Denise loves showing off her beautiful body to me, and on several occasions we had taken topless pictures of her at home. This was a great turn-on for us. She had mentioned several times that she often dreamed of me photographing her topless on a beach, but whenever I told her we should do it she chickened out. For a good reason, too, I must admit. Denise teaches fifth grade at the local grammar school. Since our town is so small, she was afraid someone she knows might see her.

This year for our summer vacation we made reservations at a popular island resort in the Caribbean. Since no one there would possibly know us, we decided it would be the ideal location for us to live out our fantasy. Shortly after we arrived at the resort we decided to go shopping for the skimpiest bathing suit we could find—one she wouldn't dare wear at home. We found a black string bikini that looked perfect. As soon as we got back to the hotel room she tried it on. It looked great. The top hardly concealed her nipples, it was so tiny. The bottom revealed almost all of her firm ass, and we had to shave most of the hair from around her pussy. Just seeing her shaved cunt gave me a hard-on. She looked ravishing.

The island was everything the travel brochure promised it would be. We had sandy beaches, soft breezes, swaying palms, and good food. It was a very romantic setting where one could easily lose his inhibitions, which is exactly what happened to Denise.

On our first full day there we were out on the beach bright and early. We walked along the shore until we found a relatively secluded area, scattered with only a handful of people. We spread our blanket and stretched out under the hot, clear sun. After several minutes of my coaxing, Denise finally got up the courage to remove the top of her new bikini. Her fully exposed breasts were a gorgeous sight, especially the tiny beads of sweat that started forming on them. I took several pictures of her in various poses. My cock was so hard during all this, I thought it was going to explode. My balls ached.

When we returned to the room a short while later, we had some of the greatest sex of our marriage. The impromptu beach photo session had heightened it to a feverish, furious pitch that left us exhausted and drained by the time we finished.

The next day we went back to the same spot on the beach and, even though there were more people there than the previous day, she took her top right off. Her nipples were erect. All the men nearby were blatantly gawking at her. I knew my wife was enjoying the newly acquired attention her body was receiving.

By the third day her top was off even before we got to our spot. Denise had become so turned on by all the attention, she even stood up and pulled the tiny bikini into the crack of her ass, leaving her beautiful cheeks completely exposed. Then, with her tits and ass out for anyone to ogle, she slowly walked across the steaming white sand and into the blue water. I quickly grabbed the camera and started shooting her as she slowly submerged.

She made the trip from the water to the blanket several times, enjoying every minute of it. Once she was coming out of the water just as two young, muscular men were walking by. They stopped to talk with her, and I watched her nipples become erect as she stood there casually flirting with them. Even though I was some distance away I could see the bulges forming in their shorts. After they left she came over and told me the two of them were on vacation from Germany. She had made a date for the four of us to play tennis the next day. Then she asked me to walk back into the water with her.

We walked into the water until the waves lapped at our shoulders. She slipped her hand down my trunks and started rubbing my stiffening cock. She whispered in my ear, "I'm so hot I can't stand it—fuck me right here." I immediately pulled down my trunks as she pulled off her bikini bottoms. I started rubbing the head of my throbbing cock against her erect clit. She placed her legs around my waist, and I supported her firm ass. Her bare breasts were clearly out of the water for anyone to see. I shoved my dick into her flaming cunt as hard as I could, and we fucked right there in the ocean. The water was so clear, people passing by knew exactly what we were doing. At that point we couldn't have cared less. We both came at the same time. It was terrific!

I returned to the blanket to towel off, leaving her to get some swimming in. When I glanced over at her a little later she was slowly emerging from the ocean, shaking her head back and forth, spraying water from her hair. Then I noticed that she was holding the bottom of her tiny bikini in her hand. She was completely nude! The thin strip of pubic hair covering her pussy was in full view. I grabbed the camera. She obliged my request of going back into the water and walking out again so I could get pictures. We both got so horny we couldn't stand it. After I got enough shots we gathered the blanket and towels and headed for our room as fast as we could.

Denise felt uncomfortable with all the sand and salt on her skin, so she jumped into the shower first thing. When she came out she sat on the edge of the bed with her hot cunt staring me in the face. I immediately got down on my knees so I could taste the inner lips of her hot, wet pussy. She pushed me deeper in.

She loves it when I munch on her pussy. I began playing with her clit, and she quickly reached a gigantic climax. She returned the favor by taking my throbbing penis and licking it from bottom to top. Then she slid her beautiful lips down over the head of my throbbing dick. She took all of it into her mouth and made me come right away. She kept at it until she had sucked the absolute last drop of my come into her mouth. Only then did she allow my limp penis to slip slowly out from between her lips.

At dinner that night we talked about what we had been doing for the last few days. Denise said it made her wet just to think about it. We went back to the room and spent all night celebrating our fifth anniversary, drinking champagne and having the greatest sex imaginable.

The next afternoon, while we were getting dressed for our tennis match with the two Europeans, I noticed that Denise had put on the shortest tennis skirt she has. (It barely covers her ass cheeks.) She also wore a tight, thin jersey with no bra. I grinned but didn't say a word. She was planning on giving our opponents something to watch besides the tennis ball.

During the first game Denise went up for an overhead smash. Her skirt fluttered up from the breeze, and I gasped—she did not have on any underwear! It was almost impossible for me to concentrate on the match knowing she was on the court without underwear. It was obvious by the size of her nipples biting through her tight top that she was getting a real kick out of all this.

Not surprisingly, we lost the first set. During the second set she had to go back by the fence to retrieve a ball. When she bent over she exposed her gorgeous ass to the two Europeans. Well, needless to say, this completely turned the match around. They were so distracted knowing Denise had no underwear on, they could hardly hit the ball. They were concentrating on her instead of the game. We kept winking and smiling at each other as we won the next two sets.

Afterward they offered to buy us drinks on the patio overlooking the tennis courts. They had ulterior motives, of course. Denise was so wet with perspiration by then that her top had become see-through. If that wasn't enough for these poor guys, she kept crossing and uncrossing her legs to tease them with flashes of thigh and bush. Their cocks were probably ready to burst right through their shorts by the time we finished our drinks. When we finally parted, they shook my hand and told me my wife was one of the most beautiful women they had ever seen in their entire lives.

We finally got back to our room and had some heated balling. Denise wanted me to fuck her while her tennis skirt was still on. I have never seen her pussy so wet and juicy as it was that afternoon.—*S.R., Palm Springs, California*

Masturbation

Solitary Sucking

A couple of years ago I was reading a letter in *Forum* about a man who wanted to suck himself off. This kind of turned me on, so I thought I'd try it.

I worked up a good, stiff erection, got on my bed, and threw my legs over my head, hooking my toes in the headboard. This left both my hands free. But no matter how much I twisted and turned, I could get my penis only about six inches away and directly over my mouth.

I noticed that my cock was going soft, and so I reached between my legs and began to masturbate. The sight of my stiff, wet cock so close to my mouth drove me wild. With my other hand I began to fondle my balls. My penis stiffened out as never before, and my breathing became long and deep. The head of my cock was soaked and still dripping. The warm feeling emanating from my balls told me that my orgasm was on its pleasurable way.

I looked at my cock and saw it turn livid and begin to throb. Then it began to pump its load. I caught it on my tongue and lips, swallowing it as fast as it came. The fingers of my other hand were still fondling my balls, adding to the pleasure of my outlandish, lust-inspired act. Just thinking of what I was doing made my penis throb and shoot even more. The pleasure that I was getting was out of this world, and I surrendered to it, letting my cock unload.

When it was all over, I lay back and reveled in my new way to masturbate. I've done this only six or seven times, because it is so overwhelming and because I don't want to spoil a good thing by overindulging. One of these days I intend to do it for my girlfriend to see.—*J.F., Sacramento, California*

LATE-NIGHT FLIGHT FUN

I am a thirty-four-year-old businessman. My work requires a lot of air travel. Over the past five years I have met and dated numerous stewardesses. I'd been around and thought I'd just about seen it all. That was until I went to Chicago.

My flight was late in the evening. One of the stews was most striking. She looked to be in her thirties, stood almost six feet tall, had long red hair, and was thin. She had fabulous, long dancer's legs and a full, round chest that she proudly displayed by keeping several buttons of her blouse open. I figured she showed off her cleavage so blatantly to see how much attention she could command from the passengers, who were mostly tired businessmen like myself. Whatever the reason, I hit on her after she served my drink, a decision I was later very glad to have made.

Her name was Darlene. She had a cute face with a long jaw, and was easily one of the sexiest-looking women I have ever been attracted to.

Darlene joined me for a drink. We talked and she let me know she wanted more from me than my conversation. She did this by raising the hem of her skirt and opening another button of her blouse to reveal more of her C-, maybe D-cup, tits. They were tucked into a French half-cut bra. Darlene's pink nipples were the thickest, longest I have ever seen.

Darlene confirmed her availability when she whispered to me,

"You know what? There's nothing I like better than a guy with a big cock, and judging from your bulge I think you qualify."

"And you, my dear, have just said the magic words," I replied as I reached for my zipper. Darlene's eager hands reached over to my lap, deftly opened my fly, and pulled my hard tool from my pants.

"Oh, I'm glad to see you don't wear any underwear," she purred. She gripped my hose and began milking my oozing hard-on.

My cockhead was dribbling a steady, heavy flow of sticky pre-come as it perched above Darlene's milking hands. Darlene began to squeeze my nuts one at a time as she expertly stroked, fondled, and handled my meat.

"My God, you are creaming a flood for me, aren't you," she moaned as my piss-hole poured its copious pre-come over her hands as they continued expertly jerking me off. Darlene continued her fabulous handling of my meat while I caressed her heavy, solid tits and pulled on her long nipples. Suddenly I felt my balls rise and my rod stiffen.

"That's it, give it to me, let me see that gigantic dick spit its hot jism for me. Come on, baby, shoot a heavy load for ol' Darlene," Darlene whispered. When I finally did burst, I myself was amazed at how much she had turned me on by her expert hand-job. When my cock began to blast ropes of semen into the air, Darlene caught each glob in her right palm until I finished busting my nut. Her palm was dripping with my thick, hot seed. She stared at the load of sperm in her palm, then slowly tongued the gooey spunk. Soon she was lustily licking her fingers and slurping from her palm.

When she finally finished, she excused herself, saying she had to go to the ladies' room to clean herself off.

"Bring me your panties when you're through," I instructed.

"I love it. Sure you can have my panties," Darlene replied with a gleam in her eyes.

She gave me her soaked panties with her phone number inside them. I sniffed her crotch until I landed. I plan to see her this weekend.—*K.G., Charleston, West Virginia*

DON'T MOVE THAT CARROT!

It started a few months back when I received a wrong-number call. The guy on the other end sounded so sweet and gentle. There was a bit of loneliness in his voice, too, which I could relate to, so I struck up a conversation. Without exchanging names, we got to know each other. As we talked, I could tell by the tone of his voice that he wanted the phone call to turn into a sexual encounter. It really turned me on to think that, through the anonymity of the phone, I could tell him all the things I've always wanted to do to a handsome stranger. That first call has led to many others. Our agreement is that we will never meet in person. It keeps the relationship mysterious and exciting.

One evening after work I was feeling so horny that, on the drive home, I pulled onto a country road and stripped off my clothes. Freedom at last! But I did put my coat back on because it was winter. It felt so good driving nearly naked. My hard nipples were rubbing against my coat. I couldn't wait to talk with Gary, to hear his strong voice and to finger myself as I listened to him speak. Unable to wait, I called him from a drive-up pay phone. My pussy was as hot as fire when I got him on the line.

He was quite surprised that I was already nude. I told him I was so horny I was calling him from the car, still miles away from my home. As much as I wanted to listen to him, I found myself instead describing what I would be doing if we were together.

I began by telling him I was rubbing his cock, letting it heat up in my hands while my lips were kissing his earlobes and neck. "I'm applying more and more pressure to your fat cock," I said breathlessly, "and my hand is sliding up and down the thick, hard shaft." I pumped his dick with my voice, imagining that my hands were wrapped tightly around the stiff pole.

"Now I'm rolling an ice cube around on the head of your prick," I continued. "The cold water feels so good as it runs down to your balls. I'm rubbing my nipples with an ice cube too. It's making them as hard as your cock, sending shivers down my spine as the icy water makes its way down my belly and across my clit. Now the cold water is dripping into my pussy. It's so wet and sticky I've got to stick my finger in it.

"Yes, I'm fingering myself now. It feels so good, but I can't have all this pleasure to myself. I lower myself onto your cock and take the bulb into my mouth. It's soft and wet, and spongy, and still cool from the ice."

I could hear Gary moaning, so I took my time, describing every movement of my tongue on his hard shaft. "I'm pressing the tip of my tongue against the long vein on the underside of your prick, Gary. Now I take your whole cock in my mouth and suck. I suck it hard, and deep, and you explode. Your come fills my mouth, sweet as pudding. I let it slowly drip down my throat, and keep stroking your cock with my lips until it's drained."

Once Gary had come, he began talking to me. He told me to rub my finger against my clit, to wiggle the button hard and fast. "Now stick your thumb in your pussy," he instructed. "Roll it around slowly, back and forth and from side to side." I did as I was told. Unable to resist the temptation to anticipate his next request, I also pumped my thumb in and out of my pussy like a cock. I could hear Gary on the phone, telling me to run my fingers back and forth over my clit. "Faster! Faster!" he urged.

The car seat was in the full reclining position and my legs were spread wide apart on the dashboard. "Do you have anything in the car that you could fuck yourself with?" Gary asked.

Remembering the bag of groceries in the backseat, I told him, "How about a carrot?"

"Perfect," he said. "Wiggle it against your clit for a moment, then plunge it into your cunt. Slide it in and out of your wet pussy. That's it, use deep thrusts." I did so and the sensation was incredible. As I fucked myself with the carrot, my thumb kept hitting my clit, driving me wild.

I could feel the juices flowing from my pussy. I imagined that it was Gary's cock, and not a carrot, inside me. I begged him to fuck me harder. "I want to come," I pleaded. "Ram me, Gary. Fuck me as hard as you can."

"God, are you hot," he said. "You're swallowing me up! That's it, take it all!"

I slid the carrot in and out, in and out. As I pumped, my moans grew louder. Fortunately the phone was in a secluded area and there was no possibility of anyone coming by. "Stick the carrot all the way into your cunt and leave it there," was Gary's next instruction. "Now frig your clit. Give it everything you've got. I want you to make yourself come. But don't move that carrot!"

The minute I started wiggling my clit, I felt the orgasm build up inside me. It started with a tingle in my toes. Then my legs weakened and the rest of my body followed. I squealed into the phone as I climaxed. The orgasm washed over me like the waves of a powerful sea. My whole body was transported, exhausted with pleasure.

"Now," Gary said, "pull the carrot out. Nice and fast." He knew exactly what he was doing. No sooner did I yank the carrot from my pussy than I came again. The sudden motion made my cunt erupt with wetness, and made my voice erupt with a moan that was probably heard for miles.

I have learned that sex is best when it holds some surprise. These telephone sessions with Gary are always different and un-predictable. They are, by a landslide, the best sexual experiences I have ever had. If any of your readers are afraid or embarrassed to explore their deepest fantasies with a lover in person, they should try doing so on the phone. I have a feeling they will be astounded by the results.—*B.L., St. Louis, Missouri*

A SOLO ORIGINAL

Like many of your readers, I grab your magazine as soon as it hits the newsstand, and like many of your readers, I am greatly turned on by the letters and pictorials. I masturbate looking at those fantastic asses, tits, and cunts. I especially like the ones showing two girls getting it on.

Now, the difference is that I am female. I am twenty-six years old, and my measurements are 38-25-37. I am divorced and live alone and I don't have to work, so this leaves me with plenty of time for my favorite hobby, mainly jerking off my cunt to fantastic orgasms. I am a compulsive masturbator. I have jerked my cunt to a juicy orgasm as many as thirty times in a day. Allowing eight hours for sleep, that's as much as twice an hour. I don't suppose this is a record, but I would like to hear from other readers on this. I never play with my pussy less than a dozen times a day. Sometimes I have three orgasms before I even get out of bed.

Although I have never had sex with a woman, my fantasies during masturbation most often involve lovely girls with big tits and nicely rounded asses and juicy slits. I have fingered myself many times looking at some photos in one of your issues. How I would love to bury my face in one of those beautiful cunts or just lie with one of the models and watch her finger-fuck herself!

With this juicy cunt between my legs, I can please myself any time I want, any way I want. I have a large collection of playthings to satisfy my cunt. (I love the word *cunt*!) With a little imagination I can get my cunt off with all kinds of things besides my fingers, vibrators, and dildos. I've used carrots, candles, cucumbers, bananas, and all sorts of other things commonly used by women. I have, however, one item for solo fucking that is probably unique. I have had a thing for high heels ever since I wore my first pair. They make me feel very sexy. I stay naked most of the time, even now, except for my shoes. I have several pairs that I never wear outside, which I bought for solo sex only.

I usually dig out one of your issues that describes a girl with her hand on her cunt or spreading her cunt lips. I get a pair of shoes from my collection. Then I lie on my bed with the shoes on and the magazine next to me. I start to jerk my clit with one hand and run my fingers along the folds of my cunt. When I start getting nice and juicy, I stop jerking and cross my legs tightly to feel those wonderful vibes. Then I take a tit in each of my hands and raise them both so I can lick and suck my nipples. This really makes my juices flow. I then go back to my cunt. I put two fingers way inside to feel the silky skin and creamy juice. I then lick the cream from my fingers, and at this point I am ready.

I take off one of the shoes and lick the heel all over. At this point, I slide the heel of the shoe against my juicy cunt and clit. I press hard to get the heel wet with my slick juices. I roll the shoe sideways slightly, feeling the smooth patent leather on my clit. My ass is bouncing like crazy by now, as I begin my mini-orgasms, building up to the big one, all of which can last up to half an hour. Then, I call out to the girl in the magazine and plead with her: "Fuck me harder, faster!" or "Please let me suck you!" I think that having some lovely doll to suck while I get off with my heel would be the ultimate. Just as I approach my big climax, I take my other shoe, wet it in my mouth, and come like a wild woman.

I should mention that I also have a pair of pointy-toed patent leather shoes. I prefer to rub the toes of these shoes against my erect nipples. I call this "toeing with myself," and I can even do it while I watch TV!—*Name and address withheld by request*

GRADUATE PROJECT

A few years ago I had just finished grad school and was living off campus with my girlfriend, who was also a grad student.

With my thesis done, I was teaching part-time and waiting for my girlfriend to finish her term. One morning as we climbed out of the shower, she mentioned that she had volunteered me to help one of our friends, Pam, with her graduate project. I knew Pam well and readily agreed, figuring what she needed was some help with word processing or editing.

At the appointed time I showed up at Pam's place—a big, rambling house festooned with ferns, wall hangings, and wicker furniture. Pam met me at the door clad in a long terry-cloth robe and carrying a mug of coffee. It was eight in the morning. She invited me inside and explained she was getting her master's in physical education, and she was doing her thesis on muscle massages. She said that her advisor thought she had a good chance to get it published and that she was going to submit it with photos. That, she explained, was where I came in.

My girlfriend, Janet, had volunteered me to be Pam's subject for the photos that would ultimately accompany the text. I was not quite prepared for this and was taken completely off guard. Pam ushered me to her bathroom, gave me a towel, and urged me to take a hot shower to help me relax. She said that she and the photographer would be in the living room, and that I could just leave my clothes hanging in the bathroom.

I showered and dried off. Feeling sheepish and more than a little apprehensive, I came out into the living room with the towel wrapped around my waist. The photographer, a female grad student whom I had seen around, and her lighting assistant—also a young lady—were waiting with Pam. On the floor a large quilt was spread out. Several candles were lit. Pam handed me a small bottle of lotion and explained that a slathering would better reveal my muscle definition in the photos. I began putting it on my arms while she spread it on my back.

In an instant she undid my towel and was putting the lotion on my buttocks. I found myself standing naked in front of the other two girls. Pam moved about in front of me and applied the lotion to my chest, abdomen, legs, and even gave my genitals a once-over. I stood there naked as the photographer moved about and, with the assistant's help, took several light-meter readings.

Pam removed her robe and was naked underneath. As she applied some lotion to her arms and breasts she asked me to apply some to her back, explaining that in order to get or give a proper massage one had to be totally naked. Thus we began the photo session with me lying on my belly and Pam kneeling beside me, working on my back and legs with her firm fingers.

The thesis required over one hundred photos. One has to understand, however, that in order to obtain that many quality photos one has to take literally thousands.

For the next week I would show up at Pam's place early in the morning, undress, and spend the day in the nude as she massaged me front and back from toes to head while the photographer clicked away. I began to enjoy the massages a lot, as one could imagine. I even grew accustomed to being naked in front of the other girls. In fact, when we took a break or had lunch neither Pam nor I would get dressed. I got a tantalizing charge out of standing around naked and chatting with the girls.

One day a couple of her friends—a guy and a girl—stopped by at lunchtime. Unabashed, Pam answered the door in the nude and introduced them to me as I stood there, also naked. We talked for a while, and they looked over some photos from the sessions.

On the last day of shooting, Pam explained that she wanted to get the photos done for the erotic massage section. She explained to me that she would understand if I wanted to back out. I told her she had to be kidding. After all I had been through, how could I quit then? Besides, the idea of getting an erotic massage from Pam sounded extremely appealing, to say the least. I didn't feel guilty either because, after all, it had been my girlfriend's idea for me to do this in the first place.

The photographer's assistant joined us for these photos, disrobing and massaging Pam as well as me. The girls massaged each other's breasts and buttocks. As the camera moved in close, they brought each other off with their fingers. Then the two of them went to work on me. I lay there on my back with a raging erection.

Finally, with the camera only a couple of feet away and the assistant watching me, Pam gave me a long, loving handjob with lots of oil while cooing about how she loved the look and feel of my cock. She knew how to bring me to the brink and then back. Finally, she brought me off and my come spurted on her loving fingers. All of this was captured by the camera.

This was undoubtedly one of my most memorable experiences. Now whenever I see her I can't help but remember the incredible experience I had with her and the other girls.

Pam's thesis did get published and is still available in some bookstores—though, frankly, it is bought more for soft porn than as an instructional manual. I am proud to be in those photos. It was a truly erotic experience.—*M.O., Milwaukee, Wisconsin*

IN LOVE WITH HER PEN PAL

I am forty years old and divorced, stand five feet four inches tall, and weigh one hundred twenty pounds. I have maintained my figure because I absolutely crave sex. The reason I am divorced is that I couldn't stand the tedium of having just one lover.

Three years ago I joined a service that enabled men and women to meet through the mail. I've met many men who've proven to be excellent sex partners. Last spring I received a letter from a man doing time in prison. Normally I wouldn't pursue a relationship with a criminal, but this man intrigued me. He was also divorced, and before his arrest for fraud was a successful professional. He described himself as six-feet-two, with a muscular, athletic build. The thought of this hunk in his prison togs made my pussy juices flow.

After several bland, getting-to-know-you letters, I decided to spice up our correspondence with some Polaroid pictures of myself, naked, in various provocative poses. As Todd is in a minimum-security facility, he was allowed to keep the photographs. He wrote back immediately to say how crazy he was about seeing me nude and itching to be fucked. He told me he jerked off three times in one hour immediately after getting the pictures.

In that same letter he provided me with a tracing of his hard cock on a piece of paper. When I unfolded the paper I was both amused and stunned by what I saw. It was the longest, most deliciously curved cock I'd ever seen. I wrote back to Todd and told him that if his cock was really the nine and a half inches it measured on the paper, I would come to visit him at the prison for a closer look. He answered my letter at once and told me the tracing was an accurate portrait of the real thing.

The prison was just a couple of hours from my home. I showed up the following weekend in a pair of skintight jeans and a very loose-fitting sweater. My plan was to raise the sweater above my big melons to give him a good look. I was disappointed that we could not have a "contact visit," as they're called, since I had visions of holding Todd's gigantic, curved tool in my hands. However, our "window visit" proved to be a completely arousing affair.

After Todd and I spoke for a few minutes I began to tempt his libido by playing with my fleshy tits. I could see from the way he was fidgeting in his seat, and from the huge knot in his jeans, that I was turning him on.

"Do you think we should play a little show-and-tell?" I asked into the phone we used to communicate.

Todd replied with a nod. Standing, he slowly pulled down his zipper. I gasped when his pink banana sprung from his jeans and grew fully erect before my eyes, bobbing on the other side of the glass like a lewd puppet. The drawing he'd sent was indeed accurate. In fact if I hadn't measured it at nine and a half inches, I would've sworn that his cock was closer to ten—or even eleven. I was so turned on that, with just a slight shift of my legs, I brought myself to orgasm right there! With my cunt sopping wet,

I lifted my sweater and gave Todd a wide-screen view of my breasts. I pushed them up to the window, rubbing the hard nipples against the cool, clear glass.

I moved away from the glass, still exposed. Todd began to fondle his enormous balls, holding one in each hand as his mammoth hard-on throbbed up and down, oozing a steady stream of clear, thick pre-come. From that point on we both steadily masturbated. I was mesmerized by the size and shape of his huge erection, and even more so by the unusually large nuts that hung low in his hairy bag. I talked to Todd on the phone as we jerked off, describing in detail how I couldn't wait to tongue every inch of his hard cock and feel the head throbbing in my throat.

As I talked and made blowjob sounds, Todd pulled on his hammer and watched intently as I played with my tits and stuck my finger in my creamy hole. I wished he could smell the fuck-me aroma wafting up from between my legs. I wanted to break through the glass divider between us and stuff his log into my cunt. The fact that I was denied this pleasure only served to make me hornier.

I watched closely as Todd continued to beat off. Suddenly his enormous, fat balls began to rise in their sac. His cock started to shake and the head swelled even more. Instinctively I opened my mouth when the first ribbon of pearly white jism jumped from his hard meat and splattered against the glass window that separated us. I moaned into the phone as I, too, came. In my mind I was swallowing his thick load in big gulps, savoring every drop. My fingers worked wildly at my swollen clit until I'd come a second and third time.

Todd wiped the semen off on the sleeve of his blue prison shirt. Then he held it up to the glass, saying into the phone that he couldn't wait for the day he could stick his cock in me and pump me full of cream. I dream of that day too, which should come in another eighteen months. Until then, we share these show-and-tell visits every weekend. When we're not together— and even if I'm with another man—I long for the moment when

Todd's massive, curved rod will find its way into my mouth, my cunt, and between my tits. Anywhere he wants to bury that treasure is all right with me.—*T.C., Detroit, Michigan*

HEAR IT AND COME

I am a student at an eastern state university and I should start by telling you that I suffer from a not-so-rare disease known as chronic virginity.

Thanks to my roommate Paul (which is not his real name), I have learned to suppress some of the adverse conditions of this disease. As you know, party life at large universities is plentiful, and our apartment is no exception. At a party one night, I found, as usual, that the female species was not attracted my way; so I retired to my room to go to sleep. Soon after, Paul brought a young lady into the bedroom to do some prolonged penis plunging, but to his surprise, he found me in bed.

Since the rest of the apartment was crowded with people, he and the young lady retired to the bathroom. Not knowing that I was still awake, Paul continued in the usual fashion of lovemaking. Knowing quite well what was going on, I had acquired one of the best hard-ons that I had ever experienced. Soon I heard the bottles in the medicine cabinet start to rattle violently and the toilet seat start to thump. I could not resist the urge anymore; so I slipped a hand down to my groin and started to jerk off. Nearly out of my mind with ecstasy, I could imagine myself inside of that chick's juicy cunt, going in and out, in and out. I had never experienced such an orgasm before and was surprised by the beautiful sensation I had received as I came all over my sheets.

Now my roommate and I set these situations up at every party we have. While he is getting a piece of ass in the bathroom, I lie violently pounding my meat in bed. The result is the best pleasure both of us have ever known.—*T.C., Baltimore, Maryland*

OLIVE OIL ORGASMS

My boyfriend and I enjoy sex, but lately we've been so busy that we haven't made love in three weeks. I love the fact that he treats me like a best friend, but I thought it was time he saw me as a seductive woman as well. One day while at the liquor store I picked up a copy of *Forum*. There was an article about orgasmic massage that seemed to be just the thing I was looking for. I went to the bedroom and put on a tank top and some panties.

My boyfriend came to the door looking mildly surprised by my outfit. It was unusual for me to take off my clothes so early in the evening. He followed me into the kitchen and we sat at the table. I showed him the magazine article.

"I've been reading this, and I want a man's opinion."

"Really?" he said.

"Yes," I said, trying to be serious. He is the reticent type and, usually, so am I. He wasn't used to me reading anything lighter than *Newsweek*. He glanced again at my outfit, my nipples showing plainly through the thin cotton.

"It's about a massage for men, and I want to know if it's something you'd like." He couldn't hide his stunned expression.

I brought the subject up again after dinner, and handed him the magazine opened to the article on massage. As he read silently, I loosened his clothing and slipped his pants down to his ankles. He began to stroke himself, but I insisted on taking over. I touched him just the way the article had described, first one hand running from the tip to the root, then from root to tip, ten times with each alternating hand and each stroke.

"Just a moment," I told him, and ran to the kitchen to find some oil. He stayed on the couch. Olive oil was the handiest, and I prayed the odor wouldn't turn him off.

"Here," I said on returning, and poured the oil over the tip as the article suggested. I stroked him repeatedly, switching hands every single stroke. I'd go outward ten, from the tip to the base of his root, then back, rhythmically. Evidently my motions suited him. He lay back on the sofa and raised his arms above his head, leaving himself totally vulnerable to my touch.

His eyes began to roll from side to side in ecstasy. His obvious descent into oblivion aroused me, too. As his excitement mounted, he reached out for me. To his surprise, I pushed him back to lie on the sofa and continued my hand motions stronger and more rhythmically. The oil seemed to be making him harder than I had ever seen him. I began to squeeze my thighs together in time with the rhythm I was jerking him to. As my hand went up and down on his cock, I could feel my pussy getting wetter. He moaned for me to pump him even harder, and I did until we both couldn't stand the tension anymore. I came with him as he spurted his load up to my mouth. I licked him clean.

The next day I got a phone call at my office. "Now I know why Popeye loved Olive Oyl," he said. I found it difficult to keep a straight face as my next client entered my office.—*T.E., San Francisco, California*

Bondage and Discipline

A Hair-Razing Tale

A few weeks ago, my girlfriend, Carol, asked me to give her a ride home after work, since her car was in the shop. When I stopped by the hairstyling salon where she works, Carol was just finishing her last cut. I asked her and Becky, the other stylist, why they were still hard at work when Linda, the owner, had already gone home. One of them told me that she was in the back of the shop doing a stenciling job.

"What's a stenciling job?" I asked innocently. The girls just smiled and laughed. After considerable coaxing, Carol explained that Linda had several customers who wanted initials shaved into their pubic hair. I asked if that skill was one they had learned in school. Becky shot back, "No, but if you are volunteering to be my guinea pig, I am ready to learn." I quickly declined. Just then, Linda and an attractive girl in her early twenties entered the main room. The girl paid Linda and left.

I struck up a conversation with Linda, kidding her about her favorite football team, Michigan, which had been losing recently. Feeling a little cocky, I asked her if she'd like to make a wager: "Linda, are you ready to lose a ten-spot on the Illinois-Michigan game?" I knew that Illinois had beaten Michigan easily in their first two meetings, and I also knew that Linda loved to gamble. Linda quickly agreed, and I thought I'd make an easy ten bucks, but she insisted that a third party hold the money to prevent collection problems. I tried to borrow the money from Carol, but she said that she didn't have enough money with her. Becky offered to put up the ten-spot, but made me promise that if Michigan won I would not only repay the loan but also allow her to practice her stenciling. I agreed without giving it too much thought.

To my surprise, Michigan won the game. The next day, Carol asked me for another ride home from work. When I arrived, Carol told me that she was running a little late and it would be at least forty-five minutes before she'd be through with the perm she was working on. "That's okay. He has a debt to pay off, anyway," Becky quickly chimed in. I gave Becky the ten bucks I owed her, but refused to let her carve any initials in my pubes. Carol, Linda, and Becky bitched that I was a welsher. Unmoved, I grabbed the newspaper and sat in one of the empty chairs.

Linda disappeared and returned a short time later. She wandered over to me and pretended to look over my shoulder at the newspaper, but after a few seconds she grabbed my wrist and clamped a handcuff around it. She attached the other handcuff to the side of the chair. With the help of Becky, Linda snapped a second set of cuffs around my other wrist and attached that pair to the other side of the chair. For a few minutes I struggled futiley with my bonds, but I quickly realized that I wasn't going anywhere until they released me.

By now, all four women in the salon were laughing out loud! Carol explained the bet and its stakes to the lady whose hair she was perming. Then Becky asked the woman if she would be offended if payment were exacted before she left. "Be my guest," was her response. "I've always felt that all just debts should be promptly paid when due."

After locking the front door, Becky forced the chair that I was in to fully recline. She unbuckled, unsnapped, and unzipped my jeans. Linda tugged on one side of my pants, and Becky tugged on the other. Together they easily pulled them off.

Becky reached between my legs to grasp the crotch of my briefs, and yanked them off with one swift motion, tearing them in the process. The customer loudly gasped, "Oh, my God, you have to move me so I can see his crotch."

With one hand, Becky pulled my rock-hard erection down between my legs. With the other she grabbed the scissors and trimmed all my pubic hair to about one-half inch in length. Then she placed the "K" stencil slightly above and to the right of the base of my prick. Becky combed out all the hair exposed by the opening forming the "K," then cut that hair as short as she could. Next, a pink gel was painted over the stencil. When the stencil was removed, a pink "K" covered the remaining stubble. Becky selected a straight razor and carefully shaved the pink area until it was completely smooth. The "L" stencil was placed just above and to the left of the base of my cock, and the process was repeated.

When she finished the second initial, Becky stood back to admire her work and to get a review from the audience. The newly permed lady got up and traced the shaved area on my abdomen with her index finger. "Why, it's just as smooth as a baby's behind," she remarked.

Carol complained, "You know, he should really have to pay some kind of penalty for trying to welsh on the deal."

"Yes," Becky agreed, "but I guess we had better just clean him up for now."

Becky washed my pubic area with soap and water to remove the remnants of the gel. However, she was not satisfied with cleaning just my pubic hair; she soaped and stroked my bulging cock as well. I came very quickly, shooting several gobs of sperm on Becky's hand. She promptly wiped it on my thigh and rubbed it in.

When Miss Perm realized what had happened, she lamented, "Damn it, if you were going to jerk him off, I sure wish you would have said something so I could have positioned myself to watch him shoot his wad." Linda appeased her by announcing that she would release my right hand, but, until I had brought myself to yet another climax, she would not release my left hand.

While I was recovering from the shock, Becky went to her car to get her Polaroid instant camera. She took several pictures of her handiwork, making sure that each woman had at least one.

"Okay, Kevin, let's see you beat your meat," giggled Linda. I slowly slid my hand up and down my limp shaft. Miss Perm lent some assistance until I was hard, but then handed me my erection, saying, "It's your show, shoot for the stars." With the ladies urging me on, I stroked myself with increasing speed and intensity. Becky stood with her camera at the ready. As my prick was engulfed with come, Becky began to take snapshots as my cock continued to pump spurt after spurt. Becky's camera just kept clicking. Carol now tells me that Becky has a lovely pictorial of my payoff displayed in the back room of the salon for all to see. My hair's grown back now, but I'll be damned if Carol ever gets another ride home.—*K.L., Gary, Indiana*

MEMORIES AFTER MIDNIGHT

How can someone adequately describe the freedom you are granted when you subject yourself to another's will? It is almost impossible to describe the release obtained in turning your body over to another's total control! If you are lucky enough to find the right master, you will experience such sexual ecstasy that you will be hooked for life!

On my part, my initiation into master/slave possibilities began innocently enough. But my master, being the adept student of female natures that he is, saw the possibilities in our relationship from the start.

I had known Jesse for a while before anything even remotely sexual in nature ever happened between us. The first time that I found myself in his bed he went easy on me.

Kissing me passionately, our tongues caressing, his hands

slipped down to my breasts and he began to gently tug and rub his thumb on the tips of my nipples. Shivers of excitement started to run down my spine, sending bolts of pure lust straight to my pussy. I was dying for him to just touch me there, in the most sensitive part of my being.

Slipping his hands over my hips, and stroking my inner thighs with a feather-light touch, he removed his lips from mine and kissed his way down my neck until his lips fastened on the hardened nub of my nipple. Quite unexpectedly he bit down on that tender bit of flesh, releasing it only to softly chuckle at my shocked gasp! Smiling at me wickedly, he returned his mouth to its task while a finger found its way through the moist fold of my outer lips, then into the dark wetness of my cunt. Oh God! What a feeling his talented fingers brought to me, as his teeth tantalized my aching nipples.

I was really amazed to discover that after the initial shock, his mouth and teeth only brought even greater pleasure as he intensified the force which he used on my nipples. My hips bucked against his hand as I strove for even deeper penetration. Due to the combined sensations from his teeth and his fingers buried deep within me, I was brought with unexpected speed to orgasm. Muscles inside my cunt began contracting, spasming uncontrollably around his fingers, and my breathing turned to ragged gasps while I humped his hand to one of the best orgasms I'd had in a long, long time.

While my breathing was quieting, and my heartbeat returning to normal, Jesse just kind of smiled with a knowing sort of look on his face. Then, with an air of innocence, he suggested that I let him restrain me. Holy shit! I almost came right then and there, as this had been a fantasy of mine for just about forever, but I'd never had the nerve to come out and ask anyone for it for fear of their reaction. Here, at last, my longed-for fantasy was being fulfilled.

Tied spread-eagle to his bed, my eyes obscured beneath a black satin blindfold, my body felt everything with an intensity that I had never known before. I had given to Jesse any control that I might have had over my body, and I was free to just experience the multitude of pleasures that his skill promised. All inhibitions fled me as I responded to his every touch.

First he took something (it felt like a tasseled cord) and started to brush it lightly between my thighs, and over my exposed and now gaping pussy. Using both hands, he pulled apart the outer lips of my pussy, spreading wide that most sensitive area. He started telling me what a nice cunt I had. I had never been so closely examined by anyone before, and it excited me wildly! When he flicked that tassel against my open gap I started coming and coming and coming, as my pussy was begging for him to put something inside it. It felt wonderfully nasty to lie there anticipating his next move, knowing I was helpless to do anything but blindly wait for whatever would come next.

Descending with a much greater force, the cord now lashed its way across my breasts. Gasping, I found myself arching my back to give my breasts even greater access to the punishment Jesse was administering. Unexpectedly the cord changed its target and descended to the swollen bud of my clit. Again my cunt started spasming, sending me over the edge. I screamed in ecstasy until I felt as if I would pass out from the sheer intensity of my sensations.

Even though I had fantasized about bondage, I never realized that the fine line between pleasure and pain could be crossed with such ease. I never imagined that I could be brought to a place where I not only desired pain, but I even begged for it. Jesse had initiated me into what he knew that my body desired, and in doing so had made me into his sexual slave. I had never known such freedom and desire as he taught me that night, and continues to teach me to this day.

Since then, my master has shaved my whole pubic area (so it will be open to his gaze, and more sensitive to the touch of his whip). He's used nipple clamps on me and, on a particularly memorable night, he lashed both my nipples and clit with a riding crop before sliding it partially into my cunt. Then he had me suck my own tangy juices off the leather crop as he finger-fucked my ass!

My master tells me that my next initiation is my virgin ass! When I learn to beg real nicely for his cock to bury itself deep within my asshole, he says that I will be really and truly his slave.

I'm begging, master . . . I'm begging! Can't you see the way the little rosebud of my asshole is begging for the attention of your massive organ? Maybe if he reads this in your magazine my master will finally believe in my submission to him, and will indulge his slave's desire for him by fucking her in the ass!—*S.B., San Diego, California*

COME NOW

"I'm afraid that I'm going to come," I whimpered.

"You should be," came her calm, patronizing reply.

I strained against the leather straps holding my body spreadeagle against the wall while this blond leather-clad goddess vigorously rubbed my erect cock.

"Don't you come until I give you my permission, or I'll paddle your ass."

"Oh, mistress, I'm afraid I'm going to come."

"You should be . . ."

Two hours earlier I had been led into the basement by a man who had instructed me to remove all of my clothing. I placed my monetary offering in the wooden bowl and knelt to face the doorway, waiting for my mistress to arrive.

As I knelt there on the floor, I glanced around the dimly lit room. There were large contraptions of wood and leather against the wall. I started to wonder what I had gotten myself into, when I heard voices and the sound of hard heels on the step. Then she came to stand in the doorway.

She gave me a cursory glance, then looked around the room.

I felt strange kneeling there, naked under her gaze. She was tall with long blond hair and wore only black: an opened vest that allowed glimpses of her otherwise bare breasts, a skirt with heavy metal zippers on both sides, high-heeled black boots.

She stalked past me and sat down in a thronelike chair, demanding that I turn toward her. I pivoted awkwardly on my knees and came to sit at her feet as she started to read the letter of application I had sent her. She asked me questions to which I was allowed to answer only yes or no. When I nervously responded "yeah" to one question I got a warning sting from her riding crop.

"You will address me as Mistress or Ma'am. Is that clear?"

I looked down at my nakedness and said, "Yes, ma'am."

"That's better. Now stand up. Now turn for me—very slowly."

I did as she told me, allowing her to view my body at her leisure. When I was halfway around she told me to stop. I heard her move in her chair, then felt the light touch of her gloved fingers run up the back of my leg. I shivered as she touched my buttock and felt a thrilling stir in the end of my penis as it started to swell.

"Keep turning," she commanded. I turned the rest of the way until, once again, I faced her.

"Well," she said, eyeing my semi-erect cock, "you're quite sensitive. That's good." She reached up to stroke my nipples, and I shivered again as they immediately stiffened. She gave a small smile.

She left the room for a moment and returned with several leather straps. I watched as she handled the instruments of bondage and discipline—*my* bondage and *my* discipline.

"Did you bring any panties?"

I was taken aback. "Just the ones I wore," I answered, not used to thinking of my underwear as panties.

"Let me see them," she commanded harshly.

Without turning my back to her, as I was instructed earlier, I retrieved my briefs from the hook I had hung them on. They were designer briefs of sheer white stretch nylon. I handed them to her.

"Hmmm," she murmured, holding them up. "These look like a man's panties. Put them on." She watched as I fitted them over my ass.

She reached out and lightly felt my ass through the smooth, tight nylon, then stroked the bulge in front, which expanded at her touch.

"You like how they feel anyway?"

"Yes, ma'am."

"Now come here," she demanded, positioning me in the middle of the room. She roughly fastened broad leather straps on each of my wrists. Turning me around, she fastened my wrists together behind my back, then turned me to face her again. I felt a twinge of fear as I stood there, feeling even more naked with my hard-on so obvious in my sheer nylon briefs. With my hands shackled, I was completely vulnerable.

She smiled and grasped the elastic waistband of my pants and pulled the briefs down under my balls. She squeezed the sensitive tip of my cock between her thumb and fingers. Flicking it, she laughed as my cock jumped. I felt helpless.

She took a strap of rawhide and bound my genitals so that my balls protruded in a tight little hairy package and my cock seemed even more swollen. She spread my legs as she buckled leather cuffs on each ankle. "You have nice legs," she said. "How do you think they would look in nylon stockings?"

I was shocked, but I knew better than to protest. "Yes, mistress," I managed to utter.

Grabbing my cock, she led me to the other room, nearly yanking me by my swollen handle.

I whimpered, "It hurts, mistress," in a voice I hardly recognized as my own.

"You don't know what pain is. What you feel now is just a little discomfort." She led me to the far wall that housed an ominous wooden frame and unhooked my hands, only to refasten them to the rack. She tied them above my head, then reached behind me to hook a finger in the top of my briefs, slipping them down off my ass.

"Now," she said, stepping back, "I want you to wiggle out of your panties."

I attempted to twitch my hips and thighs in order to get the tight nylon to slide down. The motion caused my protruding genitals to bounce and jerk obscenely in front of me while the mistress, amused at my humiliating predicament, stood by watching me.

"Keep wiggling. Get those panties off." She was laughing now. I finally managed to get the nylon garment to slide down my legs. "There. Wasn't that fun?"

"Yes, mistress," I said.

She pulled a thick belt around my waist and attached it to the frame.

"Suck your stomach in," she demanded as she pulled it tight, securing my torso to the wall. She spread my legs and fastened them to the rings on the frame.

I felt like a toy as she pulled a stool in front of me and sat down. I was naked, vulnerable, completely immobilized, and exposed to this aggressive woman. She settled herself in her seat, level with my swollen balls that protruded from their leather bindings. She stroked the smooth skin under the head of my erect shaft until I squirmed.

"Do you like that?"

"Yes, mistress," I gasped.

"Well, you can like it all you want, but don't you come until I give you permission. Understood?"

She stroked my shining cockhead faster and harder. I felt myself straining against my bonds.

"Okay, you can come," she said while she continued her rubbing. My body moved rhythmically despite my tight bonds. She stopped abruptly.

"I changed my mind," she cooed.

I sighed, and she laughed as she started her stroking all over again.

"I'm afraid I'm going to come," I whimpered.

"You should be," came her calm reply as she stroked my aching member. "If you come before I give my permission, I'm going to paddle your ass." Her strokes were brisk and on the mark. My balls ached.

"Ohhh, I'm afraid I'm going to have to come, mistress." I was begging.

"You should be," she replied once more, the threat of the paddle an unspoken promise.

"Okay, you can come," she relented. I felt my relief building when she again released my cock. Then she said in a mocking, singsong voice, "No, I changed my mind."

My purplish erection strained against the leather binding and the strap around my waist constricted my breathing, but she tightened the belt even more.

She resumed her vigorous assault on the bulbous head of my cock, and I was responding physically, fearful of losing control but unable to hold back my building excitement.

"Okay," she said again—I was beginning to dread that word— "now you may come." I felt myself building, but all the time I was waiting for her to stop her hand and deny me the relief it could bring. She continued stroking and, with a twitch of her wrist, released the leather string that bound my cock and balls. With a moan, I shot a series of white streams, ecstatic in my orgasm.

"I like a man who shoots," she said nonchalantly as she wiped my come off her leather skirt.

She released the binds that held me to the wooden frame, and I sighed out loud. She slapped me sharply on the face.

"Stop that sighing," she said.

I had to sit alone in the cold basement for a long time before she returned and allowed me to dress. As I prepared to leave, she commanded me to kneel down and kiss the pointed toe of her black leather boot. She smiled and bid me to rise as she said

good-bye. I backed out of the dungeon and up the stairs.—*N.E.,*
Battle Creek, Michigan

LUCKY GUY TIES ONE ON

One hot night last summer I was bored and decided to visit
the local bar for a few cold ones. I'd just finished my second beer when I noticed an attractive woman sitting alone at a
back table. She was tall, her long legs enhanced by a short white
skirt. Her skin was the color of chocolate, and her perfectly
rounded breasts were nearly bursting out of her green silk shirt.

With my pulse racing, I got up the nerve and walked over to
her. She accepted my offer of a drink and introduced herself as
Nancy. Soon we were laughing and joking like old friends. After
a while she put her hand on my thigh and asked me to see her
home.

Nancy pulled me into her bedroom the minute we got to her
apartment, and pushed me onto the king-size, four-poster bed.
"I have a surprise for you," she said with a grin. "Do you like
surprises?" I answered that I did, and would be willing to try
anything. "Good," she said.

The first surprise was a blindfold, which she tied around my
eyes. Then she said she wanted to tie me down, and asked if I
would enjoy that. I'd always had fantasies of being tied down and
fucked, so I told her to do it. My cock, which had been throbbing since we'd started talking at the bar, was hard as a rocket.

She expertly tied each of my hands to a bedpost, then did the
same with my legs. The ropes she used felt soft, like they were
made of velvet, and the pressure of the bonds against my flesh
made my cock ache. As soon as I was securely tied, Nancy spoke
again. "Now," she said, "the fun begins."

She unbuttoned my shirt, bent over, and gently kissed my
chest, running her tongue over my hardening nipples. Her breath
was hot, her tongue soft and wet. After kissing my chest for a

few minutes, Nancy moved lower and unbuttoned my pants. She pressed her hands against my throbbing cock, which was straining to escape the confines of my briefs. With a tug she pulled down my pants, quickly untied my ankles to slip the slacks off my legs, then retied the knots.

I was left on the bed with my hot cock pushing against my underwear. Suddenly I felt cold metal against my thigh, and then an incredible rush as my underwear fell away—Nancy had cut them loose with a pair of scissors! Now my cock stood up straight and hard. Nancy grabbed it with a hot hand. "Mmmmm," she said, "your cock is so long and thick," and with a quick motion gave the head a deep kiss. She dipped her hot tongue into the hole at the tip. I could feel my glans swelling as the come began to boil in my balls.

"Time to take off the blindfold," she said, and with a quick move she let go of my cock and undid the knot. I couldn't believe the sight that beheld my eyes! Nancy was standing over the bed, dressed in a white bra that pushed up her breasts, and a garter belt that held up sheer white stockings. The white of the fabric glowed against her black skin, and her neatly trimmed bush glistened with the dew of expectation.

At the foot of the four-poster bed was another woman. She was white, and dressed in jet-black lingerie. Her long blond hair shimmered in the light. Her lips were painted a deep red. She ran her pink tongue over her lips and smiled at me, a long finger slowly creeping into the cleft between her legs.

"This is my roommate, Maria," said Nancy, smiling as she walked over to Maria. "Her boyfriend stood her up tonight, and Maria doesn't sleep very well without a good fuck—do you, Maria?"

Instead of answering, Maria walked over to Nancy and kissed the back of her neck. Maria's long arms embraced Nancy from behind. Her red nails sought out the tips of Nancy's breasts, which hardened at the touch. "Why don't we show Arthur just how close we really are?" said Maria, her juicy lips lightly touching Nancy's ear. She turned to kiss Maria, and their lips met.

The two girls made love savagely as I watched, helpless. My hands strained against the bonds, and my cock felt like it was going to explode. Nancy pushed Maria back to the wall, sucking and licking her all over. She drove her tongue deep into Maria's pussy again and again. After she tired of sucking Maria's bush, she turned to me with a smile and said, "Maria gets so wet when she's excited. It tastes so sweet!" And then she pushed her fingers deep into Maria's pussy and moved them around, finally taking them out and bringing them over for me to lick. I sucked them hungrily, letting Maria's sweet pussy juice run down my chin. I needed some relief, and told Nancy I felt like my cock was going to explode if one of them didn't pay it some attention soon.

"Don't worry," replied Maria, "we'll take care of your cock. But first you'll take care of our cunts." She walked over to the bed and climbed onto my face. I had no choice but to relax and endure their form of torture. Then again, it wasn't really torture eating Maria's pussy, which was dripping with love honey. Her bush was wet with excitement, and I quickly slid my tongue into her pink hole, licking her clitoris as she ground her hips in slow circles against my mouth.

I could see Nancy too. Her left hand was rubbing her friend's breast while her right hand massaged her own clitoris. Within a few seconds my tongue had brought Maria to orgasm. With a shriek of joy she squeezed her thighs around the sides of my head and flooded my eager mouth with hot juice.

When Maria recovered she climbed off the bed, and Nancy leaned over and licked what was left of Maria's juice off my face. "You'll get to taste more of that later, and some of mine too," she said with a smile. "But first we have to take care of that lovely cock!"

The two of them began to kiss my legs, starting below the knees. Nancy was on the left and Maria on the right, and their hot little mouths left tracks of red lipstick as they worked their way up to my groin. I writhed with pleasure, still tied securely to the bedposts, as the two of them gently sucked my balls and took turns poking a finger up my ass. Finally Nancy took my whole cock into her mouth. While Maria finger-fucked my ass, Nancy sucked me until I released a huge load of hot sperm down her throat.

I was so hot my cock remained rigid after my orgasm, which was just what Maria wanted. With a quick motion she clambered onto the bed and quickly slid my cock into her dripping pussy. "Fuck me!" she shouted. "Drive that cock straight into my pussy, baby!" She moved like a wild woman, thrashing and grinding her hips, pumping up and down on me like a piston. Nancy put one finger into Maria's cunt and one into her ass, and together the two of us brought Maria to yet another screaming orgasm.

Now it was Nancy's turn. First she cleaned Maria's juice off my cock. Then she pushed my hard pole into her own bright pink cunt. Seeing my cock disappear into that black beauty, her tight little cunt framed by white lingerie, just about drove me wild. With my hands and legs thrashing and pulling at the ropes that held me down, the two of us fucked like savages. Maria watched and fingered her own pussy as we screwed, occasionally rubbing my lips with her juice, or licking Nancy's ass. After an hour of fucking, the two of us exploded together, shouting with unabashed ecstasy.

We had sex that night in an incredible variety of combinations, with all three of us taking turns being tied up.—*A.E., Staten Island, New York*

DALE'S EDUCATION

It is my considered opinion that men are, for the most part, immature and lazy. I reached this opinion nearly three years ago, and I must admit my marriage has really improved since then. After all, one treats a lazy, immature person differently from a responsible adult.

I require Dale to come home directly from work each day. Once he's home he's at my beck and call at all times. And to make sure nothing distracts him from his chores, he's not permitted to drink, watch sports, read the paper, or engage in any sort of extracurricular activity. Though I may sound austere and unreasonable, look at it from my point of view. On a daily basis the beds are made, the dishes are done, the kitchen is polished, the laundry is cleaned and put away, the bathtub is scoured, and the house is vacuumed. Once a week the floors are mopped, the windows are washed, the stove and fridge are cleaned, the groceries are bought, the house is dusted, and the car is washed. When I want sex, all I have to do is snap my fingers and Dale's ready, willing, and able. When we go to parties, Dale stays at my side during the entire time and then, sober as a judge, chauffeurs me home.

Sometimes Dale feels independent and balks at his daily regime. Fortunately, this is a small problem due to certain steps I've taken. First, I keep Dale penniless and possessionless. All our assets are in my name only and I require him to deposit his full pay to my personal bank account. Some time ago I supervised as he cut his credit cards into little pieces. Dale is quite aware that if I were to lock him out he'd be in a very precarious position. And to ensure my control over Dale I keep him unsatisfied sexually.

Believe me, when a man wants sex from a woman he does everything to keep her happy.

Dale travels a fair amount on business, and I found out that he liked to live it up on the road. So for the last two years I've tended my control to ensure he toes the line when we're apart. He must eat all his meals in the hotel coffee shop and bring home all his receipts and a copy of the menu. This reduces his alcoholic intake to nil. To occupy his free time I require him to "write lines." It takes about an hour to write one hundred lines, so Dale must write me four hundred lines on weekday nights and one thousand lines each weekend day. It's funny, but ever since I introduced line writing, Dale hasn't had to travel as much.

After a hard day's work, Dale really appreciates the ten minutes of gentle cock-teasing I give him most nights. Since he must endure prolonged periods between orgasms, his cock stiffens and lubricates almost to my touch. As my tongue slides along his lips and my fingers gently work his inner thighs, Dale must work hard to maintain his composure. When I finish the tease Dale is super-hard, soaking wet, and desperate for me to finish what I started. Of course, I never do.

Dale used to tell me he couldn't sleep after a tease, so in order not to disturb me, he'd go to the couch. Actually this was just an excuse so he could gain some relief by masturbating. I caught him red-handed one night, so now I insist he remain in bed with me, silent and motionless.

On nights when I'm in the mood, which happens about twice a week, I have Dale don a snug pair of underwear after his teasing. This enables him to lick my cunt with absolute abandon as the underwear protects his cock from an unauthorized eruption. He does me with incredible enthusiasm, using his fingers and tongue. And after I'm satisfied and asleep, the underwear sustains Dale's erection. I always insist he wear them until morning.

I treat Dale firmly yet fairly, and he responds very well, mainly because I'm consistent. He knows that absolute obedience will earn him one ejaculation every two months. He also knows that all failures to follow the rules bring punishment. Last Tuesday, for instance, he carelessly forgot to clean the kitchen sink. I noticed his oversight and said, "Dale, I want the kitchen floor, stove, and fridge absolutely spotless by morning. You may start work after I've gone to sleep. And your oversight will cost you another week of celibacy."

Should you decide to exert control over your man, you'll find his biggest beef isn't the housework but the loss of freedom and independence. It's a total role reversal that's difficult for him to get used to. He'll detest having to ask you for money, to divulge how he's going to spend it and to control himself when you say no. He'll also find it tough to be kept in a constant state of sexual arousal with no say as to when, how, and where you want to be pleasured. Whatever you do, don't ease his plight, even slightly. You'll find that, after a year or so of having to keep his emotions in check, he'll become more laid-back.

I've told several girlfriends about my method, and they're all very pleased with the results. Since it works for them I'm sure it'll work for you too.—*K.P., Tucson, Arizona*

Fetishism

Lover of Polished Toenails

After seeing the freedom with which your readers write, I have decided to contribute this.

I have had a secret fetish ever since my last girlfriend, who wore colored polish on her toenails. I have enjoyed fantasizing about her colored toenails while I masturbate. My current girlfriend has nice-looking feet and beautiful toes.

Recently I picked up some red nail polish and brought it with me to her apartment. I asked her to paint her toenails with it—not yet explaining my reasons. That night, after satisfying her with a good session of finger-fucking and sucking her hot and juicy love nest, I asked her if, instead of the usual fuck, she would masturbate me with her feet. She was reluctant at first, but after I explained to her that polished toenails really turn me on, she obliged.

First, I lubricated her feet with my saliva by slowly tongue-kissing and nibbling her toes. This gave me a tremendous hard-on. Then she lubricated my cock with Vaseline. She slowly started to slide her big toes up and down my shaft. Soon she wrapped all her toes around my throbbing rod. This seemed to turn her on tremendously, because she started masturbating herself violently. The sight of four of her fingers sliding in and out of her wet pussy, and her other hand massaging her clit, made me come on the spot. The sight of my semen shooting on her polished toe-nails was incredible! Then, as I massaged it on and around her toes, she had a surging, jerking orgasm herself. We both dropped to the bed, thoroughly exhausted.—*P.K., New York, New York*

JELLY ROLL WITH PEANUT BUTTER

I have often read *Forum* and the stimulating experiences presented within, but it was not until recently that I had a sensational experience of my own worth relating.

I had gone to a neighborhood bar on a Friday night to have a few beers and to score if I could. The bar was exceptionally crowded, the crowd mainly males seeking the same things I was—namely, a piece of ass and the loss of our senses. After a while I became tired of the bar and the lack of prospects, so I left to smoke a joint.

As I sat in my car and smoked, I heard a knock on my window. I turned to find myself face-to-face with a beautiful blonde. Needless to say, I rolled down my window and said hi.

She said seductively, "Why don't you open the other door and let me in so I can smoke some of that?"

I immediately responded, hardly believing the night could be so easy for me. She slid across the front seat until her leg was pressed firmly against mine. I could feel my cock begin to throb and grow.

We talked and smoked for a while, then I casually suggested that we head back to my apartment. She readily agreed to this and lit up another joint.

When we arrived at my apartment, I put on some rock music. As soon as I did, the young blonde began gyrating to the music in sensuous rhythms, shaking and kicking. I watched her for a few moments, then grabbed her and kissed her deeply, my tongue diving into the depths of her mouth. A second later I felt her left hand grabbing my bulging crotch.

She removed my clothing very slowly as I closed my eyes and swayed to the music. I felt her sweet lips encircle my rigid member and climaxed almost immediately, my hot come spilling from the corners of her mouth. With a smile on her lips, she licked it all up and swallowed it.

Suddenly I found myself standing alone in the center of my living room. I found out where she had gone when she returned with my jar of smooth Skippy peanut butter and a butter knife. My cock began to harden again as she removed her clothes, and I got my first look at her pert nipples and full breasts. She lay down on the rug at my feet and asked me if I liked peanut butter. When I answered that I did, she said that was good because I was going to have *her* as a late-night snack.

She opened the jar, handed me the knife, and told me to start spreading it all over her. I quickly took the knife and dipped it into the jar of peanut butter.

I began coating it across her hardened nipples and breasts, slowly making my way down to her belly and thighs. After I spread the peanut butter on her thighs, she opened her legs and I slopped it all over her cunt. When I was finished, I started at her tits and began licking her clean. She moaned softly until I reached her pussy, then her moans became cries of pure Skippy pleasure, and she came with a shudder.

When I finished my "snack" I got an idea of my own. I guided her to the kitchen table and bent her over it. With her plump ass sticking out at me, I sank the knife into the jar and spread peanut butter all over her cunt from behind.

Then I took my prick and slid it into her snatch, through the coolness of the surrounding peanut butter. After I came, I withdrew, and we both washed off and got dressed.

She said she had to go, but that she would love to come back sometime. That was two weeks ago, and I'm still waiting for her. Meanwhile, just to be prepared, I went out and bought half a dozen jars of giant-size Skippy.—*J.S., Reno, Nevada*

MENTHOLATED FUN

I am a twenty-year-old student at a large university that is renowned for being a party school and having many beautiful coeds. My girlfriend, Patty, is unquestionably in that category. She is a petite, five-foot-three brunette who weighs about one hundred pounds. She has lovely brown eyes and a wonderfully mischievous smile. She is completely and utterly uninhibited and will try anything to please me. When it comes to kinkiness, there are few things that occur to me that haven't already crossed her horny little mind.

A few evenings ago I was being studious and completely dull, so she went to the corner grocery and bought an issue of *Forum* to amuse herself. I knew that this was going to make her horny as hell. This was her way of letting me know to prepare myself.

A letter involving cough drops caught her eye. She pointed it out to me. Naturally, I was only too happy to give her some change to go buy a pack of Hall's. She was already sucking away on one when she came back and started disrobing in front of me. Needless to say, I put aside the book I was reading and dropped a cough drop into my mouth. Then I proceeded to go down on her delightful, pert tits. She moaned in response and humped her already dripping pussy against my leg. The very thought of the little experiment we had in mind had her very hot.

I continued to turn up her thermostat by rubbing her erect clit and licking her hard nipples. When she thought that her mouth was sufficiently mentholated, she stripped off my jeans and wrapped it around my throbbing prick. Now I'm no John Holmes, but one would think that what I'm endowed with would be too much for a girl her size. No way, folks! She took the whole length down her throat and drove me to the brink of orgasm with her talented tongue.

At this point I encouraged her to turn around, and we proceeded to a fast and furious 69. I took the cough drop from my mouth and rubbed it against her clit to spread the menthol onto her. Whenever I would remove my mouth and let air hit her clit, she would moan in ecstasy. I can only assume that she felt the tingling coolness one feels when sucking in air after sucking a cough drop.

She came a number of times before moving down to shove my dick into her dripping box. She rode me to several more orgasms on the couch while my roommate dozed in the next room. It now occurred to me that the remnants of my cough drop might be put to another good use. I removed it from my mouth and inserted it into her pussy, right about where my cock was thrusting in and out.

Moaning, writhing, and telling me how wonderfully cold and yet hot it was, she came in another series of orgasms. She dismounted me and popped her cough drop out. She slid it all along my cock and balls. The sensation was intense. Rather than describe it, I will only say find a nice, uninhibited little lady and find out for yourself.

Heightened to a fever pitch, we fucked like mad for quite some time. Knowing that her pussy must be steaming with icy fire, I bent her over an armchair and eased my tool back inside of her. With one hand I rubbed her clit while she moaned beneath me. As I approached orgasm, I felt the menthol fluids in her steaming hole start to get onto my dick. It felt hot and cold, and the hungry clasping of her cunt was heightened beyond belief. I sprayed my sperm into her raging volcano of a hole. Completely spent, we collapsed on the chair and lay there panting like dogs in heat. If you ever feel the need to add some spice to your sex life, the nearest candy store could possess the answer to your problem.——*Name and address withheld by request*

THEY BE CHILLIN'

One afternoon after a snowfall, my wife and I were going to a movie when I noticed some large icicles. I told her that after the movie I was going to go icicle hunting and find her the biggest, longest one that I could. After continually telling her how I was going to fuck her with an icicle, she told me how hot she was getting.

So on the way home, I gathered icicles of various sizes, one of them as big as my own cock. As soon as we were in the door, I put the icicles in the freezer. Then we stripped off our clothes and my wife started sucking my dick much more enthusiastically than she ever had before. I knew this was going to be good. After a couple minutes of her excellent head I came deep in the back of her throat, a load so big it started dripping down her chin.

After deeply kissing her and tasting my own come, I told her to lie down on the floor. Then I went to the freezer and chose a few icicles. When I returned, I found my wife with her legs spread wide, wanton with lust.

I snapped off the end of one of the smaller icicles and had her suck the end until it was rounded off nice and smooth. Starting on the insides of her thighs, I rubbed the frozen dildo all over her, teasing her mound and then, finally, pushing it past her cunt lips. The heat of her pussy, when it came in contact with the ice, sent up a little plume of steam.

She went wild, thrashing and rubbing her clit. After a couple of minutes of fucking her with the small icicle I got the bigger one. Once again, I had her round off the tip so she wouldn't get hurt. As soon as I slid that icy monster into her she went crazy and had an orgasm. As soon as she finished coming, I pulled out the icicle and slid my dick into her. The feeling of a cold pussy was such a turn-on, I came almost immediately. We continued like that for the next couple of hours until we were both exhausted and totally satisfied. What a night!

For those of you who live in the south where there are no icicles . . . too bad. But those of you up north, next time you get a good snow, take an icicle into the bedroom. I promise it'll be fun.—*T.J.R., Denver, Colorado*

GIRDLES FIRE HER LOINS

I am a fairly nice-looking thirty-two-year-old divorced female. There is nothing I love more than good sex, but unfortunately, since my divorce three years ago, I'm not getting all that much. Even more unfortunately, it seems as if I am always horny. Recently things began to change for the better.

Ever since I was a teenager, I have enjoyed the feeling of being confined in very tight underthings. Over the years, I have bought a variety of corsets and girdles, one tighter than the next.

I recently bought a corset that needs to be laced up, but I need someone else to do the lacing. I practically never go out of the house without wearing nylons and some type of girdle.

On a typical workday, I wear an extremely tight pantie girdle over my panty hose. The feeling of the pressure against my body and my pussy drives me crazy.

Between that and crossing my legs, by the end of the day, my crotch is soaked. I can hardly wait to get home so I can masturbate.

Sometimes, during the afternoon, I get so turned on that I can no longer control myself. I slip into the ladies' room. Once in the stall, I finger myself to one glorious orgasm. I limit myself so that I am still horny when I get home.

After I arrive home, I am still horny and on edge. I need relief. Usually I undress, but I leave on my girdle and panty hose. I begin by caressing my small breasts and rubbing myself through the girdle. I can feel the wetness through my crotch. Then I take my vibrator out of my nightstand and hold it next to my crotch. In what seems like only a moment, my need to come is overwhelming and I am crazed with desire.

I literally rip off my girdle and my panty hose. My hand races to my clit and my other hand thrusts my vibrator against me. My orgasms arrive in one crashing wave after another. Then I lay there exhausted, but satisfied. But I will usually masturbate again before I fall asleep. I guess I'm just greedy.

Among my more recent (and tightest) underwear purchases is a long-line bra and pantie girdle that is all one unit. It has a small slit in the crotch so I can pee. If this isn't the tightest thing I have ever worn, it is very close.

With this particular girdle, I have to wear regular nylon stockings because if I wore panty hose, I would have to get completely undressed in order to pee.

One evening I had a date with a man who works in my building. This was our second or third date and we had not yet made love. I was hoping that this would be the night. Eric is very handsome, and there was a certain something about him that attracted me. It had been nearly nine months since I had felt a cock inside of me.

On this evening, I had decided to wear my new all-in-one girdle. However, I didn't have a pair of regular nylons, so I wore panty hose. I also wore a very sexy dress.

Eric picked me up and took us to dinner at a restaurant overlooking the harbor. It was a beautiful night and everything was perfect. It was very romantic. At the same time, I could feel the wetness at my crotch. I decided that tonight I was going to make my move. After dinner, we walked out to his car. Originally, we had planned to go to a club to listen to music. Once in the car, I put my arms around him and gave him a long, deep kiss.

Happily, Eric responded. While kissing me, his hands wandered over my body. He asked me what I was wearing under my dress, because it felt so hard. I told him about my all-in-one girdle, and asked him if he would like to see it. His answer surprised and aroused me. He told me that it was always one of his great turn-ons to see a woman in a girdle.

We promptly scrapped our plans to go to a club, and we went

back to my house instead. As we drove, I felt his hard cock through his pants. I also described in delicious detail what my girdle felt like. I described how tight it felt and how it pressed against my stomach, my ass, and my pussy. With each word, his cock seemed to get harder.

Once we got into my house, we began to kiss intensely, and I was grinding my crotch against his. I felt his hand reach under my dress and up my leg until it felt my wetness. Hand in hand, we then walked into the bedroom, where I removed my dress.

Eric's eyes got wide. I stood with my legs crossed while he kissed me. Eric lowered me to the bed and his hands were everywhere. He wanted to touch every inch of me.

His hand felt inside the slit at the crotch of my girdle, where he felt the crotch of my panty hose. It was soaked. I felt his fingers press against my clit and begin to massage it. It felt so good. I knew it was not going to take long for me to come.

Just when I was about to come, Eric stopped. I moaned, and put my own hand where Eric's was. He promptly removed it. He then pressed against my aching mound, and I moaned again. Finally, after so many months, I was going to feel the pleasure of a good fucking.

Eric's strong fingers then tore out the crotch of my panty hose. He separated the material and put his finger inside me while his thumb gently massaged my clit. My hips rose to meet his touch. Just then, Eric's glance saw my vibrator where I had left it on my nightstand.

He took the vibrator and put it inside me. With the vibrator inside me and his fingers on my clit, I exploded in orgasm. All I could think of saying was, "Please fuck me, please fuck me now. It's been so long since I had a cock inside me."

Again, he separated the material at my crotch and plunged his engorged cock into me. Eric was ravenous and as turned on as I had ever seen any man. He fucked me to one gigantic orgasm after another, until I could feel his hot come inside me. He later told me that it was the sight of me in my girdle that did it. Because of the tightness of my girdle, my orgasms were the most intense of my life.

Eric got on top of me. Between his weight and the pressure of my girdle, I now had to pee. I moved from under him and dashed to the bathroom. Thankfully, the crotch of my panty hose was all torn out so I could separate the material to pee. I don't think that I could have held it until I got undressed. I then took off my girdle and what was left of my panty hose.

While we cuddled in bed, I told Eric about my underwear collection. As I was talking, his cock got hard again. With my mouth, I showed him how appreciative I was.

The following morning, I showed him my collection and asked him to pick out something for me. Our minds must have been in sync, because he picked out my favorite corset—the one that needed to be laced up. By the time Eric was done lacing the corset, the all-in-one girdle I had worn the night before was loose by comparison.

For the next few hours we cuddled, kissed, and felt each other. Eric's hands were busy moving all over my corset and stroking my nyloned legs. His hands would come close to touching my pussy but then move elsewhere. I felt the corset pressing tightly against me.

Then Eric's hand, for the first time that morning, touched me between my legs. I raised my hips to press against his hand. Through the crotch of my panty hose, I felt his fingers against my clit, and I moaned in pleasure. He then took his hand away and I replaced it with my own. After a moment of touching myself, Eric took my hand away. This man seemed to be a real tease, and I was beginning to love it.

Soon Eric's fingers found my clit. He kept bringing me to the edge of an orgasm and then stopping. I heard myself begging him to let me come.

It was frustrating, and also the most arousing thing I'd ever experienced. Eric finally unlaced the corset just enough to pull off my nylons. Then he proceeded to give me a fucking that will live long in the annals of sex. After we both rested for a while, Eric told me that I satisfied his greatest turn-ons. I told him that he had done the same for me.

This was about six months ago. Eric and I are still going strong; in fact, we are now living together.—*S.A., Oakland, California*

TWO CUEBALLS

I am a twenty-one-year-old junior in college. Since I was about twelve, I've fantasized about being totally bald. When I saw that *Star Trek* movie featuring a lovely bald actress, I was fascinated by her shaved head, and I tried to imagine myself without hair. I even told some friends about my fantasy, and most of them thought I was nuts. I was disappointed by their attitudes, and began to think they were right.

One night last fall, I was watching MTV, and saw Sinead O'Connor for the first time in one of her videos. Her head was completely bald, and I was mesmerized by her lovely head and big, beautiful eyes. My fantasy was rekindled and I couldn't resist the urge any longer. I wanted my head shaved, and I was determined to do it!

I've always been a little extroverted, which is why I was able to do something so bold. I purchased a wig matching my strawberry-blond curls and wore it for a couple of days, to see if anyone noticed the difference. Not one person asked about my hair, so I knew that if I shaved my head, I could hide it without worry.

I borrowed some electric clippers from a neighbor, and when I got home from my waitress job that Friday night, I proceeded to shave off my hair. Clad in just my bra and panty hose, I stood in my bathroom, plugged in the clippers, and started shearing before I could chicken out. I removed clump after clump of hair. My crotch became very damp and my heart was pounding wildly as I sheared off my hair.

I stood before the mirror with my head cropped, looking like

a Marine. I then coated my head with hair remover and massaged it in. I waited five agonizing minutes before I rinsed off
my scalp and dried it with a towel.

My hair was completely gone. I stood and admired my new
look. I was even prettier than I'd imagined. I was afraid my ears
might stick out too much, but they looked just fine. I'd done it.
I was really bald! I was in heaven that October night. My biggest
fantasy had come true, better than I expected. I fingered myself
into a wild orgasm and fell asleep in ecstasy.

I wanted to show off my new look to all my friends, but was
afraid of negative reactions. I decided to go public with it anyway, and I planned to unveil my shaven head at the college's upcoming Halloween party. I dressed as Dolly Parton, wearing a
slinky, black, sequined party dress with a sexy slit in the front,
sheer black hose, and four-inch black pumps. I stuffed my bra
with panty hose, and topped my costume off with a huge plat-
inum blond wig and phony diamond earrings. I had no boyfriend
at the time, so I went alone.

Everyone loved my costume. I was having a great time and
was really buzzing after drinking a couple of wine coolers. Then
someone said I should do my Dolly Parton imitation, so I got up
in front of everyone and sang a chorus or two of "9 to 5," receiving numerous catcalls for my terrible singing.

"Well, I could sing better without these," I retorted, reaching
in my bra and pulling out the panty hose I'd stuffed in it. Everyone cracked up as I threw my hose everywhere, reducing my
chest to normal size. Then I said, "Have you ever wondered what
Dolly looks like without her wig? I've heard she has no hair at
all. If so, she'd look like this!" I then pulled off my wig and
shocked everyone with my baldness. A sudden silence overcame
the room as I stood in all my bald glory. Then I received a standing ovation. I was so surprised at their reactions, as they came
up to me for a closer look. I explained, "I've always wanted to
be bald, so I took a chance and *voilà!*"

My friends were stunned, but very supportive of me and my

bald look. I received numerous compliments from both the guys and girls. Everyone buzzed about it the rest of the night. I put my wig back on, and as I collected my hosiery, a guy in a dress came up to me and asked me to dance.

It was Jeff, a guy from my philosophy class. We'd borrowed notes from each other a time or two, but weren't all that close. This was the first I'd seen of him all night. He was dressed from head to toe as a woman. He wore a red dress, black tights, black flats, a curly red wig, and full makeup. "My goodness, you're adorable!" I exclaimed.

"So are you," he replied. "That took a lot of guts, shaving your head. You look sensational."

We danced for a while, and spent the rest of the evening together. He walked me home to my apartment, and I invited him in for a nightcap. I removed my Dolly Parton wig and we relaxed on my sofa. "I can't get over how beautiful you are totally bald," Jeff said. "You have a lovely scalp."

"Thank you," I replied. "I've fantasized for a long time about being bald, and I finally went through with it."

"I've fantasized for a long time about dressing as a woman," Jeff admitted. "I've been curious about what women's clothes feel like. I'm really enjoying this."

"You look really cute," I said. "How do you like wearing a wig?"

"Actually, I'm quite used to it, because I wear one all the time. You see, I'm bald too!" Jeff then removed his curly red wig, and sure enough, he was just as bald as I was! I never would've guessed that he wore a wig all this time.

"Oh my God!" I exclaimed. "You are bald! I don't believe this. Did you shave your head?"

"No, my hair fell out when I was fifteen, and I've worn toupees ever since. I was so thrilled when you took your wig off at the party, because I knew you wouldn't reject me if you found out I was bald. I've never had a real relationship with a woman before, because I was so afraid of rejection."

"But why? I think you're very handsome without hair," I said, and I meant it. He looked very nice, despite his feminine makeup. "You have nothing to be ashamed of."

Since then, Jeff and I have become lovers. I helped him lose his virginity a few weeks later, and we are now almost inseparable. I shaved my head twice a week until last month, when I had my hair removed permanently. I have to wear my wigs to work, but otherwise I go wigless at all times, even to school. I even had my driver's license photo taken without a wig on. I love being bald, and I'm not ashamed to show it. Jeff has also lost his inhibitions about his hairlessness, and goes wigless in public most of the time. Sure, people stare and sometimes laugh at us, but we don't care. If they can't realize that we like the way we look, that's tough shit. Being bald isn't as bad as you think. I find it very exhilarating, and I hope some of you feel the same way.—*Name and address withheld*

An Itty-bitty Problem

I have a very slender, sexy figure and am very attractive, but I have a problem. My breasts are virtually the same size they were when I was ten years old, and that is no exaggeration. I'm twenty-seven now and have worn falsies and padded bras since I was thirteen.

When I first left home at twenty, my social life was fairly good. I lost my cherry to a guy I was really in love with. He split, though. He never told me why, but I know it's because he was turned off by my flat, shapeless chest. I couldn't blame him. After that happened, I tried my best to fool everyone. I stuffed my bras and wore tight, revealing blouses that accentuated my nice, firm, fake 34B tits. I was stupid, because as soon as a guy slipped his hand inside he would realize my tits came off with my bra.

I have really big, thick nipples that stick out a good half-inch all the time. I began to feel it was such a shame to keep them covered up all the time, so I decided to go honest. First I went to a 34A padded bra and looser tops, so friends wouldn't notice too much of a drastic change. Then I went to a lacy little training bra, always wearing a loose blouse or jacket over it. It was easy to see guys check me out, then lose interest when they saw how flat I was. At first it was almost enough to make me go back to my rubber 34Bs. I came up with a strategy. I would call attention elsewhere.

I started wearing very short skirts (I've got perfect, long, slender legs and sexy feet) and skintight slacks with four-inch heels, garter belts, and sheer stockings. The first impact was always effective, but the guys still lost interest when they saw how flat I was. Finally a friend of mine, Kristina, a nurse, suggested I pierce my nipples and decorate them with gold rings.

It wasn't long after that that I was going to work braless and wearing tight, silk blouses. My nipples were hard and stuck straight out all day. The feel of the cloth sliding over them nearly gave me orgasms several times! Although it was very obvious to everyone that I didn't have any tits, the rings were outlined under the blouse whenever I leaned back, and I noticed lots of lingering stares from both men and women.

I go braless most of the time now. As much as I wish I had tits, I find that a lot of guys accept my flatness because they're turned on by the sexy nipple rings. Kristina, whose tits are quite small and saggy, is so impressed with my attitude change and the transformation of my social life, she's thinking of piercing hers too.

So, to all you flat-chested women out there (and I know there are lots), forget the idea of implants and decorate what you have—*D.S., Quebec*

DESSERT IS SERVED

About two years ago, on the day we moved, my wife and I worked hard, diligently packing, labeling and cleaning up.

About seven that evening, after the movers had left, we were gathering up the remaining items in the house. We had bought a new mattress for the new apartment, so the old one was lying on the floor in the back room. I commented to my wife, Janet, that the mattress had a lot of good memories and that maybe we should give it one last fling. We were both hungry and tired, she informed me, and we still had a lot of work to do. With that, I started cleaning out the fridge. I found a full bottle of wine and handed it to Janet, telling her to finish it up as I defrosted the freezer.

About forty-five minutes later, I finished cleaning the fridge and freezer. I wandered into the back room and found that Janet had finished the bottle of wine and was pretty drunk. She smiled and said she had changed her mind. She wanted to put the old mattress to good use one last time.

I told her to stand in the middle of the mattress and went to get the stuff I had removed from the fridge: cherry pie filling, chocolate topping, caramel topping, a can of whipped cream, and a bottle of cooking oil.

The first thing I did to Janet when I got back was pull out her waistband and dump the entire can of cherry pie filling down her pants. She started screaming wildly as the thick, sticky stuff slid down her thighs. I laughed and told her to relax and enjoy. She began squirming as the cool filling slowly soaked her crotch.

I abruptly spun her around and poured cooking oil down the back of her pants. It was delightful watching the oil soak through the tight jeans covering her shapely ass. I began fondling her tits, and squishing the cherries around as I massaged her mound through her jeans and panties. As I removed my own clothes, I told Janet to prepare herself for the kinkiest fuck of her life.

Her tits were my next target. By now I had a rock-hard erection and was anxious to complete my dessert. I quickly unbuttoned the top three buttons of the old pink blouse she was wearing and poured chocolate sauce over her front. The sticky brown syrup quickly ran down the valley between her shapely mounds. After a few sloppy, sweet kisses, I quickly dumped the caramel topping, then pointed the nozzle of the whipped cream can down her front and emptied its contents into her blouse.

Janet was giggling and squirming. It was time to get my hands busy. I eagerly dug in, grabbing and groping with both hands and my tongue. I nibbled her neck, kneaded her ass cheeks, and rubbed her tits. I quickly removed her jeans and blouse to fully observe the delicious mess I had created. God, she looked good enough to eat. I laid her on the mattress and attacked her with my tongue, lustily licking her caramel-and-cream-covered tits. My taste turned to cherries as I moved down her body and began nibbling around her hot cunt. I feasted on her clit for a full fifteen minutes. I could not wait any longer. I drove my cock into her cunt and began thrusting in and out. Janet squirmed on the mattress, her glistening tits bouncing as I exploded into her cunt and collapsed on her.

Janet and I have laughed about that night many times since. She still has the stained bra and panties. I'm looking forward to our next refrigerator cleaning.—*F.L., Atlanta, Georgia*

Anal Sex

Poolside Threesome

My husband Jim and I moved into this neighborhood about ten months ago after he was transferred to the main plant near here. His new position pays very well, so I have no need to work. I spend my days puttering around the yard and pool. By the way, my name is Audrey. I'm thirty-six, ten years younger than my husband, and we've been married twelve years.

We soon got to know our neighbors on the left side of our property. Their kids, a son and daughter, were both away in college. Early in July I finally met their son, Val. It was July 21, a day that I will never forget. Val was with his friend Raul, a young black man who lives in the Virgin Islands. They were cutting grass next door while I was puttering around the pool. I had glanced over there more than a few times. The boys were wearing cut-offs that revealed their bulging muscles. I was probably gawking too often. Val's parents were at work and the two guys were horsing around, mainly just playing grab-ass.

I was wearing my string bikini and had just settled on a chaise to get some sun. Val came up to the fence and asked if he and Raul could take a dip in the pool. I said, "Sure, and bring over a few beers." In less than a minute the boys were on my patio with a full cooler. We all popped a top and jumped into the pool. We finished off our beers and they started ducking each other.

They soon grabbed me and under I went. I felt a hand on my ass as I went under. I thought it was accidental until they ducked me again. This time I felt a hand on my ass and one on my tit. I didn't say anything about it to the two guys, but they had my juices flowing.

I got out of the pool and had another beer. The boys soon followed. We sat around drinking. Val asked if I ever swam in the nude. I said, "Once in a while at night, when it's dark."

Val said, "How about now?" He and Raul pulled off their cut-offs. Before I could say anything, they had me standing up and out of my bikini. I glanced at their cocks. Both were hard and big. This all happened in about fifteen seconds.

They picked me up, and into the pool I went. When I came up, Val was behind me, holding me by my tits. Raul was in front with his hand on my pussy. I started to say, "Knock it off," but Raul covered my lips with his and Frenched me. I was turned on since it had been a month since I had had any loving. They kept playing with my body. Val said, let's get out of the pool. Raul got out and lifted me up on the edge and gently pushed me back. My legs were still in the pool. Val got between them and started eating my pussy. I was so hot I couldn't hold back, and I flooded his mouth with my first orgasm. Raul straddled my chest and offered his cock to my mouth. His cock was at least nine inches long and the head was the size of a plum. I had a hard time getting it in my mouth. I licked all around the head and soon had him moaning. My cunt was on fire, and I shot off again.

I soon had Raul fucking my mouth. I was getting more and more cock down my throat. My husband never shoots his load in my mouth, so when Raul said, "Here it comes," I thought he would pull out; but he didn't. He shot his load down my throat. He shot so much I had a hard time swallowing it all.

Val said, "I want to fuck you, Audrey," and carried me over to the chaise. I sat down on it with my legs over the sides. My cunt was wide open. Val got between my legs and told me to put his cock inside me. He was almost as big as Raul. I put the head at my opening and humped my cunt, taking most of it. He fucked like there was no tomorrow. He lasted about two minutes before he said, "Here it comes." I felt his cock pump as his come flowed in me.

Then it was Raul's turn. Val stepped aside and his friend took his place. He put the head at my cunt hole and pushed. It felt like a tree trunk was being pushed in me. My cunt felt like it was spread as wide as possible. I said, "No, Raul, it won't go." He just flexed his hips and grabbed my ass. Once the head was in, the rest of his cock followed. I could feel every inch as it slid into me. His cock was so big that the top of it rubbed my clit. I started to come—in fact, I don't think I ever stopped coming. His cock was way up in my belly when he shot his load. He kept fucking until he got soft.

I could feel cunt juice and come running out my hole, so I jumped into the pool to wash off. When I came out the boys handed me a beer. In between sips the boys would kiss and play with my tits and pussy. Raul was fingering me and Val was sucking on my nipples. They sure knew how to turn a girl on. I had a hand on both their cocks. Raul said, "Let me lay down and you sit on my cock."

I said, "Okay, but let me put it in myself. I'm still a little tender." I straddled his cock and put the head at my hole. The head went in easier this time. God, his cock was big. I took in about half on my first try. His cock filled my love canal. I fucked up and down and soon had him in up to his balls. He started fucking me nice and slow. His cock was rubbing my clit, and he soon had me coming.

Val said, "Pull her down to your chest." Raul did. Val then got behind me and started fingering my asshole, rubbing my juices into it. After he had me nice and wet he stood up. He put his cock at my asshole and eased it in. Thank God I had been fucked in the ass a couple times in my life before that day. It hurt at first but soon I was into it, fucking back at his cock. They were both fucking my holes. It was a first—what a sensation! They soon had me coming and coming.

We fucked for a good fifteen minutes before Val said, "I'm coming," and Raul said, "Me too." Both their cocks swelled up and I could feel their spunk shooting into me.

It felt so good I almost passed out. They kept fucking until their cocks got soft and slipped out of my holes. Juices ran out of my cunt and ass and down Raul's balls.

I was limp as a rag. We just lay down and caught our breath. We finally got up and jumped in the pool. I told the boys it was getting late and reminded them that my husband would be home soon.

As they left, they asked if we could use the pool again. I said, "Sure, anytime."

Well, since then, I've been sucked and fucked twice a week all summer long. I'm sure going to miss those boys when school starts up again.—*A.B., Orlando, Florida*

MAKING LOVE IN A CHEVY VAN

I am not an American, but I have lived here since a young age. I've been married to a good-looking woman for eleven years, and had never made love to anyone else until just recently.

Two Sundays ago I was in my car dealership, answering calls on a few ads I had placed in the paper. It was raining and it was a very slow day. There was no one there but me. The phone rang around one, and this sexy voice asked me about the van I had listed in the paper. I told her all about the van, and she was very interested. My dick started to jump when she said in a lusty voice that she'd be over in a flash.

I went back to reading my latest copy of *Forum* and forgot about the time. When I finally looked up from the magazine, I saw this very good-looking woman standing in front of my desk.

She saw the book in my hand and with a smile said it was she who had called about the van.

I gave her the key to the van she wanted to test-drive, and after twenty minutes she pulled back into the lot and came into the office. She wanted to look around the inside of the van and, since it was still raining, she asked if she could drive it into the shop.

I opened the door and she pulled in. Inside the van she asked me the few questions she had and told me she'd really like to buy it. When I told her the price, though, she said she was five hundred dollars short. Before I could say, "It's okay. You can have the van for the cash you have," she started rubbing my hardening dick. In a flash she pulled my zipper down, freeing my aching cock. When her eyes opened wide, I knew she was pleased with the size of my dick.

She slowly put her mouth around my pole and started to suck me off, taking half of my dick down her throat, rubbing my balls with her hands. The fact that a woman other than my wife was sucking my dick got me harder than usual. I moved her to the floor of the van and we got into a 69 position with her on top. As I was eating that young pussy, I thought of something I wanted to do that I had never done with my wife: I wanted to fuck this woman up the ass.

I put my finger in her asshole while I ate her pussy, and she moaned like I had never heard before. By now she had all nine inches of my pole in her mouth and working it like there was no tomorrow. I was certainly ready to come, but I pulled out of her mouth and told her I wanted to fuck her doggie-style.

I went behind her and entered her wet pussy, slowly shoving my dick into her, pumping her pussy faster and faster. She came in no time.

Now my dick was wet and ready for the coup de grace. I pulled out of her wet pussy and put the head against her asshole. She said, "It's going to hurt, please do it slow." Inch by inch I shoved my dick into that tight asshole. When I had seven inches of my pole in her, I slowly pulled it out to release the pressure before shoving it back into her again. Going like crazy, I lost control and pumped her ass like I had done her pussy. She screamed, "Please, shove it in all the way." With one thrust I had all nine inches of my dick in her asshole. She came again as I pumped a big load in her ass.

After we cleaned up, we lay down on the floor of the van, where she sucked me one more time. She said that I was the best fuck she had ever had. I sold her the van and now she comes in twice a month for a tune-up of her ass.—*S.R., Las Vegas, Nevada*

WE'VE BROKEN UP, BUTT...

I was at a party that one of my friends was having. As it turned out, one of my old girlfriends, Nancy, was also there. She came stumbling over to me when I was already half plastered on some cheap wine. And very stoned, too.

Nancy, who was pretty high herself, kissed me wetly on the lips and started going on about how she was now into anal sex. I was curious and horny, so I let her lead me by the hand to one of the bedrooms up on the second floor, away from the smoke and laughter and loud music. When we got upstairs she opened up a door. The room was empty. She put her drink down and started to undress. She turned to me, naked, and said, "Go into the bathroom over there and see if there's any K-Y jelly."

I asked, "Why?"

"It will be easier for you to fuck my behind if it's lubricated first," she replied. "Don't you know anything?"

I rummaged through the medicine cabinet and, sure enough, found some K-Y jelly. The tube was nearly full. Nancy grabbed it from me and squeezed the tube. A glob of gel came out. She smeared the whole load on her ass and started working it up into her asshole. I could tell she'd done this before.

Nancy got on the bed, facedown. I slowly inserted my cock

into her asshole. It was unbelievably tight, squeezing my cock like a strong hand. I slowly eased into her and pumped in and out.

"Go faster, Nate, go faster," she urged. Our pace quickened. I moved into her deeper, deeper. Feeling the deepness and tightness of her asshole was incredible. I felt my balls give that familiar sensual tingle and knew I was about to come. She'd already had two orgasms and was working on a third when I erupted.

When I pulled out, she told me to lick her asshole.

"Are you kidding?" I asked.

"You'll love it," she said.

So I bent over and rimmed her anus with my tongue, loving all the combined flavors of both me and her. I alternated between her asshole and cunt, plunging into each hole with equal delight. When she'd come, I leaned up and kissed her. She eagerly lapped up her beaver juices from my tongue. More turned on than ever, she asked me to fuck her. Actually, the way she put it was, "Fuck me into oblivion."

I plunged my dick into her snatch. Back and forth, back and forth, harder, faster. She screamed with delight each time I drove it in deeper. I sucked both tits, licking the soft flesh, kissing the hard tips of her nipples, enjoying her every smell and taste, every sound she made as I fucked her.

Suddenly I felt my balls being squeezed. I looked behind me and there was my friend, Wayne. I'd never had any homosexual urges, but now I was ready for anything. I motioned to him to join us. Wayne quickly obliged. He took the jelly and smeared it on me. Then he sank his fuck-meat into my asshole. He was huge! He moved with me when I fucked Nancy. She looked up at the both of us, smiled, and said, "Nate, you finally got to take it up the ass. Now you see why I like it so much."

I said, "Yeah, it feels sensational." I then told him to get off so we could switch. But Nancy wanted to suck both our dicks at the same time. After we'd washed our cocks off, she licked, nibbled, and chewed them until Wayne and I came into her mouth

at the same time. After he'd finished pumping, Wayne pulled out
and flipped her over. He then pulled her ass up to his dick,
rammed into it, and began pumping away. I stood on the bed
and put my dick back into her mouth, not wanting to be left
out. She sucked it like a baby would suck a tit. After about an
hour, we were all thirsty for something other than sex, so we
went downstairs and rejoined the party.—*Name and address withheld*

He Hates to Leave Her Behind

I am currently serving a one-year tour overseas in the air force.
Just before tour, my wife gave me a special gift. Our daughter was already asleep in bed, and my wife had drawn a bath for
us. She set the mood by lighting several candles in the bathroom.
The water was steamy hot and the wine was ice cold. Relaxing
in the tub, stroking her breasts as she lay next to me, I reached
for the soap and began to lather up her body. She turned around
so I could soap up her legs and crotch. She said she would miss
this most of all, as we'd often taken baths together. Getting up
on all fours, she lifted her firm ass only inches away from me. I
lathered and massaged the cheeks, playfully sliding a finger all
the way inside her soapy pussy. She was really starting to enjoy
herself, pivoting her hips to give my fingers a workout. I wanted
to do some extra teasing, so while fingering her tight cunt I
slowly entered her anus with a finger. At first I thought she would
stop me, but instead she whispered, "Yes . . . yes!"

I now had my middle fingers in her pussy, my index finger
working in and out of her ass—and my pinkie was toying with
her clit! She was enjoying herself rather well, and I was as excited as she was. I wanted to be inside her, but not wanting to
interrupt the mood to stop for birth control, I decided to try
fucking her in the ass. I positioned myself and ran my cock up
and down her crack, teasing her even more. Then, grabbing her

by the hips, I eased my cock into her tight, soapy ass. She pulled away at first, but then started to push back against my hardened cock with all her might. I reached around her, one hand massaging her large tits while the other played with her swollen clit. Her hips were doing double-time, jerking back, allowing my cock to sink to its full length inside her asshole. It was so nice and tight, it didn't take me long to shoot my load deep into her.

I slowly pulled my cock from her asshole and sat back to let my wife wash me off. This was the first time we'd had anal sex. And it was only the beginning. We went to our king-size bed and stretched out. My wife crawled up between my legs, gave me a devilish grin, then took my rigid cock between her warm, soft lips. She knows exactly what I like, and my member was standing hard and tall. She gave me long, slow licks, then quickly took me all the way into her mouth. It took all my control to hold back the flood of come building in my balls, but I held off in order to enjoy her wonderful technique.

She pulled her mouth from my cock and gave me that devilish grin again. As she moved up my body, she swayed her breasts before my hungry mouth. My hands were all over her tits, my fingers pinching her erect nipples. My mouth couldn't get enough as I sucked them both. She held my cock and positioned it at the opening of her hot, wet pussy. She impaled herself on my tool in one slow motion, moaning with relief and enjoying the warm, tight feeling. She slowly rocked her hips, leaning forward to feed me her breasts. As we fucked, she slipped a finger into my asshole. She had never done this before, and the feeling was extraordinary.

"Good, isn't it?" she asked. As we fucked harder and harder, she pumped her finger in and out of me, using it like a small dick. Then she raised up her hips and quickened the pace. We were both very close to coming. My hands were rubbing and caressing her tits and ass. The excitement was too much, and we orgasmed in a chorus of moans, wave after wave of pleasure overcoming us.

My wife then collapsed on top of me. I rolled her over, inserted my penis in her cunt, and with long, slow strokes brought her to several more quick climaxes. We kissed tenderly, licking each other's ears and fingers. I moved down her body, leaving a trail of kisses. My tongue gently licked her swollen clit. With a few light licks on her ass cheeks to get her ready, I then plunged my tongue deep inside her asshole. Pulling my tongue out and sticking it back in, I finger-fucked her pussy and tongue-fucked her ass. Increasing speed, I brought her to orgasm once more.

Now that I'm away, I hope she thinks of our last evening together as much as I do.—*Name and address withheld*

ACCOUNTANT IN LUST

I know most people usually preface these letters with a disclaimer about how they never thought they'd be writing to you. But I always had the feeling that one day I would write to you. I always get horny reading other people's experiences and thought I might do my part by telling everyone what happened to me last year.

I was twenty-five years old and the manager of a small company. At the time of this story, I had broken up with my girlfriend about a month earlier, and was feeling particularly horny. I had always playfully flirted with my accountant, a thirty-seven-year-old divorcée. Denise is Oriental, lived alone, and was in terrific shape. She often joked that she worked out more than she worked. She had big tits that were still incredibly firm.

So I made plans with Denise to have dinner one night. She looked incredibly hot when I picked her up. She was wearing black tights that hugged her curves and a big, loose blouse. We had dinner at a Chinese restaurant and then went back to her place.

After a couple of glasses of wine and some small talk, she turned on the television, and I began to massage her shoulders as we watched the tube. She sat in front of me on the floor, and I sat on her couch.

I couldn't believe how quickly I got hard. It was as if somebody had turned on a switch. Still unsure of what was in store, I was wary of mixing business with pleasure. The wine got the better of us, however, and slowly she leaned back into my crotch, pushing up against me. I couldn't conceal my hardness, and as soon as she felt me, she ground her back into my crotch to let me know that she wanted me.

Then she stood up, walked across the living room, and said, "Enough television," as she turned it off. She took me by the hand and led me into her bedroom. There was a double bed with no pillows, and she lay down on it and pulled me on top of her. When our lips met, her tongue immediately probed my mouth. I couldn't believe I had my tongue in my accountant's mouth and my hands on her gorgeous tits! I ground my hips into hers, and she pushed those slim hips right back against my crotch. After a few minutes of exploring with our hands, I slid down her body and unbuttoned her blouse. Off came her bra. I slid both hands under her pants and slid those and her panties off with one motion.

So there Denise was, naked, panting and wet, legs spread and waiting for me. I slid farther down and began to lick her inner thighs and her hot slit. God, she tasted good! Her snatch was dripping wet, and I lapped her up from stem to stem. It drove her crazy. I was kneeling on the floor, leaning hard into her crotch as she lay on the bed. I held her hips up to my face and licked her from her asshole all the way to her clit. Her moaning was driving me to new heights. She started panting and then she started to come, bucking and screaming while I sucked and flicked her clit, my fingers buried in that hot hole where I wanted my cock to be.

After she came, she reached down and pulled me up onto the bed. I lay on my back and she straddled me, placing her gorgeous pussy right over my face as she sucked my cock into her hot mouth. I licked and sucked even harder now that I was deep in her throat. I couldn't stand it any longer. I had to have her. She started to play like she wanted it rough, so I rolled her onto her back and spread her legs wide with my knees, but then stopped, kneeling over her, my nine inches hard over her belly.

"It's so big," she said, "and so hard."

I rubbed the head up and down against her dripping cunt and whispered into her ear, "Do you want it? Huh? Do you?"

And she replied, "Fuck me. Fuck me with it. Give it to me hard."

I slammed that baby home, all the way up into her, and she gasped. She wrapped her legs around me and tried to grind her clit up against me. I pumped her hard, taking long strokes. Then I went deep into her, grinding my hips up against her, pulling her up into me with my hands under her ass. Spreading her from behind, I stroked her snatch and her asshole. When I slipped my index finger into her asshole, she grunted and then her panting got louder. She loved it. I'd never fucked anyone who was so wild. She came again right then, holding tight.

At this point I had to back off before I blew my wad, so I pulled out and flipped her over onto all fours. Looking at her ass raised to me—pussy open and inviting—made me crazy. I rubbed the globes of her ass and spread her pussy again with my thumbs. I wanted to fuck her like she'd never been fucked before. It was like I was possessed by an animal desire. I leaned over and licked and tongued her cunt and ass from behind. I got back up and positioned myself behind her. Then I pushed the small of her back down, so she was arching her ass into the air. She was moaning, "Fuck my ass," over and over again! I wanted to, but knew I wouldn't . . . not yet.

She was flowing with juices. I placed my huge cock against her wet entrance, and it slipped in easily. Deep inside her, I pumped her hard again and again. Then I leaned over and put my weight on her. I reached around and grabbed those great tits with my hands. I pushed hard, and she collapsed under me, flat on the bed, ass raised. I reached under her arms and grabbed her forearms so she couldn't move. She said, "Oh yeah." She was really getting off on my dominating her! I was fucking her hard from behind, and she was totally restrained by me. With our sweat mixing, both of us groaning and the hard, pumping motion of me inside that tight pussy, I thought I was going to break the bed. She began to come again. I'd thought that maybe I was getting too rough, but then she started begging me for more! What a great fuck!

I couldn't hold back. I had to finish this. I pulled out of her again, pulled her back up on her knees, and rubbed her juices in and around her asshole. She moaned in anticipation and arched her back, readying herself. I pushed myself up against her, and she grunted, bearing down because she knew I wanted in. I slipped the head of my prick into her ass, and she started bucking against me, panting and moaning. I held her hips tight and steady, and then leaned into her so that my throbbing cock was forced into her to the hilt. My rod was so thick—I'd never seen it so big. Then I pumped hard until I couldn't hold back. I reached around under her and fingered her clit and pussy. She was practically screaming, telling me to come, that she couldn't take it anymore, she was going to come again. Her screams and moans set me off. I came like a geyser. Let me tell you, coming in Denise's ass was the most intense orgasm I'd ever had. What was also incredible was that I felt Denise's ass contract real tight as she and I came.

We lay there for a long time and then fell asleep. That morning I woke up with Denise's mouth on my cock. She sucked me off until I came, spurting all over her face. She rubbed my dick around her face and then licked me clean. Jesus, that was good. I had had no idea that she was the kind of woman that got off on a good, hard fuck. I continued to see Denise for about six months until I moved on to a better job. We would fuck like animals in heat, the rougher or more animalistic the better. She loved for me to come either in her ass or on her face. We even got to the point where she liked me to tie her up, but that's another story. She ultimately got remarried, and I smile every time I think of what that lucky guy goes home to every night.——*Name and address withheld*

JAILHOUSE ROCK

I've been in a federal prison for five long years. There is a family reunion program available here that any man who qualifies can't wait to sign up for: Men who are married can utilize conjugal visits to have some very hot sex with their wives. Unfortunately, I'm not married.

Recently a few of my friends were visiting me here in prison. They talked about all the hot girls they have had until I made them change the subject. Just then we heard a woman giggling, and I peeked out the window to see who it was. There was a man and a woman out in the trailer yard. I'll call them Andy and Terry.

We moved to the window to get a closer look. Andy was an older man, in his fifties. The woman was gorgeous! She had frosted hair, firm tits, a big ass, and the nicest pair of pussy lips I've ever seen bulging through her sweat suit. A few hours later I was wandering alone, through the trailer site during clean-up duty. To my surprise, Terry appeared and called out to me. There was a tingle in my stomach. I definitely wanted to get to know her. She licked her glossy lips as I approached, and her eyes ran all over my body. I was sure she could see my hard-on, but I didn't care. I had been without for too long to care about hiding things like that.

We talked and flirted a bit, but I knew I had to get away from her quickly or I would have jumped her right then and there. As I started to walk away, Terry said, "I think you are a handsome guy. Would you like to make it with me?"

I became numb with panic. I didn't know what to say, so the first thing I did was ask about her husband. She replied, "My hus-

band lets me do what I want, whenever I want, and I want you."
I told her I would return in a minute, then turned and ran back
to my trailer. I needed to gather my thoughts.

When I had collected myself and returned a few minutes later,
Andy and Terry were drinking coffee together. Andy told me not
to worry, that he loved his wife and whatever made her happy
was fine with him. He suggested that I take Terry into the bedroom so that she and I could get to know each other better.

As soon as we got there, Terry gave me a passionate kiss that
left me hot all over. She ran her hand over my stiff cock, and I
immediately thought that I would come too soon. I nervously
told Terry that I wanted to do all the touching at first. I peeled
off her sweat suit, exposing the loveliest pair of breasts I've ever
seen. And her pussy lips were meaty and inviting beneath a pair
of white silk panties.

I gently placed Terry on the bed and began kissing her from
the neck down. I nibbled on her breasts, squeezing them together
tenderly. She moaned as I worked my way down to her stomach, flicking my tongue into her belly button. When I did that
she started pulling my hair and humping my leg. I could feel her
love juice oozing through her panties.

I took Terry's panties off. She opened her legs wide, and I nibbled the insides of her thighs. I then licked her gigantic pussy
lips for a while before pulling them back to work on the inside.
She was moaning a lot and becoming wetter and wetter as I
sucked and licked. I inserted my tongue into her love hole, then
pulled it out quickly and tickled her clit. This put her right over
the top. She was screaming with pleasure and gripping my head
between her legs. My face was soaking wet. I never knew a
woman could come so much.

At last she told me to fuck her. I jumped to it, plunging my
eight-inch cock deep into her sweet, hot, tight pussy. Terry was
bucking wildly and tearing at me. She grabbed me by the ass and
pulled me into her as hard as she could. I shot a streaming load
that seemed as if it would never end.

Terry asked me where I learned to do the things I'd done to her, but I just smiled and said nothing. To her surprise my cock was still as hard as a rock. She grabbed it and began rubbing her tongue over the head until I almost wriggled out of bed. She caressed my balls and began sucking them while stroking my dick at the same time.

"I'm going to come if you keep that up," I told her, but a moment later she pinched my cockhead with her fingers and did something to take away the sensation.

"That's the squeeze technique," she told me. She then took my whole prick deep into her warm mouth, slowly moving up and down on it. Her mouth was like a hot, wet, vacuum cleaner, and it wasn't long before I exploded again. She slurped up the leftover semen and again was amazed to see that I was still hard.

I knew our encounter would not be complete until I'd fucked that inviting ass of hers, which was fine with Terry. She began thrusting her ass up at me. I kissed it all over, and even put my tongue in her asshole. I warmed and lubricated her asshole using plenty of saliva, then I pressed the tip of my cock against her hot hole. She let out a little yell and began bucking and ripping a pillow apart as I worked my cock inside her. I reached down and played with her clit, which got her off just as I was shooting a good load of jism deep inside her ass.

On my way out Andy thanked me for showing Terry such a good time.—*Name and address withheld*

MIND OVER MATTER

I dedicate this letter to a very special man in my life.

I might as well be honest. Over the past six months I've had dates with over thirty-five different men, and I've had sex with more than half of them. The man to whom I'm dedicating this letter has tamed me, somewhat.

We met in a bar. He told me his nickname, which made me

curious and flirtatious right from the start. It's Bones. His friends call him that because he has several degrees already, and now he is going for a master's in psychology. That impressed me because I have a thing for smart guys. Anyway, to get on with my story, Bones and I went home to my place the night I met him. The only thing I told him on our way home was that I liked anal sex very much, and that it's a rare man who is gentle enough to do it right. Bones was that man.

We relaxed in my bedroom with our clothes on for some time when we arrived at my place. After a while we had built up the motivation to have raw, hungry sex. It was great. I sucked on his cock for some time and he really knew how to enjoy it. I couldn't believe what a nice touch he had. He would gently stroke my face and himself while I was sucking. But I became impatient. I had to have him inside me. I was hoping he would enter me from behind, and he did. I knelt on the bed while he positioned himself behind me. He thrust hard at first, but then eased up for a long ride. I told him to put his thumb in my ass, because I knew his throbbing cock would be there soon. While he was pumping my cunt I would rub my clit and grab his balls at the same time. Then I told him I was ready to come and that I wanted it in my butt.

Just before I came, he did as I asked. He put his cock in my ass and I came several times—eight or nine, to be exact. Each time I came I squeezed my cunt and rubbed my clit, arching my back and moaning all the while. Bones more than took care of my sexual needs for that night, and he's done it on several more nights since that one.

I've decided that I also want to dedicate this letter to those guys out there who are trying to work their way through college. I know how hard it is, but keep up the good work. I'll be the first to admit that I don't have a degree in anything, but my brainy lover makes me feel as hot as one hundred and fifty degrees—and that's a wonderful feeling.—*D.S., Baltimore, Maryland*

Group Sex

The Gift That Keeps Giving

My girfriend, Mary, and I share an apartment in Anchorage, Alaska, and the night before I left town on business for a few weeks, we went out to dinner and to a bottomless disco bar (at her request, because she was curious).

As we sat watching the show, the subject of my birthday came up. She asked me what I wanted for a present. I pointed to the stage and said, "See the young one on the right?" She said, "That's pretty sexy. I'll see what I can do." We both laughed about it, and I said, "Well, you asked me!" —and I soon forgot about it.

Well, last Saturday I flew into Anchorage to celebrate my birthday, and after picking me up at the airport and driving back to our apartment, my girlfriend said, "Your present will be here tonight." I still didn't give it much thought—after all, it was just another birthday present.

About half an hour later, while we were talking and having another birthday drink, there was a knock on the door. Mary said, "That must be her." I asked, "Who?" And she said, "Your birthday present."

Mary went to the door and returned with a girl who was tall, slim (but not too slim), beautiful—and had eyes that showed her approval when Mary introduced me as the "birthday boy." She was young and delicious.

Mary apologized for not getting the dancer I had pointed out, but explained that this gal was only nineteen and that it was her first professional job. I could hardly believe it, but my cock must have, because I was as hard as the permafrost we have up here.

Mary gave me a phone number and asked me to call her when we were done. Smiling devilishly at me, she went out the door.

I felt a little awkward, and the girl was obviously nervous, too. We had a few drinks and made some small talk, and soon we were both very relaxed. Finally, I said, "Well, why don't we go into the bedroom?" She smiled as I took her soft hand and led her into the bedroom.

I can't describe the feeling as she slowly stripped the clothes from her long, slender body and, getting in bed, molded her young body against me. She held me tightly, as if afraid, but her body grew warm and pliable as my hands explored it. Her kisses—tender at first—became wild. She opened her mouth and sucked my tongue as my hand found her pussy. As I moved my mouth down across her hard nippled breasts to her belly button, her body began to shake in anticipation. By the time I got to her clit, I was surprised to find out how small her pussy was. I was able to cover the whole thing with my mouth as I sucked and licked it. In the meantime, she had twisted around and was working with tender nips and licks on my eight-inch cock. Soon, she pushed hard against me with her sweet little pussy, and she came once in a long, low moan.

But, seeing that I was still hard, she repositioned herself between my legs. I looked down into her eyes, which were smiling up at me with a pouting, hungry look, as she moved her mouth forward and sucked me slowly into her mouth. It wasn't long before I shot a load into her tender mouth and had her gulping to swallow it all. And all the time she was looking into my eyes, loving every drop.

We had both been asleep for a few minutes when we heard the door open—and there was Mary. "Jesus Christ," she muttered. "You've been at it for two hours." She then turned and went into the living room.

I suggested to the girl that we ask Mary to join us and, with her approval, I went to get Mary—who kept saying no until the girl came out and said, "Come on, Mary. It's really good."

I took Mary by one hand, the girl took her by the other, and we all went back into the bedroom. Mary sat at the end of the bed as I laid the girl down and spread her legs so Mary could see.

"Have you ever seen such a small pussy?" I asked. Spreading the lips and smoothing back the sparse hair, I held it open for a couple of seconds. Then I began to eat the girl while Mary continued to watch. I soon heard a moan and looked back at Mary, who was rubbing herself (her dress was hiked above her waist) and was having a hell of an orgasm.

Mary left us alone then, hinting that it was time for her to go. So the girl and I fucked until morning.

When Mary returned with breakfast for three on a tray, she whispered, "Happy Birthday!" and held me close. I said I'd never forget this birthday, and the girl smiled and said she wouldn't either.

Later, when I thanked Mary again for the present, she said, "Every man should have a nineteen-year-old on his forty-fifth birthday. Next year I'll get you an eighteen-year-old."

I never thought I'd say it, but I'm actually looking forward to my next birthday.—*T.B., Anchorage, Alaska*

BOTTOMS UP, BOYS!

I'm usually a pretty quiet girl, but give me a couple of drinks and all hell can break loose.

I woke up this morning with a terrible headache. It was the morning after our baseball wind-up party, and my entire body hurt. The apartment was in a shambles. I remembered having a lot of fun with the guys.

"You want to watch the tape we made last night?" my boyfriend asked.

I told him I did. He got up, went over to the television, and placed a tape into the VCR. He hit the play button. I stared at the scene of the party that appeared on the screen.

It was pretty late, and almost everyone had left. There was only me, my friend Laura, and about eight guys. Someone suggested we put on a stag movie, but I got up and said, "No. Live entertainment is always better." I started to do a striptease in the middle of the room. All the guys cheered me on. I climbed up on the coffee table and kicked off my pants, then slowly ran my fingers inside my panties and rubbed my cunt. Then I undid my bra and let it fly across the room. I pushed my tits up and licked my nipples. My panties were next to be removed. I started playing with my cunt. "Now I'll show you a real show," I shouted.

I walked over to Laura, took her by the hand and pulled her toward the table. She was reluctant, but everybody started shouting, "Come on, Laura, do it!" and she gave in. She stood there as I slowly undressed her. When I had her naked, I started licking her nipples, working my way down to her pussy. She lay down on the table, and I climbed on top of her in a 69 position. We ate each other out for the longest time. I loved the taste of her pussy. Neither of us were bi—we just felt like trying it.

I sucked her hard clit while sliding my index finger in and out of her wet pussy. She was doing the same to me. It felt great, but it got even better when two of the guys came over. They stood at each end of us and drove their cocks into our cunts. Our tongues continued to flick each other's clit as the cocks kept banging in and out. It felt great having a man's huge cock and a woman's soft tongue working on me at the same time.

It wasn't long before the guy in Laura came. I tasted his come as it ran out of her cunt. Then I got up off Laura and two of the guys took her over to the couch. She sat on one and took the other in her mouth. I lay back on the coffee table and said, "I'll fuck the rest of you—if you can handle me."

One guy came over, held my legs up in the air and drove his cock into me without warning. I thought I was in heaven as his cock drilled in and out, in and out. Another guy knelt at the other end of the coffee table. I bent my head back, and he drove his cock into my mouth. The next thing I knew I had a cock in each hand.

The guy in my mouth was the first to come. He caught me by surprise, and I almost choked as he filled my mouth with sweet-tasting come. He held my head with his hands and continued pumping my mouth. I kept swallowing until he pulled out. Then there was another cock in my mouth. He started to come and yet another load went down my throat. Just then, the guy fucking my cunt started coming. He pulled out and shot his load all over.

Another cock was soon sliding in and out of my pussy. It wasn't long before I felt a warm rush inside as he let go in me. I went back to sucking somebody, and soon more come was filling my mouth. I swallowed as much as I could.

Because my back was sore, I got off the coffee table and knelt on the floor. I took a soft cock in my mouth and proceeded to get it hard. While I did that, someone came from behind and slammed his cock into me. He was no sooner done than someone else ran their flagpole up my cunt. When *he* was done, someone turned me over and fucked my tits. I held my tits tight around his cock as he rocked back and forth between them. When he finally started coming, I tried to catch as much of it as I could in my mouth.

I figured I must have fucked everyone there at least two or three times that night. I'm sure everyone blew a load in my eager mouth at least once. I can't really be sure, because the camcorder ran out of tape.

It was a fantastic night. I don't regret what happened, but I don't think I'll drink when there's more than one or two guys around anymore. Well, maybe three or four, but that's it.— *K.T., New York, New York*

THE ICEBREAKER

I attend a state university in upstate New York and finally had the type of adventure that I've been waiting for since I first began to read *Penthouse Forum* a couple of years ago. As it happened, I had to drive up to school in the middle of a snowstorm last winter. I was with two female riders who were very pretty but very unfriendly. Halfway up to school the car got stuck in a huge snowbank, and before I knew it the car was covered with snow.

The girls showed signs of panic, so I tried to convince them that everything would be all right. They started to talk about being buried alive and about how much they would miss getting laid!

Before I could voice my opinion, Cindy (a small blonde with a really fine ass) had her hand in my pants and had a firm grip on my very surprised cock. Meanwhile, Eileen (a brunette with huge tits) was rubbing Cindy's crotch to the same rhythm that Cindy was working my tool. I couldn't believe that this adventure was happening to me! Next thing I knew, we were all stripped and in the backseat of my car, having the time of our lives. Cindy and Eileen were really getting into each other, and their girl-to-girl gig turned me on more than I imagined it could. Eileen's rapid tongue darted in and out of Cindy's blond bush and Cindy was joyfully playing with Eileen's silver-dollar-sized nipples. The cold was rapidly taking its toll on my now flagging penis. Cindy, noticing this, quickly warmed it back to its previous rock-hard state by using her obviously experienced tongue and mouth. When I was about to explode, the girls switched off and Eileen took my throbbing cock into her mouth and sucked down every last drop of my semen.

We took a quick breather and, realizing that our survival meant maintaining body warmth, got right back into things. I started to eat out Eileen while Cindy fondled my balls. The next thing I knew, Cindy mounted me and took my entire eight inches into her hot hole. Cindy's moaning, groaning, and wild gyrations took my attention away from Eileen, who inserted my fingers into her cunt. We all erupted more or less at the same time.

Taking another breather and realizing we didn't have enough energy to continue the present mode of heating, we put our clothes back on and huddled together to wait for our rescue. After a two-hour wait and one more fuck session, we were rescued by the state police.

Eileen and Cindy went back to their unfriendly ways, and when we bump into each other on campus all I get is a quick smile. But I still remember the ride up to school (and I can tell that the girls do too), and I will never forget that threesome in my four-wheeled igloo.—*Name and address withheld by request*

MIAMI SPICE

I read your magazine every chance I get. I'm twenty-eight, six foot one, and I work in the sales department for a large company. My job requires me to attend conventions at least once a month. My letter concerns something that happened on my last convention.

The convention was in Miami. As usual, I spent the first two days meeting the vendors. By Wednesday things were going full blast. I never thought the day would end. We finally wrapped things up around ten in the evening.

Afterward I headed back to the hotel and stopped in the lounge. I was on my second vodka when I noticed a striking blonde at the other end of the bar. She looked to be in her early forties and was extremely well built. The man she was with looked to be in his fifties. I had seen him at a few of the meetings. He caught my eye and motioned for me to come over and join them. I really didn't feel like talking shop, but decided it was better than drinking alone. When I got to their table, he introduced himself as Martin and his wife, Liz.

We started discussing the convention until Liz got bored hearing about it and pleaded for us to change the topic of conversation. She asked me if I would like to dance with her. I looked over at Martin and he said, "Go ahead. I'm bushed and she's been wanting to dance all night."

When she stood up she looked even better. She was about five foot six and only slightly over a hundred pounds. Her figure looked to be about 36-27-36. We danced a fast number, then a slow one. She enjoyed snuggling. I felt a little uncomfortable, but she put me at ease by telling me Martin liked to see men holding her close.

She kissed me on the neck a few times, and my cock was growing by the second. She asked if I would like to have some fun before it got too late. I said, "Sure, but what about Martin?"

She said, "He'll be part of it."

When we got back to the table, Martin was gone. I asked where he was and she said, "He's waiting for us." We finished our drinks and took off for her room.

When we got to the room Martin was sitting in his shorts, sipping on a drink. She asked me to unzip her dress. Off it came. Her black bra and bikini soon followed. I started taking off my shirt. She was busy with my belt and zipper, and soon I was down to my shorts like Martin. Then she pulled them off and said, "Oh, yes. God, it's beautiful."

My cock is about eight inches and pretty wide. She lay down on the bed, her legs spread wide, and said, "Come on. Let's 69." I knelt above her head and she started sucking on my cock, taking almost all of it in her mouth. I leaned over and started eating her sweet pussy. She was sopping wet with love juice, and it wasn't long before she started moaning loudly. Her ass came off the bed, and she flooded my mouth with her come.

When her orgasm was over, she said, "Martin, let me suck your cock while Bill eats my pussy."

I was between her legs, licking her cunt, and Martin was kneeling by her head, his four-inch cock in her mouth. No wonder her eyes had lit up when she saw my eight inches! I kept licking her pussy while my fingers were inside her. Martin got off in about three minutes, and she swallowed all of his load.

She said she was almost there, but wanted my cock in her when she came. She kneeled on the bed, and Martin slid under her in a 69 position. I knelt behind her and eased my cock into her wet hole. She moaned as I slid inside her. I moved in and out while Martin vigorously sucked her clit.

I held her tits as I pumped her slick tunnel. While I did this, Martin kept licking her clit, and she was sucking away at his cock. All of a sudden, my cock flopped out of her hole and into Martin's mouth. I thought, Oh, shit, this is crazy. He put it back in her pussy after licking it a few times. Then he started rubbing my balls and licking my shaft as I pumped in and out of his wife.

I don't know how I lasted as long as I did. Liz started screaming, "I'm coming! I'm coming!" and flooded my cock with her juices. That did it. I started to come with Martin pumping my balls as I unloaded in her cunt. I kept fucking till my cock got soft and wouldn't stay in her. Then Martin put my cock in his mouth and licked it clean of the juices.

I lay back on the bed and watched as Martin licked and sucked his wife clean.

We all sat back and had another drink. Then Liz started stroking my cock, bringing it back to life. She asked if I would be able to make it with her again. I said, "Sure, but it'll take a little work." She said she'd take care of that, and started giving me head. I looked over at Martin. He was watching my eight inches slide in and out of Liz's mouth. His little cock was getting hard, and he started jerking it off. Liz was now deep-throating my cock. She was good. Her throat muscles were squeezing the head of my cock.

After about five minutes, I said, "Okay, honey, I'm ready to fuck your hot little pussy." She stretched back and spread her legs. I put my cock against the tip of her lips and slowly drove it all the way inside her. She moaned and soon started fucking me back, wrapping her legs tightly around my ass. She had a nice, tight pussy. It clung to my cock like a glove. I knew I couldn't hold out much longer. Liz's cunt muscles started squeezing my cock. We cried out and I flooded her cunt with my come. My orgasm seemed to go on and on. I finally pulled out. By then, I was exhausted.

I got dressed and walked to the door. I was about to wish them a good night, but suddenly realized they weren't paying any attention to me. Martin was eating Liz's cunt, and judging by the way she was moving and moaning, I knew she was coming again.—*B.C., Los Angeles, California*

BROWN SUGAR

I am a black, nineteen-year-old woman whose fantasy of being involved in a threesome finally came true.

I went out to a popular nightclub looking for some real action. At the club, a tall, handsome white guy named Roger asked me to slow dance. On the dance floor Roger slowly ground his dick against my hot pussy, squeezing my ass and sticking his wet tongue into my ticklish ear.

After a few dances I was literally about to come all over myself, so I asked Roger if we could go to his place. On our way toward the door, he stopped to talk to a short redhead. Then Roger, Red, and I left the club. When we got outside Roger explained that Stacy (the redhead) was his girlfriend and that they wanted me to be the third in a threesome with them. I just smiled and said, "I'd love to."

In the car I sat in between Roger and Stacy. Roger had one hand on the wheel and the other on my thigh. Stacy was moving her hands to my pussy. I opened my legs wider to give Stacy better access. When she finally reached my pussy she gasped in surprise because I was not wearing any panties. Stacy lifted my skirt and stuck two fingers into me and began to give me the best finger-fuck I'd ever had. I undid a few buttons of my shirt and pulled out my breasts so Stacy could suck on them. At every stoplight Roger would kiss me and let his fingers join Stacy's for a while. I was in heaven, and we hadn't even reached his apartment yet.

The elevator in Roger's building was crowded, so he led us to the back stairs for a little privacy. There, in the hallway, they sandwiched me between them. Stacy pulled the back of my skirt up and fondled my bare ass. Then she pushed her knee against mine, indicating that I should open my legs. I opened my legs wider, and she stuck two long fingers up my hot love-box. I couldn't help but moan, it felt so damn good. Soon Stacy knelt and began to nibble on my ass. Her lips were moist and her fingers were working faster and harder on my pussy. Meanwhile, Roger began fondling my breasts and kissing me passionately. Soon he pulled my breasts out of my bra and began kissing them. I was so hot that I unzipped Roger's pants to grab his hard tool. I couldn't stop myself; I came and Stacy sucked me clean.

When I finally floated back to earth, I realized that we had an audience. I smiled at the shocked old woman on the stairs and said, "I bet that was better than any porn movie you ever saw."

In Roger's apartment, he led us to the bedroom and quickly undressed us both. Roger licked, nibbled, and tongued his way down my hot body. I grabbed his head and pushed it down farther as we slowly sank to the floor. I spread my legs wide and he moved my pussy lips apart and stuck his long tongue into my hot pussy. Roger ate me like an expert.

After I came back from cloud nine, I saw that Stacy was on her back giving Roger a blowjob. She was also nude. I got up and lay down beside her. I caressed her pointy breasts with my tongue. I slowly kissed my way down her shapely body. When I got to her cunt, I dove in. As I played with her clit and ate her, she raised her hips to meet me. When Stacy came I slurped up all her delicious love juice.

Later we moved to the bed, where I spread my legs and said, "Fuck me hard, long, and fast, Roger."

"Roger," Roger said.

We had a little trouble getting Roger's long rod into me because it was thicker than I was used to, but I was way too horny to let that stop me. Roger fucked my brains out—just how I like it—and Stacy kissed, nibbled, and fondled me all over. After a short rest, we went at it again. And again. We must have gone around the world three times that night.

Now every time I think of that night, I come all over again.—
T.C., Charleston, South Carolina

He Had His Cake and Ate It

It all started on my birthday. My girlfriend Karen and I were on our way back to her apartment. Unbuttoning her shirt, she said she had something for me in her room. As I caressed her tits, my dick swelled up in my jeans.

We arrived at her apartment and she ran right inside her bedroom, yelling for me to undress and sit on the couch. When she came out of her room, I was surprised to see Cindy, her friend, standing next to her, totally naked and playing with herself. As they walked toward me, Karen told me to lie on the floor. As I hit the rug, Cindy grabbed my tool and started to suck it. Karen then jumped on my face, moaning, "Lick me dry."

Cindy was sucking the living daylights out of my tool. My hands were on Karen's plump tits and my tongue deep in Karen's hole. Then Cindy sat back to watch and play with a dildo she had found under the couch. As Karen saw my rod free, she slid off my face and placed my cock deep in her mouth. I came down her throat within seconds. While I was squirting my juice, Karen got off my rod and Cindy let my come flow onto her bush. Exhausted, I sat back on the couch and watched Karen lick my come off of Cindy's cunt. Seeing Cindy spread-eagle on the floor with Karen's face buried deep in her bush, I grabbed the dildo and entered Karen with it from behind. With loud moans she spread her legs, letting the dildo get deeper into her hole.

After bringing Karen to orgasm, she insisted I finish eating Cindy. I dove right in, licking the juice from her soaking wet clit. I sensed that she was close to orgasm, so I dove deeper into her pussy, shoving my tongue as far down her hole as I could. Following several tremendous thrusts from my tongue, Cindy let out a moan, crying, "I'm coming."

After licking her clit dry, the three of us sat on the couch. Cindy told me that she had to leave, but said she would stay long enough to help Karen with my birthday cake.

They went into the bedroom and, after a few minutes, Cindy came out and told me to go in. Cindy left as I entered the room. Karen was on the bed, whipped cream covering her stiff tits, her hard red nipples like cherries on top. Moving closer, I noticed that her pussy looked like a banana split—complete with three different flavors of ice cream, colored frosting, and whipped cream. Karen asked me if I wanted some dessert. I nodded. For the rest of the night, I had my cake and ate it too.—
Name and address withheld

HEAVY METAL

I'm twenty-one years old and a pretty hot item. I fantasize a lot, and enjoy getting myself off while watching porno movies, even though I live with my boyfriend. Sex between us has been pretty boring the last three years we've been together, and I must resort to other means to sexually satisfy myself.

Aside from watching adult films, I also enjoy living out my fantasies every once in a while. The mission is usually easily accomplished because my dreams of lust aren't too outrageous or wild. My hottest fantasies require a guy with long hair, good looks, and a nice body. Preferably, he should be in a heavy-metal band.

One evening my girlfriend, Rachel, and I got dressed up in leather and went to a local rock club to see our friend's band. Rachel wanted the drummer. He was a really cute guy named Charlie. I would've gladly let him screw my brains out too. I never told Rachel this, because I didn't want to start trouble. As we watched them play up on the stage, we both got pretty drunk and exceptionally horny. After the show we partied with them backstage for a while. To make a long story short, I ended up going back to the hotel with Charlie. It seemed he wanted me just as much as I wanted him.

Of course, Rachel had been pretty upset when she realized who I was leaving with. Thinking fast, I told her to wait a half hour, then go to the hotel room we would be in. She agreed, and Charlie and I were off.

Charlie was more than ready after we got inside the simply furnished room. As he put his hand up my black silk minidress, I pulled his pants down and watched his cock grow long and hard. I urged him to lean back. I put my lips around his large cock, taking every inch into my mouth while running my fingers slowly across his hairy balls. He was sent into ecstasy, moaning and groaning. Soon I could taste drops of his come on my tongue. It was exciting me beyond belief. As I kept fucking his cock with my mouth, I ran my fingers across my wet cunt.

It was then that my friend entered the room. Without saying a word, she removed her skirt and top, sat on the bed, and started kissing Charlie. I pulled my lips from his hard cock, ran my wet pussy up and down his leg, then joined them on the bed.

Rachel reached into her purse and pulled out a long vibrator. She put it aside for the time being. I sat on Charlie's face while Rachel sucked him off until he shot his load onto her tits. I reached out for a sample of his come to taste, but instead I gently rubbed it all over her tits, making them shine.

Charlie started tonguing my hot pussy while Rachel and I worked on making his cock big again. It wasn't difficult. With her sucking his balls and me going down on him, he was hard within seconds.

He said he wanted to watch me and Rachel get each other off, so I hopped off his face. We were a little uncomfortable about it, but the drunkenness made us say, "What the fuck?" She grabbed the vibrator, turned it on and rubbed my clit. Then she teased me with the tip of it, putting it in just a little, then removing it.

All this time, Charlie was jerking his rod, very pleased with the show. Rachel started fucking me hard with the vibrator, and I was on the verge of coming within moments. Then Rachel removed it and straddled my face. I started eating her wet cunt, savoring its warm sweetness. I grabbed the vibrator and ran it along her thighs.

"Give it to me all the way," she moaned. I licked her pussy one last time before jamming the vibrator into it to the hilt. I moved it in and out of her, at the same time licking her clit. Soon she screamed my name and came. I licked her juices away and continued fucking her pussy with the vibrator. All this time she was busy chowing down on my bush.

I got so excited watching Charlie jack off to our show while

Rachel was eating my cunt, that it wasn't long before I was coming. I was still fucking her with the vibrator, but before I realized what was happening she grabbed it and started fucking me with it. We came once again.

With all of this going on, Charlie soon started coming. Rachel and I promptly licked it off his belly, and it wasn't long before we all became excited again.

I got down on the floor on my hands and knees and started eating Rachel's pussy while Charlie fucked me doggie-style. I could feel his balls bouncing off my clit. I ate my friend until Charlie shot his hot load inside me.

While he recuperated, Rachel and I got into a 69. We eagerly lapped at each other till Charlie was ready to join us once again. He fucked Rachel doggie-style while I knelt behind him and sucked his balls. Suddenly he grunted and pulled his dick out of Rachel. I quickly grabbed it, put it in my mouth, and sucked his hot spurts.

Before we knew it, it was morning. But we didn't care. My friend had yet to fuck Charlie, so we started up again. Rachel started eating my pussy to excite him, so I fucked her with the vibrator to add to the show. I was becoming very excited and came almost immediately. Charlie went over to Rachel, put her ankles on his shoulders, and started fucking her. I watched as he thrust in and out of her tight, wet pussy. We all got what we wanted, and it was the greatest fantasy come true I ever had.—
M.D., Roanoke, Virginia

ALWAYS KEEP FILM HANDY

My husband and I read *Forum* every month. The letters concerning women with women really turn me on. My greatest fantasy has always been to make love to another woman. When I admitted this to my husband, he wholeheartedly wanted me to go through with it.

One night, while drinking in a bar, my husband and I met Cathy. She was petite, with tiny breasts—the complete opposite of me. She had never been with a woman either, and we were both nervous. After a few drinks and some conversation, we got up the nerve to proceed. My husband asked if he could take pictures, and we agreed.

She drove with us to our house. I hurried out of my clothes and slipped under the sheets. I watched her undress. When she finished, she came over to me. She kissed me on the neck. I was so excited I was panting, dying to feel her smooth, warm nakedness slide against me. She was soon sucking on my big breasts. It felt so good, I came with a soft cry.

She put her hand on my legs. I relaxed and let her do whatever she wanted. She slowly moved down my body, kissing, licking, touching. I couldn't stand it any longer. I wanted to feel her sweet breath on my wet pussy. I gently moved her face toward my love box.

When her lips touched my clit, my hips started quivering and I moaned uncontrollably. She gently slid one of her fingers inside me and worked it in and out while sucking my clit at the same time. When I came, she wantonly lapped up my pearly love juice.

It was my turn. I could smell her pussy, and wanted to taste her. I moved her on her back and went for it. First I sucked on her small breasts, then I slowly worked my way down her body to her love box. Her come was dripping down her ass cheeks by then. I licked, sucked, and put my tongue deep inside her pussy. Her body started shaking from orgasm in no time.

My husband was watching and taking pictures all this time. His big hard-on looked as if it was going to burst through his shorts. It was time for him to get involved.

He fucked me from behind while I sucked on Cathy's breasts and finger fucked her. Then he pulled my vibrator from the night table dresser and playfully put it in her pussy. He fucked me while moving it in and out of her. Our moans of pleasure filled the room.

Cathy was soon begging to be fucked, so my husband pulled the vibrator out of her pussy and filled her cunt with his big rod. I sat on her face. After I came I decided to grab the camera and take some photographs of them.

I watched and photographed his big, shiny cock as it slid in and out of her hot, juicy box. Then he took his cock out of her pussy and fed it to her. She couldn't take all of him, but she gave it the old college try.

By then I was hot again and ready for another good fucking. I got on my knees on the bed and he put his cock into me. He fucked me hard and deep. It wasn't long until he filled my box with his love juices.

It was an experience I'll never forget. Thank you, lover!—
J.G., Las Vegas, Nevada

Men With Men

Stroking in the Men's Room

Sometimes it begins with no warning whatsoever. I'll be sitting at my desk, tackling a difficult problem, and suddenly my cock will begin its familiar stirring in my briefs. At first I try to ignore it, as I'd rather finish my project, but my cock has a mind of its own and begins to swell, slowly at first, until it is pressing up against my pants. The pressure adds to the excitement and before you know it I'm sitting there with a rock-hard dick pressing against the tight material of my pants.

So, I put down my keyboard and reach down to my dick, trying to rearrange the swelling tool to a more comfortable position. Having done that, I head for the men's room. When my cock demands attention I have no choice. I have to go beat off or I'll have a thick, hard piece of swollen meat in my pants for the rest of the day. Luckily, it's not too obvious as I walk down the hall that I'm sporting a hard-on, though if you were to look down at my crotch you would see the clear outline of my tool, pointing straight up, begging to poke its head above my waistband.

In the few years that I've worked here and jerked off in the men's room, only a few women have noticed my hard-on, and then only in clandestine glances. Everyone else seems oblivious to my sexual excitement. As I push open the heavy wooden door to the men's room I find that the stall is occupied, so I stand at one of the urinals at the far wall. It feels so good to let the hot skin of my cock out to the cool air. I get excited as I pull my dick out of my tight pants. Looking down at it, I am amazed, as always, that this thick throbbing flesh actually fits in my tight briefs. As I start stroking my cock, the guy in the stall starts making noise and I begin to wonder what he is doing in there. I think I know. My mind wanders to events that happened just last week.

I was working late to finish up a project, when the familiar urgent need of my cock made itself known. As I entered the men's room, Raymond, the night custodian, was wiping down the sink. Now, Raymond is hot: Young, dark and handsome, there is a cockiness about him that's very attractive. He has a body-builder's physique and soft brown eyes. I said hello and his eyes immediately dropped to the outline of my thick tool that strained the fabric of my pants. It was obvious that he saw my hard-on. He looked back up at my eyes. I was nervous and excited. Talking all the time, he followed me to the urinal and we both took our cocks out at the same time. Looking down at my cock, he started to stroke his thick meat. "You sure get hot working late," he said. "I sure do," was my reply.

He turned and locked the door, then walked over to the sink where there was a large wall mirror. I followed him and let my pants fall to my ankles, exposing my thick cock. He positioned me so that I could see everything in the mirror, then he stepped out of his jeans and, stroking his cock, knelt down to lick the underside of my shaft. His tongue was warm and soft, and my cock got even harder as he played with my balls, swollen with my hot come that begged to be released. He worked his sweet tongue around the entire shaft, then began to suck each ball gently.

I ran my fingers through his soft black hair as his head bobbed up and down over my hot tool. With his other hand he started to stroke my cock, letting his tongue run down my thigh. His sucking and stroking were really turning me on. Standing up, he looked into my eyes and drew his face close to mine until I could smell his sweet breath. I reached over and touched his swollen meat, rubbing my hands between his legs, holding each ball in my hand while I gently squeezed his thick shaft until his breath came in short excited puffs.

We knew we had little time, so we turned to face the full-length mirror. Looking over our two beautiful young bodies was such a turn-on. We each stroked the other's cock as we kissed. I jerked the hot skin of his cock and his body went stiff as he let out a groan and spurted his come all over the counter. My hot balls contracted and my sperm shot out again and again from the end of my cock. I just kept coming and coming as I shot my sperm all over the counter, mixing it with Raymond's.

Noise from the stall brought me back to reality. Remembering my fantasy was enough encouragement to make me shoot my load into the urinal. Just as I was about to come, the stall door opened and Raymond walked out. He looked at the door quickly, then came over to grab my cock. He jerked me to a powerful orgasm as I shot my load of thick white come into the urinal.

As I walked back to my desk with a smile on my face I realized that I might be working late a lot more often, particularly when Raymond was on duty.—*G.P., Bangor, Maine*

A MAN'S JOB

A few years ago my wife and I were living on the campus of a major southern university. I was enrolled in the school and my wife, Dana, was working on campus. We lived in a housing complex for married students. We became friends with several couples who lived in the complex, and shared many good times together. Yes, I even managed to get some studying done.

During this time we also became sexually intimate with another couple, Tom and Susan. At first we would just neck and pet with our respective mates in the other couple's presence, but slowly we grew bolder and started getting nude and making love in front of one another, sharing our most intimate activities and fantasies as well.

After a couple of these lovemaking sessions, Tom remarked that he would love the freedom to touch anyone in the group, and wanted to know how we all felt about it. We agreed that this would be acceptable conduct, and then continued our foreplay as usual.

I was sitting beside Dana on the floor, caressing her beautiful, firm breasts and sucking on her cherry nipples. She was fondling my heavy sack and pumping up my erection. Tom had pushed Susan to the soft carpet and was eating her wet pussy. She was beginning to moan with desire for more from her lover. Her cries became so intense, Dana and I started watching and listening more than doing. All of a sudden, while they were changing positions, to my great surprise Tom reached out and grabbed my shaft. He began to rub and squeeze my prick, and to caress the inside of Dana's thighs at the same time. I was instantly rock hard from this unexpected action and, with a reassuring glance from both girls, I touched Tom's hard member in return. This was the first time I had touched or even seen another man's hard cock.

We made love to our respective mates that night without any further explorations, but the incident was on my mind for days. I had truly been fascinated by the sight and touch of his hard shaft.

Several days later Tom was at our apartment without Susan. She had to work that night. After the usual conversation and refreshments, I started to kiss and fondle Dana in the hopes of instigating some action that Tom would become involved in. As things grew hotter and I began undressing my wife, we looked at each other, then at Tom, and invited him to come with us to the bedroom.

Tom sat on the bed with us and gently caressed Dana while I

kissed her and continued to peel off her clothes. I laid her gently on the bed, and Tom and I both shed our clothes while she watched. I lay down beside her on the bed while Tom sat on the opposite side. I began to squeeze her warm, ripe breasts and pinch her hard, cherrylike nipples, kissing her deeply all the while. Tom rubbed her stomach and played between her hot thighs with his hands. She opened her legs to allow him further exploration. I ran my hand down to her bush and found her dripping wet.

I started rubbing my cock between her breasts while Tom ate her flowing pussy. I had never seen her so hot. Being ravished by two men at once was obviously a great turn-on for her.

Then Tom and I exchanged places. I sank my hot prick into her wet hole and started a slow, deep pumping action. Tom began caressing her soft mounds and placed one of her hands on his throbbing meat. She came several times while I was inside her, but I held back and kept myself from shooting off. This was not an easy task, trying to bring her to climax while watching her jerk off another man's prick at the same time. Finally, after Dana came several times, I looked into her beautiful, blissful face. I loved this woman so much, I wanted to give her as much pleasure as possible. I stepped aside and let Tom take my place.

Tom's expression was one of pure joy at the chance to share Dana's beautiful body. He mounted her quickly, and I watched his rigid prick disappear in her cunt. I think, judging by the expression on her face, that she had another orgasm right then. Tom was nearly motionless as he lay on top of her warm body. It was obvious he was also trying to keep control of his juice, as I had. I moved behind them for a better view of their union and watched spellbound as their bodies slowly bounced off one another, his shaft easing out of her slippery well as her lips brushed its length. When all that remained inside was the purple tip, she would fight to get him slowly back inside her.

I have no real sense of how long this went on, though to me it seemed forever. Tom stopped himself several times to maintain his control, and finally he exchanged places with me once again. When I reentered Dana, she was so drenched with her own juices I sank to the hilt with no resistance whatsoever. I shot my load inside her instantly.

She was on the verge of passing out, so I arranged her comfortably back on the bed and we left her to sleep. Tom and I were still as horny as hell, and the only woman available had passed out from an overdose of our loving. What were we going to do for release?

Well, I thought, what better time to try something new than now. After all, I had been thinking about Tom's cock for days.

We went into the living room, both of us still totally naked. I checked the curtains and the locks, and asked Tom to sit down in a chair. I sat on the floor between his legs and looked at his beautiful cock. I reached out for his member. The first gentle touch of my hand made Tom suck in his breath. I held the tip right up to my face as I slowly slid the soft skin back and forth. I drew his pre-come from the slit and spread it evenly over the large, purple head.

Tom slid forward in the chair to give me better access to his crotch. I cupped and lifted his heavy balls with one hand while I slowly stroked his beautiful cock with the other. When I glanced at his face and saw a look of true urgency, I placed his cockhead in my mouth. I really enjoyed the salty taste and the fullness in my mouth. The heat of his member really turned me on. I slid my tongue around the head and sucked on the slit to get his fluid. I started inching my way down the full length of his hot, hard shaft. When it hit the back of my throat, I let it slide farther in. I was actually astonished at how easy it was to swallow cock. I eased him out, then started a steady piston action up and down his slippery shaft.

Tom was soon gasping for breath. "Slow down," he moaned. When my wife says that, she usually means for me to hurry up and get her off, so I didn't slow the pace at all. In fact, I sucked harder. After some more of my sucking, Tom cried, "I'm going to come any second!" I pulled my mouth from his cock and yelled, "Go ahead!" Then I quickly dived back for more. I was so turned on, I couldn't wait to taste his sperm.

I didn't have to wait long. He moaned, threw his head back, and the jism spurted out of his swollen prick in hot, sharp jets. The first one went straight down my gullet and the next one filled my mouth. I struggled to keep the flood contained, but to no avail. By the fourth squirt my mouth was overflowing. I swallowed about half of his jism, and kept the rest in my mouth to swirl around his cockhead with my tongue. As the throbbing in Tom's cock began to ease, he quickly became too sensitive. I wanted to make sure I got every drop of that wonderful spunk, but Tom could take no more of my sucking and said that he was totally used up for the time being.

I had now, with Tom's help, totally satisfied Dana and single-handedly done the same for Tom. I felt terrific, even though I hadn't come myself. I learned an important lesson that night—satisfying two people I really loved was just as good as satisfying myself. I also learned that I could totally love two different people at the same time, and that their gender made no difference. These were some of the best lessons I had in college.—*Name and address withheld*

WHILE THE CAT'S AWAY

My wife and kids were out of town, and I was feeling exceptionally horny for something out of the ordinary. I pulled up to the parking lot of the Grotto and shut off the car. I was a little nervous, not being used to the gay scene, and felt unsure of what I would find within. As I walked toward the door I loosened my tie and unbuttoned my vest. Once inside I walked straight to the bar. My mouth was dry and my heart was racing. I hardly glanced at the hunks surrounding me. After a few sips of beer I started to relax, then lit a cigarette and proceeded to scan the room.

Sitting on the stool next to me was Eddie. He was about my height, six feet two, dark and handsome. His open shirt revealed an exceptionally hairy chest, and dark hair covered his arms as well. We struck up a conversation, and when he stood up I got a good look at his balls showing through his tight jeans.

He ordered us both another beer. We sat and talked for quite a while. He slowly maneuvered himself so that his knee lodged between my thighs, slowly rubbing and kneading my groin. I loved the feeling of exhibitionism in the crowded bar and couldn't believe how hot I could get in a public place.

I wanted to get out of there and get down to business, and it seemed he wanted the same thing. We finished the beer, paid the bill, and walked out into the parking lot. By now my cock was straining through my wool slacks, and a huge spot of pre-come shined through. I patted his ass as I got into my car. As I followed Eddie back to his house I could hardly stand the fifteen-minute drive to sexual bliss.

We pulled up to an art deco entry to a private tropical garden. It was a beautiful entrance to his small bungalow. Inside we drank some cool water and then I stretched out on the couch. He soon joined me and we began fondling each other, slowly at first, then more frantically. I pulled off his shirt and reveled in the sight of his chest and erect nipples. I lost myself in his matted hair while he disrobed me.

We went into the bedroom and got naked. His phallus stood like a rigid peak of marble crowned with a single glistening drop of dew. I began encircling the top ridge with my tongue, slowly working toward the crater at the top of the purple volcano that would soon activate. I smelled the base of his cock and nudged his balls with my nose. I then licked each one with my tongue while he groped for my groin. I shoved him back against the headboard so that he was half sitting up, with his knees bent close to his chest.

As I spread his knees his hairy thighs framed two balls the size of ripe summer plums. His cock was fully ten inches long and so thick that I could barely get my fist around it. It twitched with anticipation and another droplet of come slid down the ridge. He held his knees apart while I burrowed between his thighs.

His hairy, well-formed chest began to heave, and I knew he was on the brink. I began massaging the fleshy underside of his shaft with my thumb and suddenly sucked his entire member into my throat. It took only a few heaves before he was moaning and writhing with pleasure. I slid him out of my mouth and sat back to catch my breath.

His cock stood straight up toward his hairy navel, swollen, purple, ready to release. He looked me straight in the eye as if to plead, "Finish me," but this was an erotic moment that I didn't want to end.

By now my cock was also purple with anticipation, dripping its glistening nectar down my shaft. I straddled his legs and gripped his cock, pressing it closely to mine. There we were, connected by our love probes, both electric with anticipation. Holding firmly, I began to thrust up and down. He soon followed my lead. The headboard was slamming against the wall as our groans grew louder, our musky scent permeating the atmosphere. Our cocks slid together, wet with our pre-come. He lifted his ass and started gasping in orgasm. The eruption came from the depths of my balls and I came with him, simultaneously spewing white lava all over our chests and balls.

We both leaned back, cocks covered with come, and relaxed. He stretched out and I quickly took the opportunity to mount him, French-kissing him and rubbing our lubricated genitals together until we both began stiffening. He then flipped me over and went down on me. I hungrily sucked the cock that stiffly dangled before me. I grabbed his hairy ass and he grabbed mine as we began to face-fuck each other. We formed an unending doughnut of sexual tension, my head locked between his thighs while his cock slid up and down my throat. His grip on my ass got firmer and his cock began to engorge. Simultaneously we rocked in pleasure, groans muffled by the tube steaks we were both eating.

Reluctantly we separated, cocks red and shrinking, come oozing from their heads. I fell asleep rubbing his hairy stomach and legs. The next morning I awoke, showered, and kissed him goodbye. I haven't sought any more men since then, but I have the memories of an unforgettable night!—*P.D., Tucson, Arizona*

GLANDS IN THE SAND

I live in Florida aboard a thirty-foot sailboat. Although at times it seems a little cramped, the low cost of dock rental and the ability to escape to remote beach areas on the weekends more than offset the small living quarters. I am in my thirties yet still have a good many boyish features, and I keep my pubic hair shaven to call attention to my boyish cock.

I love to sail off to remote areas and sunbathe in the nude. Sometimes I stay on the boat and sometimes I pick a deserted island beach area or a clearing in the mangroves. Just a short time lying naked in the sun gets me horny to the point that I have to whack off to a glorious orgasm.

On one such occasion I had an experience on a beautiful, remote beach that I have to tell you about. I had sailed for about three hours and found a nice, sunny, private anchorage for the boat. I stripped down to my birthday suit and felt the warmth of the sun tantalizing my skin. I especially love the sensation of the hot rays of the sun striking my tender bare behind. After about half an hour I was hot and sweaty, so I jumped into the water. The water was warm and still felt good, as my cock and balls floated freely as I swam.

Thinking I was totally alone, I swam far from the boat and eventually to the beach, still naked as a jaybird. When I reached the beach I just lay there. I spread my legs wide open, loving the sensation of the small waves lapping at my behind and hairless balls. After a few minutes I felt my dick grow into a firm, long rod.

I continued to lay there in the warmth and then started to rub my cock against the soft sand. (It wasn't exactly sand, it was more of a silt.) Anyway, it felt great, and I eventually buried the shaft deep into the soft silt. It was as good as any pussy I'd ever felt.

Still thinking I was alone, I pumped harder and harder, arching my back to get maximum penetration. It was at this point, to my horror, I noticed another person in the bushes watching me. I knew I was caught in the act. I stopped and just lay there, pretending to be sunbathing. I hid my head like an ostrich, hoping that the intruder would go away (just the same as my tremendous boner).

But then a lump came into my throat when two feet came and stopped inches from my head. I looked up and it was another man, a little younger than me. He was in good shape physically and had a nice tan and lovely blond hair. He was wearing a skimpy racing-style bathing suit and I noticed a huge bulge in front of it.

Then he said, "Hey, that looks like fun. Mind if I join in?" I didn't know what to say, so I just smiled. Apparently he took that as an invitation, because in a flash he had stripped and was lying beside me. It took no time for him to get a large hard-on, which I could see peeping out from under his firm belly.

I felt mine returning as well. This was a new experience for me. I'd never had an erection in front of another man before. But after a few more minutes I really felt very comfortable. Before long we were both pumping our dicks madly into the soft silt. I saw him arch up and smile and I knew he was coming. Then I felt my own orgasm begin, and I arched as well as I shot a tremendous load.

We still didn't speak. A smile said it all. We climbed farther up the beach and lay on our backs, letting the warm sunlight soothe our spent cocks. It was a wonderful feeling, and I realized that I enjoyed sharing it with another person.

I looked over at him when his eyes closed and saw the most beautiful cock. It was very manly compared to my boyish member. It was thick and fully large even when flaccid, and just curled up on his body while he lay there. Although I'd never done this sort of thing before, I had the urge to touch it. I resisted the temptation and closed my eyes for some sunbathed relaxation of my own.

As I lay there I felt my cock coming back to life in the warm sun. It wasn't hard, but it was getting bigger and was shifting position. It felt so good I just let it do its own thing, resisting the impulse to turn over and hide my condition.

Suddenly my eyes darted open as I felt a hand gently touching my cock. My heartbeat quickened, but again I did nothing to make him stop. He rubbed my cock harder and fingered my hairless crotch. I parted my legs wider to let him explore all of that wonderful part of my body.

He fingered me marvelously until I had a huge erection. Then he got to his knees and lowered his head to my groin area. I felt a wet mouth engulf my throbbing cock. It worked its way up and down my now slippery shaft.

I felt the explosion building up inside me, and then my cock erupted uncontrollably. His head tilted back, and he grinned as he felt my hot juices flowing into his open mouth. Then, suddenly, his own orgasm began. His cock shot a magnificent load all over. Some of it landed on my chest. I scooped it up and put it in my mouth. I'd never tasted come before—it tasted sweet yet salty. He licked what remained on my chest and slowly stood up. I passed out, drained and satisfied, on the beach.

He lost his strength too and toppled over next to me. We lay there spent for a while, then cuddled some as the sun dropped lower and it got cooler. Then, all of a sudden, he kissed my limp cock and grabbed his swimsuit. He disappeared back into the bushes. I eventually returned to my boat and spent the night dreaming of this marvelous encounter.—*H.L., Fort Lauderdale, Florida*

UNCUT AND UNINHIBITED

I've read many letters in *Forum* from men and women about their bisexual experiences, and many letters with views on circumcision. I have enjoyed reading both. Since my own experience has involved both, I am writing to share it with your readers.

In the rural Nebraska community in which I was born and raised, being uncircumcised is not unusual. I never gave it much thought, until my family moved to Boston when I was eighteen. I soon found that a foreskin was a rare oddity in this city.

During this time I had my first homosexual experience, with a boy on my block. He was circumcised, and we explored each other's penises in every way imaginable. I still recall feeling that he had the most beautiful penis. I often wished that mine felt and looked like his. I have since had a great fascination for circumcised penises. Though that was the only homosexual experience I have had until just recently, I have always known that I am bisexual.

I had recently joined a Nautilus center to firm and tone my body. I was immediately impressed with the beautiful bodies of the other men. I caught myself admiring them in the showers. I got excited just thinking about touching their circumcised penises. I had never let any of them know about my secret desires, my fantasies.

One recent Friday night, Kevin, one of the guys from the club, called and asked me if I'd like to come over and join Rick—another guy from the club—and him for a few beers. I eagerly accepted his offer.

When I arrived they handed me a cold beer. We sat on the floor and listened to the stereo. We sat around for hours until we were totally smashed. The talk had turned to sex early on, and continued to get more intimate with every beer.

During the conversation, Rick was sitting directly across from me with his legs crossed. He was wearing a pair of jogging shorts. It was obvious that he wasn't wearing any underwear. His circumcised cockhead nearly hung out the leg of his shorts. I had a tough time keeping my eyes off it. Though he said nothing, I knew that he must have been wise to my peeking.

Since my experience with women is minimal, I mostly sat and listened to Kevin and Rick talk about the girls they'd had. When Kevin asked me if I'd had many girls, I admitted to only having had a few. He replied that I must have to masturbate a lot. I tried to be macho, saying something about preferring the real thing.

Rick responded, "Hey, don't sweat it. We all masturbate sometimes. In fact, I love to masturbate." The tension broke and we all laughed. Kevin quickly followed up by saying, "Seriously, though, Frank, talking about jerking off, how do you uncircumcised guys do it? Do you use the foreskin or pull it back? Or do you just rub the shaft? I've never seen an uncut guy masturbate before."

Kevin caught me looking at his dick. "Do you like what you see? How about a closer look?" he asked. "I've seen you checking me out in the shower. Would you like to watch me jerk off?"

"Yeah," said Rick. "You show us how you masturbate, and we'll masturbate for you." Kevin was already playing with the head of his semi-erect cock. I was lost at the sight of it. We slipped off our shorts and compared penises and methods of jacking off. They were amazed that my foreskin still covered my glans, even when erect, and were fascinated to see me move it back and forth over the head.

I asked Kevin if he'd been sucked off by a man before, to which he replied indignantly that he wasn't gay. "You don't have to be gay to enjoy it," I said. I was eager to take his bulbous, circumcised cockhead into my mouth. He was too excited for words. I guided his penis into my mouth. I hadn't felt anything this wonderful since my teenage experience. I continued to suck until he came.

While I was involved with Kevin's cock, Rick began stroking my uncut dick. When I had finished Kevin off, he joined Rick in jerking me off. They argued over who got to bring me to orgasm, they were so fascinated with my foreskin.

Afterward, we sat around, had a few more beers, and discussed the evening's activities. We decided that Friday night would be bisexual night. Kevin and Rick talked about inviting some girls in on the fun. They said that I shouldn't keep my interesting cock to myself. They said that they knew some girls who would find it fascinating.

That was several months ago. Bisexual night has become a regular feature of our weekends. I let the girls explore my uncircumcised penis any way they choose. Sometimes I masturbate for an audience of over a dozen men and women. I really got off on these performances and I feel privileged to be both bisexual and uncircumcised.

I hope that other men in the same situation will take advantage of any opportunities that might come up. I urge them to write and share experiences.—*M.R., Boston, Massachusetts*

GIVING AND RECEIVING

My best friend moved away shortly after he graduated from college. John and I, along with our wives, had actually been more than best friends. We had become sexually intimate as well.

A few months after John and his wife had moved away, my wife, Debbie, and I arranged to go on a camping trip with them. When we arrived, John had already found a secluded site for us to use. It was near their new home, but extremely private and set beside a beautiful mountain stream.

We spent the first evening catching up on old news. Then, while Jane and Debbie were sitting at the campsite talking, John and I decided to take a hike up a little mountain road.

After we had walked for a while, I began to feel a desire to renew the sexual experiences we had indulged in back at school. I really didn't know if John would be willing to take up where we had left off or not, but I was longing to suck his hard shaft again after so many months without it.

I told him I had to take a leak and stepped into a tiny clearing off the path. John followed. He stepped up beside me and pulled out his beautiful, thick cock. We both looked at each other, and I knew he wanted me, too.

It was almost dark as I dropped to my knees there in the clearing and took his shaft tenderly in my hands. He sighed as I gently rubbed his shaft, which quickly swelled to full erection. I deeply breathed in his male aroma and flicked out my tongue to taste the drop of clear fluid quickly forming on his purple tip. I couldn't wait any longer. I dived down on his hot pole, taking it all the way into my throat on the first plunge.

It wasn't long before I had John moaning that he was about to come. When he did, I drank down his sperm as if I couldn't get enough, which of course was true. After I had cleaned him thoroughly, he reached for my bobbing shaft and began jerking it off with real fervor. He cupped my balls with his other hand and had me ready to shoot in no time. I quickly let go several spurts of white, hot spunk into his strong hands. We quickly cleaned up and headed back to camp.

We spent most of the next day together at the campsite. They left late in the afternoon because Jane had to go back to town for work that night.

John returned about dusk to spend some more time with us. As night fell, we went into the camper and turned out the lights. It was so dark in that little mountain valley that you could literally touch your nose and not see your hand.

Debbie was sitting on the edge of the bed between me and John. I caressed her breasts and discovered another hand there with mine. It was John's, of course. Somehow, in the dark, we managed to get out of our clothes and onto the bed in record time. While I was kissing my wife and kneading her firm breasts, I could hear John doing something down between her legs. I couldn't tell what. I worked my caresses down her shapely body and into her bush. When my fingers reached her clit, I found a tongue busy at work.

John moved up and started playing with her left nipple. She

had her hand on his hard cock. I was playing with her other breast while we kissed deeply. She suddenly pulled my head near to her face and whispered, "I want you to suck John's cock for me. I know how much you want it."

I was so overcome by her loving desire to see me pleased that I rolled on top of her and rammed my hard shaft between her moist thighs. At the same time I pulled John's hot member up into my reach. As I sank my rod into Debbie's love well, I slid John's pulsing prick into my mouth. My mind was reeling as John's heated shaft was massaging my throat. As I played with his cock with my tongue, I could taste his pre-come leaking out his slit.

Debbie's hole was offering its own massage on my prick, sending thrill after thrill into my crotch. I was totally lost in the deluge of sexual sensation. The more Debbie worked on my cock with her gripping pussy, the more I worked on John's shaft with my mouth.

Soon I felt my come racing through my shaft and flooding Debbie's hole with jet after jet. Seconds later, my body received an equal amount of spunk from John's throbbing pole buried deep in my throat. I swallowed every drop of that delicious come and sucked his softening shaft clean.

We all just lay there for a while, catching our breath. Then John had to leave for home. I was so totally satisfied that I don't remember anything else until the next morning when we had to pack up for the trip home. I've heard it said that it's better to give than to receive, but I've never had a better feeling than when I was giving and receiving pleasure at the same time to two people I love.—*Name and address withheld*

PART TWO

Letters to Penthouse IV

Crowd Scenes

In This Sex Olympics
It's Spain—3; Brazil—1

I'm a twenty-year-old sophomore at a prestigious California university. During my freshman year, I became acquainted with two other students from my country, Spain. We became close friends immediately because we like the same things—tight pussies, big tits and juicy clits.

During finals week, Facundo, Carlos and I decided to rent an apartment on the beach for the summer and the following year. Our exams were over on a Wednesday and all three of us were filled with mixed feelings. We were none too pleased with the outcome of our exams, but we were anxiously anticipating an enjoyable summer on the beach that was to begin sooner than we expected. On our third night at the beach, we decided to go out dancing and, hopefully, to find some obliging pussy.

When we arrived at the disco, we were feeling pretty loose as a result of several joints apiece. We were there no more than fifteen minutes when this brown-eyed she-devil slithered up to Carlos. She said nothing, but grabbed his hand and led him out to the dance floor. Facundo and I scanned the place for the same kind of action, but things looked dismal.

The song ended and Carlos and the girl returned. He intro-

duced her to us as Andrea and, as it turned out, she was Brazilian. She must have taken an immediate liking to Carlos, for her
right hand was down the back of his pants, tweaking and rubbing his ass. Carlos was reciprocating by rubbing his fingers up
and down her hot little crack through the material of her dress.
He was also showing off a huge bulge in his trousers. This little
Brazilian gal, who turned out to be eighteen years old, was dressed
so sensuously that Facundo and I were on the verge of whipping
out our love tools and jacking off right there. She wore a black
slit skirt that showed off the most supple calves and thighs I have
ever seen. Her red Spandex top was about to rip apart as her
big and beautifully shaped tits strained against the material.

Our conversation began as small talk but soon turned to the
subject of sex. She made several direct suggestions and, the longer
the conversation lasted, the bigger and longer our cocks grew.
The more they bulged in our pants, the more she licked her
lips—staring at our cocks all the while. At one point, she turned
to Carlos and said that she would like to go someplace more
quiet. Carlos agreed readily and was about to abandon Facundo
and me, but Andrea declared that she would like to be alone with
all three of us at the same time.

Normally, it takes fifteen minutes to get from the disco to our
apartment, but that night we made it in five. Andrea and Carlos
sat in back of my Camaro, feeling each other up, while Facundo
and I rode in silence, listening to the impassioned moans of those
two sex-starved humans.

Once inside our apartment, we went wild. We stood at arm's
length from her as she stripped slowly in front of us. Then, one
by one, she undressed us, licking and nipping every inch of our
naked flesh. When we were all naked, she returned to Carlos,
whom she had stripped first, and began to stroke his ten-and-
three-quarter-inch hunk of meat. She licked and sucked his glans
and parted the tip with her hot tongue. Meanwhile, Carlos was
running his hands through her hair. Suddenly, he grabbed her
head and impaled his thick spear into her mouth. She gagged a

little at first and then began a serious effort to deep-throat him. All the while, Facundo and I watched in fascination as all of Carlos's swollen prick gradually disappeared between her glossed lips. If she liked his ten inches, she was going to love Facundo's eleven and positively idolize my twelve.

She did about a dozen deep strokes and stopped abruptly, feeling Carlos's dick swell with his jism. She kissed it lightly on the tip and turned her attention to Facundo's mighty monster. She moistened it and then took it into her mouth. She took it out again and began to rub it against her huge tits. Moaning with pleasure, she squeezed her tits together around his sausage and proceeded to tit-fuck him. As she did this, I used my unique powers of concentration and stayed a limp five inches. When it was my turn, I noticed a slight frown of disappointment as she looked at my dangling soft meat. She looked into my eyes as if to say, "Is this all you have to offer me?"

"Suck me," I said, "and while you do so, close your eyes and fantasize about sucking something bigger." She obeyed. The warmth of her tight mouth and the sharpness of her teeth were too much. When she opened her eyes, my cock was at its full twelve-inch size. What she saw made her eyes bulge with joy. As she continued to suck and gurgle, she began to hand-job my two friends. After about five minutes of this, she stopped everything and begged us to fuck her hard and good.

Well, chivalry is not dead and our Latin upbringing demanded that we aid someone in distress. Carlos lay on his back. His thick pole was jutting up from his groin. As Andrea straddled him, she massaged and rubbed her tits, while I rubbed Carlos's pulsating bazooka on her clit and juicy lips. Slowly she let herself down on him as I guided it in. She was so hot and ready that her juices cascaded down his shaft and balls. Facundo then positioned himself over Carlos's face, in front of Andrea. Without any hesitation, she hungrily devoured his sizzling sausage. I began to lubricate her tight ass with my tongue, preparing her threshold for my stage-center entrance.

Andrea began to moan throatily as I slowly penetrated her tight asshole. Her twat must have been sizzling, for I could feel it contracting around Carlos's pecker. With one violent thrust, I reamed her rear hole. At first, our rhythm was awkward, but the four of us soon got it together and fucked away harmoniously for what seemed hours. All of a sudden, she began to shake violently, and I could feel her cunt pulsing and throbbing at a hectic rate. Carlos and I slowed down to give her a rest, and when she relaxed again, we were back to poking her from everywhere. She couldn't get enough. My God! This woman had over thirty-three inches of cock in her and she wanted more!

We each fucked her twice that night in the same fashion—with all of us giving it to her at once. The second time, Facundo pulled out just in time to unload all over her face. She thirstily lapped it up, rolling her tongue around to slurp up every available drop. Then she rolled off Carlos and simultaneously pulled her ass away from my cock. I promptly began to eat her luscious cunt, while Facundo and Carlos played with her glorious tits. She had a smile that split her face from ear to ear. Then she did something we never expected. She reached for the phone and dialed with trembling hands.

Twenty minutes later, we were joined by her seventeen-year-old sister and another girl who looked about sixteen. What ensued was absolute mayhem. We fucked ourselves silly, all six of us. Around two in the morning, we were pretty hyper and really sweaty, so we went down to the Jacuzzi and continued to fuck around. These girls were insatiable and, after a two-month dry spell, we were, too.

We finally collapsed in the living room of our apartment, utterly exhausted. The girls left around three in the afternoon, after another round of sexual fun. Since then, they have moved to an apartment in the same building as ours, and we see them often. It looks like this summer is going to be the best since our sexual awakening, and our only wish is that it may never end. Well, I have to sign off now. Andrea and Company have just walked in and it looks like they mean business—I mean pleasure.—*J.M.C., Irvine, California*

FIVE-CENT RAISE IN PAY LEADS TO A GREAT LAY

I recently gave a party that was supposed to be quite innocent. It was just to celebrate a stupid little five-cent raise I'd received. At the store where I work, no one else got a raise, so when I got a whole nickel, we thought it was some kind of a joke. I bought the wine, Mindy bought some beer, and Tim just brought himself and a deck of cards. I invited a few other fellow employees but they didn't show up. That was their mistake.

It started with Tim and I drinking just about all the wine as we waited for Mindy to show up. (She works the late shift at the store.) Tim and I were pretty bombed, so Mindy had to catch up. She drank two six-packs within forty-five minutes!

We started playing a little poker and Tim suggested that we pick up from where we had left off at our Christmas party. Mindy said, "Not strip poker!" and Tim said, "That's right! You didn't come to the Christmas party and we want you to see how much fun we had!" "Not yet!" Mindy screamed. "Just give me a few more drinks and a little time."

Well, she got pretty smashed and the three of us started playing strip poker. Mindy and I soon lost much of our clothes, and Tim didn't lose any. Why were we girls having all the bad luck? After a few more hands, we were down to practically nothing and Tim was fully dressed. I watched him deal the next hand and, sure enough, he was cheating! "And what do we do to cheaters?" Mindy said. "Get even," I said. So we pulled Tim to the floor and started ripping off his clothes. He fought at first, but we could tell he was loving it.

We wrestled around on the floor for a while, stopping for a few kisses and feels as we tried to get Tim's clothes off. Finally he said, "OK, I won't fight you off. Go ahead and rape me." And we did! Just as we pulled off his pants, Mindy and I saw the biggest, most beautifully shaped cock we've ever seen. Mindy grabbed it and started licking it like a kid with an ice cream cone. Man, what a hunk of meat! "I want some of that, too!" I said. So there we were, fighting over Tim's cock. I couldn't believe it!

Mindy finally made room for me and we then took turns sucking off Tim. He shot his load in Mindy's mouth and crawled over to me, pillowed himself on my soft boobs and sucked on them like a baby. I saw his member grow hard again and I suggested that he put it to use. He slipped my panties off me and rammed his giant cock into my box. I thought I was going to go through the floor! Meanwhile, Mindy was getting jealous, sitting and waiting for this to end, so she lay on the floor and masturbated. We all came at the same time, screaming louder than the stereo.

"Now it's my turn to be fucked," Mindy said. Tim moved over to her and started feeling every inch of her long slender body. While they were getting it on, I stood up and dressed. I'd never spent such a night with my fellow employees or anybody else!— *Name and address withheld*

Doctors Team Up to Cure Nurse's Itch

I am a nurse in the gynecology section of a large metropolitan hospital in the South. My duty shift lasts from eleven at night to seven in the morning. During these quiet hours, I've often wondered what it would be like to have a sexual encounter with a gynecologist. I've worked with many of them, of course, and these doctors certainly seemed to know everything about the female anatomy.

One night, my fantasy came true, and it was even better than I'd thought. It began about midnight. As I was charting my patients' vital signs, I noticed one of the resident doctors in the nurses' station gazing at my legs. I pretended not to see him, but turned a little to afford him a fuller view of my shapely legs and crotch. I could tell by the bulge in his scrub pants that he was interested. Soon, an intern walked over to him, and the doctors conversed in a whisper. They began to kid me about how "such a nice-looking" nurse got such an odd shift to work. Then one of the doctors asked if I had ever experienced nitrous oxide (laughing gas). When I said I hadn't, they did not have to do much convincing before the three of us had slipped upstairs to a quiet delivery room and I was lying on an operating room table, breathing a mixture of nitrous oxide and pure oxygen.

I was feeling great when one of the doctors suggested that my legs should be in the stirrups and my hands strapped out to the sides, so I would not fall off the table. As my legs were placed in the stirrups, my skirt rose above my thighs. Four eager hands were then undressing me. As my mind began to clear, I felt my white panty hose being removed; then the zipper and buttons on my dress were undone. Soon I was wearing only bra and panties. At this point, the mask was placed back over my nose and I felt great again after several breaths. Since my arms were bound to the table, it was difficult for the two men to remove my bra, although they had no difficulty with my panties, which were already soaked with my juices. They cut away my bra with surgical scissors. I was really getting hot and high at the same time.

Completely nude and helpless, I felt shaving cream being smeared over my pubic area. Then I was being carefully shaved by the intern, and the resident was sucking my nipples. When the shave was complete, the resident came around to stand between my widespread legs and ordered the intern to the head of the table to continue administering the gas. I could feel the resident's hands spread my labia and pull the clitoral hood out of the way of my now protruding clitoris. The juices from my cunt ran down my buttocks and onto the floor as the resident mouthed my clitoris—sucking, tonguing, and chewing for what seemed like hours. He licked up and down my cunt lips and around my clitoris, until I was begging him to fuck me.

Finally, the resident dropped his scrub pants and unceremoniously began to ram into me again and again with his throbbing penis. Just as I was about to come, he removed his penis from my vagina and greased my anus with some Vaseline. He then began to ram his big thick rod into my ass. The intern, meanwhile, had shed his scrub clothes, climbed on top of me, and shoved his stiff cock into my mouth as he went down on me in a 69 position and the resident continued to fuck my ass. The fantastic feeling I had is indescribable—the nitrous, the cock in my mouth, the one in my ass, and my cunt being devoured in new and inventive ways!

Believe it or not, we all came simultaneously, which left me with come in my mouth and my rectum, and with me screaming in ecstasy. As the two doctors laughingly told me later, I made so much noise when I screamed that they became afraid of being discovered, and so they gave me one-hundred-percent oxygen, woke me up, and handed me some scrub clothes to put on (my uniform was in shreds). Later, when I was back at my station, I explained to the other nurses that my uniform had been soiled by a very sick patient. I got away with it—and I'd learned that gynecologists really do know their territory, just as I'd suspected.—*Name and address withheld*

Friends That Orgy Together Stay Together

During my first week back home from college last spring, my best friend threw a big party. As the party progressed, a group of eight of us was getting along particularly well, and we all agreed to stay after the party broke up.

By one-thirty in the morning, everyone else had left, and the eight of us sat down and talked about how amazing it was that we had become so close in just one evening, particularly since many of us had been complete strangers when the party began. The group consisted of myself, my two best friends from high school, John and Butch; a friend of John's, named Stephen; an ex-girlfriend of mine from high school, named Julie; Julie's friend Laura; and two girls who went to college with John, named Cindy and Heidi. I would say that all four of us guys would be considered good-looking, and the four girls were definitely foxy.

Well, someone suggested we play truth-or-dare, and we all thought that it sounded like fun. The questions started off pretty tame, but when someone asked me who in the room I would most like to kiss, I said I would show them rather than tell them. Then I walked over to my old girlfriend, Julie, and pushed her down on her back. Before she could react, I lay on top of her and gave her the French kiss that I'd been longing to give her during the whole year I'd been away at college.

About half an hour after this, our game degenerated into a discussion of sex.

After a while, I guess, we all got horny from the discussion, and we were all definitely drunk, so when Butch suggested that the eight of us could probably pair off into twosomes that would be acceptable to everyone, we agreed to give it a try. To avoid hurting anyone's feelings, we agreed that the four guys would each write down the names of their first two choices, and after comparing them to be sure that each girl was chosen at least once, we would give the list to the girls, who would then go and make the final selections.

I chose Julie, whom I had never slept with, despite eight months of going together, and I named Heidi as my second choice.

After about ten minutes, the girls came back and said that they had made their selections. Before telling us who the pairs would be, however, they wanted to play strip poker. Naturally, we guys thought that was a great idea.

Let me tell you, seeing those four beautiful women slowly undressing as the game progressed, and not knowing which one I would soon be making love to, was one of the most exciting experiences I have ever had. Before long, Laura, Cindy and Heidi were gloriously naked, as were Stephen and John. Julie, Butch and I were down to our undergarments. Butch lost the next hand, and as soon as he removed his jockey shorts, Heidi crawled across the circle and began kissing and caressing him.

Although the original plan called for each couple to go to a separate room, that idea was quickly forgotten. Julie pulled off her panties, then nearly tore off my boxers, and suddenly I lost track of what everyone else was doing.

She and I immediately went to a 69 position, and the sweet taste of Julie's pussy nearly drove me crazy, as did the skillful work of her mouth. I shot my first wad in about a minute, but I kept sucking and nibbling on Julie's love box until she was screaming in ecstasy. By now, I was hard again. Julie quickly climbed on top of me, and we fucked together for the first time. Before I could come again, though, she climbed off and Heidi climbed on. Then Julie sat on my face. Although this obscured my view of Heidi's large and totally tanned tits, I didn't complain.

Soon the whole scene turned into a huge orgy, and I began losing track of just whom I was fucking, sucking, or being sucked by. I do remember that Cindy had the tightest little cunt I'd ever had the pleasure to enter, and that I was extremely surprised to find that Laura, who had seemed like such a shy girl, was multiorgasmic.

The most pleasurable experience of the night for me was being expertly deep-throated by Heidi, whose shaved pussy was the sweetest I have tasted. And Cindy was definitely the most energetic lover I've ever had, bouncing up and down on me like a jackhammer, with someone else's come smeared all over her jiggling breasts.

There is, however, one sad aspect to this episode. I'm convinced that my friend, John, is losing his mind. I say this because he actually took a ten-minute break from the action to shoot two rolls of color slides of us, individually, in pairs, and as a group, from every angle, performing every imaginable act. Of course,

I may change my mind about his insanity after I see the slides.—
Name and address withheld

GAIL, DONNA AND JOE TEACH HARRY TO GET DOWN

My name is Harry. I never read your magazine until my present wife asked me to. Once I began reading the letters you publish, I got hooked on them. So I thought I would jot a few lines about what happened to me between marriages.

After I received the final judgment on my former marriage, I was invited to join a well-known club so I could meet people and try to get rid of my blues. After a few nights at the club, I got to know Gail, one of the waitresses, and asked her for a date. We met the next evening and went to an X-rated movie, then to her apartment for the night. And this was where I learned more about sex than I ever had before.

When we arrived at Gail's apartment, we had a few drinks. She lit up a joint and asked if I wanted to smoke it with her. Since I'd never used the stuff, I refused. I just took another drink. Then she went in to shower, saying that she was hot from having seen the movie earlier. When she returned, she practically attacked me and said she wanted to "get it on." We started French kissing and she began rubbing my cock through my pants. Then she wanted me to take a shower. I didn't want to, but I did anyway.

When I came out of the shower, Gail was lying on the rug. Her legs were spread apart and she was playing with her pussy and pulling her nipples. She just looked at me and said, "Eat me out!" I had to admit to her that I had never done that before, but she just laughed and said that she would coach me. Well, I was scared at first and my stomach turned over several times before I got up to her pussy and started licking and sucking on it. God, that first taste of cunt juice tasted good! She kept telling me what to do next, and after about a half hour of this, I shot my wad all over the rug. When she saw that, she told me to turn around so she could suck my cock hard again. Well, after she'd been giving me head for about fifteen minutes, the damn doorbell rang.

Gail went to answer the door in her birthday suit. I was grabbing for my pants when two of her friends, a girl and a guy, walked in. To my surprise, Gail immediately told them about my never having eaten pussy before. They got a big charge out of hearing this. Then she introduced me to her friends. Their names were Joe and Donna. Gail lit another joint and they passed it among them. After a few drags, Donna suggested that I eat Gail's pussy again. She said that she had done it many times and that she would get down and show me the most sensitive areas of Gail's pussy.

Well, for a while, Donna and I were both tonguing Gail's pussy. Donna was a good teacher, too. But then, Joe began to eat her pussy and she rolled over and began to play with my cock and Joe's at the same time. Then Joe turned around so Gail could suck his cock and Donna went down on me. I came first and it was a while longer before Joe shot his wad. The two girls French kissed with our sperm in their mouths and, while they were kissing, some of it started to run out of their mouths. Joe got up there and began to lick up the overflow. When I saw this, I felt a little sick. I just closed my eyes and kept eating Gail's pussy.

Later on, Joe wanted me to suck his cock. I refused and said that pussy-eating is as close as I'll get to sucking cock. Then he wanted to suck mine and I told him, "No way." I spent the whole weekend with them, sucking pussy and fucking. It was a weekend that I'll never forget.

Gail, Donna, Joe and myself spent several other wild weekends together after that, and sometimes there were more participants than just the four of us. But I never ate anyone's pussy but Gail's and Donna's, because I knew that they would coach me if I went at it wrong.

Gail also used to drive over to my apartment some nights and, once in a while, Donna would come with her. I often found them eating one another out when I walked in from work. Once when they were there, my ex-wife dropped in unexpectedly. They really got on her. When Gail asked her if she would like to have her cunt eaten, my ex-wife departed at a full run. She never did come back to my apartment without calling first.

Well, I don't know what's happened to Gail, but if she reads this, it will ring a bell for her and she'll know that what she taught me has really changed my outlook on sex.—*Name and address withheld*

Horny Coed Enjoys Gang Sex with Frat Pack

I am a student at a small college. I don't claim to be a model, but I feel I am good-looking and have an admirable body. A month ago, I broke up with my boyfriend of five years, with whom I had a fairly active sex life. He was the first person I ever had any sexual relationship with.

Last weekend, I was sitting in the dorm, feeling lonesome and horny. I noticed a sign on the bulletin board, announcing a fraternity party, and I decided to go.

When I got to the frat house, it was so crowded that I figured I would only stay long enough to have a beer. When I wandered down to the basement there were about ten guys standing around playing a drinking game. One of them asked if I wanted to join in. When I declined, he quit the game to talk to me.

After about an hour of talking and beer drinking, I began to feel a bit loose. At their repeated invitation, I joined the guys in playing their drinking game, which they called "buzz." It went on awhile and we were all quite drunk when I realized I was the only girl still at the party—along with nearly a dozen horny studs. I said I should get going, but they asked me not to, suggesting that we play just a little longer. I was hesitant, but since each of those guys was kind of cute, I figured that if I stayed, the worst I could do would be to wind up with a cute date for the rest of the night.

The game went on for about another half hour, and soon after, I found myself on the third floor with the winner. We fooled around for about ten minutes, and then undressed each other. I was cock-hungry as a bitch in heat, and I immediately went for his with my lips. It took only about ten seconds for me to bring him off. To my pleasant surprise, I had an orgasm myself.

As I was wiping the overflow of his come, from my chin, I looked up and saw two other guys standing naked over me. At first I was scared, but then I got excited and went for one of their cocks. The other fellow proceeded to fuck my boiling cunt. It had been so long since my last screwing that I was in ecstasy, having a cock in my mouth and another in my cunt. I bucked like a bronco and soon reached my second orgasm, but I still continued sucking and fucking.

Then I heard more voices. Seven other guys were waiting in line. I had never had group sex before, but I was so hot by now that I would have taken on the entire fraternity. The brother whose cock was in my cunt shot off when the other guy pulled out of my mouth and covered my face and hair with come. It didn't take long for someone else to shove his cock in my mouth, but I also felt someone spreading my buns apart and rubbing some K-Y jelly around my asshole. I started to protest when he drilled my rear entrance so deep that I thought his dick would hit the one in my mouth. I reached an incredible climax that was better than ever before.

I was in seventh heaven when a third guy positioned himself underneath me and plugged my already come-saturated cunt. I pumped back and forth furiously for my three guests. As soon as one would come, he would immediately be replaced by some-one else, and I had orgasm after orgasm.

At various times, I reached around me and grabbed one or two cocks to play with by hand. That night and morning, I took on all ten of them at least twice, and they deluged my face and tits with semen. Two of them took me back to my dorm the next morning and escorted me to my room. I thanked them and gave each a good-bye kiss.

I haven't been back to the frat house yet, but if any of those guys read this, I promise to return—and next time, I'm going to do the whole fraternity.—*V.T., Buffalo, New York*

GROUP GETS INTO THE SWIM AND DIVES INTO EACH OTHER AT SPLASHY POOL PARTY

I read your magazine regularly, and I, too, have had an experience that I'd like to tell the world about.

It happened when my wife and I attended a Christmas party at the home of the president of the company where I work. He had invited fifteen people from the company, and a few key suppliers, for a formal dinner. As my wife, Sharon, and I discovered, the president's home is very big. Among its luxuries are an enclosed swimming pool, a whirlpool, sauna and steamroom, a game room and bar, plus a gymnasium with a basketball court and an exercise room.

After dinner, our host announced that the house would be open for any activities we desired.

Sharon and I went out to the pool. There were people swimming already, and two couples were in the whirlpool. Swimsuits were available in the dressing rooms. I put on a pair of bikini briefs and waited for Sharon, who soon emerged in a white, halter-style maillot that was cut low between her breasts and in back, it barely covered her ass. Sitting in the whirlpool, we made small talk with the others. The men seemed to pay a lot of attention to us, and I soon noticed why. Sharon's suit was virtually transparent when wet—her tits and pussy were plainly visible. I couldn't blame them for gawking—Sharon is twenty-six, five-foot-seven, one hundred and six pounds; her measurements are 34-22-34, with a C-cup bra.

After we hurriedly left the pool, Sharon put a towel around her and sat on a chaise lounge. In a few minutes, her suit was dry and opaque again. I asked if there were other suits available. "None that fit me," she said.

I went to get some drinks, and when I returned, I saw a woman running topless around the edge of the pool. A few men and women were swimming nude. Sharon was standing in the water with some men. When she came out of the pool to get her drink, she didn't bother to put on a towel—she just stood and drank, while everyone who was interested watched. I asked Sharon what I had missed while I was at the bar. She said that there were no more bathing suits, and some people were swimming in their underwear, and some were naked. Sharon also said that Ray, a man in the pool, had already given her a drink. She then swigged down the one that I had brought her. "I'm just starting to feel really good," she said. "Would you mind getting me another drink before we go swimming?"

Just as I returned, Sharon and Ray walked out of a cabana. She said that she'd had to go to the washroom, and that Ray had guarded the door for her. All this time, the pool kept filling up with people, until there were more naked and half-naked people than ones wearing swimsuits.

Sharon and I entered the pool together, but before long, we became separated. When I finally located her, she was standing in the shallow water with Ray and two other men. I could see her tits and nipples through her suit from the other side of the pool, so I could easily imagine the marvelous view that those three guys had. Suddenly, Ray kissed her and started squeezing and playing with her breasts. As I was about to swim over to Sharon, a naked woman tapped my shoulder and said that I was "it," because I was wearing a bathing suit. She said I had to remove my suit and then tag someone else who had one on. She pulled my suit down to my thighs, and watched me as I took it all the way off. I was swimming toward Sharon when another lady, with a suit on, passed me. I tore off her suit and told her the rules.

As I started swimming again, a woman grabbed my prick and said that her name was Jane and she wanted to fuck. At the same time, Sharon was leaving the pool with the three men. Her suit was stretched out of shape, so that one tit was completely exposed to the night air.

As Jane wrapped her arms around my neck and her legs around my waist, I started fucking her like wild. She was kissing my face, licking my ears and pulling my hair as I squeezed her tits and pumped my cock into her like crazy.

While enjoying my aquatic fuck with Jane, I saw Sharon sitting on the chaise lounge. Ray and the other two men stood in front of her. She pulled down Ray's swimsuit. She grasped his cock and started kissing it, at the same time rubbing his balls. Ray reached behind Sharon's neck and undid her suit, releasing her other breast. Ray's two male friends removed their suits and helped Sharon out of hers. She lay back on the chaise, and Ray mounted her, inserting his stiff cock into her pussy. The other men stuck their pricks into her face and started working on them as Ray pumped away.

Ray must have come quickly. Hardly two minutes had passed when I saw him getting off Sharon. One of the other fellows quickly took his place. Sharon started licking Ray's limp cock as well as the third man's hard one. Just then, I felt myself releasing into Jane, who kept her legs around my waist for a few more minutes before swimming away without so much as a goodbye.

When I got to Sharon, she had gobs of semen smeared all over her hair, face, tits, stomach and pubic mound. She smiled when she saw me and promptly took my cock into her mouth. The three men were gone, but another guy was jacking off, ready to come on Sharon's belly and breasts. She grabbed his cock, and he instantly shot all over her. I felt I was ready to pop, but I didn't want only to be blown, so I pulled my pecker out of her mouth and slipped it into her sloppy pussy. I pumped a few times before depositing my load.

As we walked to the pool to dive in and wash off, I could see globs of come trickling slowly down along Sharon's legs. Once in the pool, we washed each other off and watched the other people.

During the rest of the evening, we each had plenty of hot sex with other people. Sharon had seven men enter her pussy, including me and the company president. I fucked three other women besides Sharon and Jane. When we left, our host thanked us for coming and invited us to a "super" New Year's Eve party, saying it would last at least a day. He said he wanted to give Sharon something by which to remember the evening, and he presented her with the white swimsuit she had worn. He told her that she had really looked good in it—and out of it, too. If the New Year's party is as good as this one was, I might have another story to share with you.—*Name and address withheld*

HOT-TO-TROT FRIENDS BECOME FAST-PACED FIVESOME

I have been reading *Penthouse Letters* now for two years and have often doubted some of the stories—up till now, that is! I'm twenty-one, married, and I live a comfortable life. My wife, Rose, is twenty and has black hair, brown eyes, and a fine body with firm tits and a nice thick bush. During our two years of marriage, we have discussed the possibility of swinging with other people but have always changed our minds for one reason or another.

Last week, however, a friend of mine, John, came over for dinner with his girlfriend, Liz. Rose has always been turned on by John, and I in turn dig Liz. During dinner, another friend, Denis, came by. After dessert and coffee, my wife complained that she did not feel well and went to lie down in our bedroom. The rest of us were in the living room, smoking a few joints and sipping some wine. John excused himself and went to the bathroom.

After a while, when John did not come back, I went to see if everything was all right. Finding the bathroom vacant, I looked in the bedroom and saw John sprawled on the bed with my wife holding his stiff prick in her hand. When John noticed me, he jumped up. But my wife grabbed him again, smiled at me and said, "No more reasons why we shouldn't." She then took his cock and sucked it into her mouth.

Not knowing how to react, I walked back to the living room to find Denis and Liz playing with each other on the floor. Denis was feeling Liz's big tits. I was amazed! John was fucking around with my wife, Liz was fucking around with Denis, and I wasn't fucking around with anybody! I watched Denis pull Liz's pants down. He started to eat her hairy cunt. I couldn't take any more. I whipped out my prick and stuck it in Liz's mouth.

After a while, Denis and I switched positions. As I was eating Liz, I felt a warm mouth on my cock. It was Rose. John's come was still dripping from her face. She was sucking me while John was fucking her pussy from behind, while I ate Liz and Liz blew Denis. After a few minutes, Denis couldn't hold back and came all over Liz's face. At this sight, I let a load fly into Rose's mouth as John came in her cunt.

A while later, my wife leaned over and started sucking off Denis as we all watched. Denis came all over her tits. Then Liz sucked me for a while and John started fucking her in the ass—something that completely turned me on. John asked if I would like to give it a try and I quickly accepted his offer. Rose licked my cock to get it wet. My cock went straight in and I came within a minute. Everybody being spent, we decided to call it an evening but promised to get together again soon.—*Name and address withheld*

FINICKY PUSSIES FIND PERFECT FIT IN SHOE STORE

I am a twenty-year-old student at a West Coast university who just last week had an experience that gives me a "rock hard" every time I think about it—and I find myself thinking about it a lot. About two months ago I was short on funds, so I answered an ad and got a job selling shoes part-time at a local shopping plaza. This allows for plenty of girl watching but little else since our store's clientele consists of eighty-year-old ladies.

Anyway, on Tuesday evenings it is my responsibility, and that of another part-timer, Don, to close up shop. Tuesday evenings are generally dull, as are most evenings when business is slow. However, this last Tuesday I received a call from someone who asked if it was true that the "Naturalizer always gives you a perfect fit." The girl's voice was sexy and her soft tone had me turned on in an instant. I said, "That all depends on what size you need," and when she said eight wide, I told her I'd be able to help her "personally." She said that was great and she'd be right down. I could hardly wait for her to arrive.

About an hour before closing, in walked two of the best-looking ladies I've ever laid eyes on. They were around twenty-one. The dark-skinned one had black hair, a nice set of lungs and an ass as tight as my boss come raise time. The other was a little taller and had a smile that would make a guy stand at attention. She was endowed with some nice big tits that were well displayed in her tightly stretched tank-top. On a scale of one to ten, these two lovelies were definitely elevens.

After a little small talk I showed them around and asked them if they saw anything they liked. The dark-haired girl said, "Yes, I called earlier about needing an eight wide. My name is Marta, and this is my friend Lori. She'll need something that can fill an eighteen-inch box." I suggested that Marta come in back and check out my stock in order to get a perfect fit. Lori would have to wait for Don to come back from his break.

Once in back, I could tell from the way Marta was staring at me that she'd have no trouble finding the style she wanted, so I decided it was time to make my move. I pulled her close, my hands cupping her tits, by which I could tell she only had on the dress, which was good because we didn't have much time. She was moaning and shaking, and I knew she was dying to be fucked just as I was dying to fuck her. I slipped off her top and exposed the loveliest set of tanned tits, which I quickly sucked into raisins.

At this point I heard Don walking back from his break mumbling something about what a rip-off the next-door deli was, so I broke away from Marta and went out to talk to him. But Lori didn't give me a chance; she literally jumped him, and they were going at it hot and heavy in an instant right in the middle of the sales floor. So I quickly lowered the front gate electronically, turned off the lights and went back to business.

Marta was super horny by now and was screaming, "Fuck me, fuck me," working herself up into a furious frenzy. I slipped my pants down, freed my swollen cock and entered her glorious muff. She was awfully tight and I thought of offering her a shoehorn, but instead I was soon lying back and letting her lower herself onto my waiting timber. She bounced up and down on it with a vengeance till she had multiple orgasms and I blew an enormous load into her.

In the meanwhile I could hear that Don and Lori had finished, and Lori was saying that she usually had such a hard time finding something to fit. Fully satisfied, Marta eased herself off, and we went back in to join Lori and Don. The girls smiled and said, "See ya next week." Don and I turned the lights back on, raised the gate and let them out. After straightening our ties, we were once again ready for business. I sure do like those Tuesday nights.—*J.D., San Diego, California*

YOUNG SWINGERS TASTE SEASONED COCK AND CUNT AND CAN'T GET ENOUGH

Barbara and I are a couple who've been happily married for six years, and swinging for four of those years. We are in our twenties and we have restricted our swinging to those in, or near, our own age group. Until last month, that is.

In early summer we placed an ad with a photo of us in one of the national swingers' publications, stating that we were bisexual and interested in similar couples or in single bi women, but we didn't specify any age limitation. Within two weeks of the magazine's publication, we received a total of seventeen responses, all but a few from people who lived too far away or who were too far-out in their sexual preferences.

One reply was from a fifty-two-year-old woman who wrote that she and her fifty-four-year-old husband were interested in meeting us for a look-each-other-over drink. Enclosed were two sharp color photos of them totally nude. Moreover, they lived less than five miles from us, both were bisexual and their time was quite flexible.

The following day I sent them a short note with our phone number and a request that they call as soon as possible. That was on Tuesday, and Thursday evening the woman called. Barbara spoke to her and set a date for us to meet them for cocktails on Saturday.

The couple, Glen and Evelyn, were pure British gentility. He was in the import business, and they had come to the United States eight years before with the intention of staying no more than six months. Once they had experienced the California weather, however, they decided to remain and planned to become citizens. Barbara and I were greatly impressed by their manner and speech and found them to be even more attractive in person than their photos had indicated. After downing two rounds of Scotch and soda, the four of us left in their car and in twenty minutes we reached their lovely condominium.

Glen put a tape on the stereo, Evelyn fixed the highballs and we sat down to drink and chat. There was no pressure on any of us, nor were any overt advances made until Barbara commented how much she had been impressed by Evelyn's photo and I said something flattering about Glen's genital endowment.

"Perhaps seeing the genuine article would be more satisfactory," Evelyn said, rising from her chair. "Come, Glen, let us disrobe and be completely immodest."

They disappeared into their bedroom and returned in a few minutes stripped to the buff. "We find nudity ever so comfortable and always go about the place like this in the evening and on the weekends," Glen explained.

Limp, his cock hung down to an honest six inches, and I felt certain that it would swell to eight inches at least. Evelyn's pubic hair was cropped quite close, though not shaved, and the lips of her cunt were plainly visible. Her eyes fastened on Glen's cock, Barbara began removing her clothes, and I also started to undress.

Evelyn made the first move by grasping my cock gently and offering me her mouth. My right hand went to her cunt, my left to her breast, and we tongue-kissed fervently for a full minute, my cock rising to full erection immediately. Then Glen knelt in front of my wife, pushed her legs apart and tongued her clitoris lightly, his hands lovingly caressing her tits at the same time. Evelyn leaned down and expertly went to work on my cock. Barbara, moaning softly, pressed Glen's head into her crotch, and in another minute she went into the ecstasy of a violent climax that seemed to last a long time. Then Glen took her to the bedroom.

Evelyn ceased sucking my cock, and we followed them to the bedroom, where our orgy got into full swing. Barbara guided Glen's pulsating cock to her cunt, and he was soon fucking her with a steady rhythm. Evelyn asked me to lie on my back, and then she impaled herself on my cock, which penetrated her snug vagina right to my balls after a few lubricating strokes.

Being a gentleman, Glen made certain that Barbara enjoyed a

solid orgasm before he exploded in her body, and the sight of her in a state of such intense gratification brought my own discharge gushing into Evelyn's vagina as she grinded down to drain every last drop of steaming love juice from my cock.

Moving off my body, Evelyn bent down to kiss Barbara lightly on the mouth, and then she slowly kissed her way down her body until her face was between her legs. Tenderly, Evelyn licked the moist flesh for a few moments, and then she drew it into her mouth, sucking and swallowing her husband's come with the help of Barbara, who was bearing down to force the fluid into her mouth.

Glen and I sat quietly watching the lesbian scene, and when Evelyn swung around to get into a 69 position with Barbara and Barbara began sucking her cunt hungrily, my cock rose slowly and was soon hard and stiff. Glen, too, was beginning to get erect, and, as if by prearranged signal, we reached for each other's cock and were quickly fondling each other with frenzied motions. Our eyes met, and without having to say a word, we silently arranged ourselves on the bed, cock to mouth, and ardently gave each other head with wild abandon.

About ten minutes after Glen had been sucking my cock, Barbara and Evelyn began having a series of continuous orgasms. The incredibly exciting sounds that came from them at each release made me ejaculate. Just as my spurtings subsided, Glen's warm come splashed onto my tongue. With his huge, thick cock filling my mouth, it felt as though he had discharged a torrent.

That ended our first visit with the Britishers. We've partied with Glen and his wife three times since that night and have also become acquainted with another middle-aged couple, Collier and Janet. Our advice to other young swingers is: Don't sell older people short; you might be missing the most beautiful sexual experience of your lives!—*Name and address withheld*

MIDTERM STRAIN WIPED OUT IN SUCK-AND-FUCK FREE-FOR-ALL

After reading a recent issue of *Penthouse Letters,* I'm prompted to relate a wild incident that happened to me and some of my buddies at a small Pennsylvania college. We were first-semester freshmen and it was around the time of midterms. Everyone was tired of being bogged down with studying, so we decided to have some fun.

A friend of mine, Jeff, called his girlfriend at a neighboring girls' dormitory and asked if she and her friends would like to take a break and smoke a few joints. They were willing, and in a matter of minutes four girls were outside the door of our apartment.

After a few casual hellos, Jerry lit up a bowl of some good Colombian. The girls had a few hits and began loosening up. They took their jackets off and made themselves comfortable.

About this time Jeff and his girlfriend, Lynn, grabbed a six-pack and said good night as they headed for the bedroom.

I took my cue from Jeff and started necking with a cute little blonde, Chris, who had the finest set of tits I'd ever seen. As I was caressing her hips, I was very aware of her large nipples peering out at me through her sweater.

By this time everyone had gotten into the act and paired off. Seeing that it was pretty crowded in the living room, I whispered something to Chris, and she eagerly followed me into Jeff's room.

To our delight, Jeff and Lynn were lying nude on the bed. She had taken his swollen cock between her crimson lips and her head was wildly pumping in an up-and-down motion. Jeff smiled when he saw us enter the room, because he realized he now had an audience. I could feel Chris's body trembling as a reaction to what she was witnessing and maybe in anticipation of what was to come.

Deciding to take matters into my own hands, I reached over

and undid the front of her jeans. I could now feel her woolly wonder and she arched her hips forward in response to my caresses. Her wandering hands released my purple-helmeted soldier of pleasure.

Soon we were completely naked. I proceeded to stimulate her now-moist muff with my probing tongue. Her body shuddered violently with each stroke of my tongue and she was quickly approaching orgasm.

Suddenly she wrapped her legs around my head and released what seemed like a fountain of delicious juice into my thirsty mouth. She groaned in ecstasy. Then, after she'd moved down to take my throbbing cock into her mouth, Jeff appeared behind her and mounted her doggie-style with his ten-inch dick.

While I was leaning back in sheer pleasure, Lynn came over to me and lowered her luscious pink jewel box onto my waiting lips. Meanwhile Chris, who was enjoying her late-night snack, deep-throated my iron-hard member. We all came in what seemed like a mutual orgasm.

We were exhausted and covered with each other's love juices, and Jeff suggested we go back out and smoke a few more joints. The girls threw on our bathrobes and we pulled on some jeans.

But we were in for a shock when we opened the bedroom door. Our two friends, Jim and Jerry, were having an orgy of their own. Jim was stroking his huge circumcised rod, and then he plunged it into the precious pussy of one of the girls. Jerry and a cute redhead were devouring each other in the 69 position.

Not at all disturbed by our presence, Jim, after pounding furiously, shot his hot come deep into the girl's convulsing hole. When the other two were through, Jerry suggested we switch partners. Everyone agreed and we fucked long into the night. Around three o'clock in the morning, the girls insisted that they really had to get some studying done. We kissed them good-bye, promising to get together again sometime. I can't wait until finals!—*Name and address withheld*

MOTORCYCLE FREAKS GIVE GIRLS A ROUGH RIDE DURING HELL-FOR-LEATHER FOURSOME

Until last spring I'd always had a low opinion of motorcycle freaks, because of the Hell's Angels stereotype. But last April I changed my mind—lady's prerogative, right? Anyway, I'd like to tell your readers how it happened.

My best friend, Candy, and I took a drive in my camper into the Virginia mountains last spring. After we'd set up camp, I looked out and saw two big guys on bikes pulling into the campsite next to ours. I turned to Candy and fearfully said that we ought to move before those guys tried to rape us. Candy suggested that we wait awhile to see if they'd move, but they didn't, and by then we were too tired to find a new campsite before dark. When we stepped out, it was obvious that the guys hadn't expected to have two sexy chicks camped next door because they both stopped in their tracks. Candy introduced herself and me, and we found out that their names were Doug and Eric. Doug, a tall, strong blond with blue eyes, was togged out from head to toe in jet-black leather, which glistened and rippled when he moved his beautiful, muscular body. Darker and with very rugged features, Eric was also tall and strong. He wore a tan jacket, brown riding breeches and tan knee boots.

Candy and I wanted to get to know them better, and so when they asked if we'd like to go riding with them, we jumped at the chance. Then Doug told us that we'd have to put on some leather before going riding, to protect our beautiful bods. Since he put it that way, we could hardly disagree. They had extra jackets with them and leather chaps that we were able to put on over our jeans.

In a few minutes we were all set. I slid down onto the bike saddle behind Doug and soon realized that I'd be pretty well jammed up against his ass. Before long I was holding on for dear life, and I began to appreciate the sensation of gripping him through his leather suit, which made me feel as if I were stroking his nude body. About then we rounded a turn and were leaning into the curve; I ended up grabbing Doug below the belt to keep my balance and was excited to learn that he was just as turned on as I was. His big cock was straining against the leather. I stroked the ample bulge and wished wildly that I could get my hand inside his tight jeans. By now the crotch of my jeans was becoming wet from my pussy's love juices. Not only did I have this big, handsome guy locked in my arms, but also the motorcycle was vibrating under me like a huge electric dildo.

Soon we reached the mountaintop and stopped to rest. The guys spread out their sleeping bags. Then Doug, giving me a piercing look, said, "Why don't you girls take off your regular clothes and then put the leathers back on? Leather isn't just good for biking, you know. Besides, you'll find it's a tough chick who can take what we're about to give you. When we fuck, it's as physical as that run up the mountain was, but you both look like you can handle it and maybe dish out a little rough and tumble of your own." They helped us out of our clothes, and I ended up wearing only a waist-length leather jacket, a pair of chaps belted tight at my waist (leaving my tail and crotch all exposed for Doug to play with) and a pair of knee boots. Candy wore the same things, except that she had on a skimpy vest instead of a jacket.

Doug and Eric, obviously excited by our outfits, began to fondle us feverishly. By the time Doug finally let me pull his cock out of his leather pants, we were both ready to explode. He took me down in almost a football-type tackle on the rocky, dirty hilltop and rode me like a wild man. Finally he thrust one deep last time into my cunt, and we both exploded in a thundering climax.

Eric and Candy were still at it meanwhile. He had mounted her from the rear, grinding her bare nipples into the rocky ground as he plunged against her backside. She was shrieking hysterically, but obviously out of passion, not pain. I was turned on again by now, so Doug lay me down across his motorcycle and mounted me from behind. Then he lifted me up and let me sit on his pulsing tool, pushing me forward so that my breasts dangled on either side of the gas tank. He began to hump me as if this were the last fuck he'd ever have. It seemed the more Doug got, the rougher he wanted to play. I was glad that I was wearing the leather, because he was almost brutal in the way he handled me. It wasn't exactly S&M, I guess, but it was the closest I ever came to it, and it wasn't bad at all!

That night we went back to the camper and slept together, but the next morning Doug and Eric were up and packing before Candy and I were quite awake. Doug asked me if I wanted to come with him, but I foolishly decided that I should return to my job in town. It was the best sex I've ever had in my life, and if I ever run into a Hell's Angels type again, I won't be so quick to pass any negative judgment; I'll just grab him and never let him go.—*L.E., Silver Spring, Maryland*

COUPLE DIVE INTO FIRST THREEWAY ON HOST'S WATER BED

My wife and I are avid readers of *Penthouse Letters* and thought you and your readers might like to hear how your magazine has helped add a new dimension to our sex lives. My wife, Jodi, is twenty-five and I am thirty. We are very liberal in our sexual attitudes and are considered a very attractive "together" couple by our friends and most people we meet.

One afternoon, as we were drinking a bottle of wine and reading a cross section of *PL* letters to each other, we decided to discuss the ones that most turned us on (those that had stimulated the hottest fantasies). To make a long story short, we were surprised to find that we were both extremely turned on by a letter about group sex in the "Crowd Scenes" section. Over the next four weeks we frequently and openly discussed the subject and decided we would like to try swinging.

Being novices, we didn't have any idea on how to go about it.

We finally agreed that if a good swinging opportunity arose, we would discuss it and go with it if we decided that the vibes were right. We wanted to be totally in control of any scenario we got ourselves into. Little did we know that our first "seduction" would take place much sooner than we could have ever imagined.

At a party later that same week we were talking to the host, Jim, a slight acquaintance whom we had met through a mutual friend. After Jim left us to mingle, Jodi told me that she was extremely attracted to him and was at that moment fantasizing about the three of us getting it on in the water bed she'd seen in one of the bedrooms. My cock almost burst through my slacks on hearing this. Although our fantasies had mostly involved swinging with other couples, we were now both very excited at the possibility of a three-way with Jim. I suggested to Jodi that she flirt with him at every opportunity. During this time I would mingle and observe them from a distance. Visions of my luscious young wife being driven crazy by hot, horny studs had been preoccupying my thoughts lately, and I was eager for some real action.

Jodi managed to talk to Jim several times, to tease him with fleeting caresses and to rub her nylon-clad legs against him. He became very flushed and sexually excited, but my presence in the room obviously prevented him from returning Jodi's attentions.

Jodi returned to me, very disappointed at the outcome of her flirtation. I told her we'd just have to take the bull by the horns, so to speak. Just follow my lead, I told her, and play it by ear.

Little by little the other party-goers started to leave, but we lingered until we were the last two guests still there. Jim played right into our hands by offering us the use of a spare bedroom so as to save me a twenty-mile drive in my somewhat inebriated condition. We accepted his offer and thanked him for his hospitality. Then we all sat for a while, talking, telling jokes, listening to music and smoking a few joints. We didn't discuss sex at all, but the vibes were definitely good and there was a lustful energy in the air.

Jim then asked us if we'd ever slept in a water bed. Jodi replied that we hadn't, but that she'd always thought it would be a very erotic experience. Jim urged her to go ahead and take the room with the water bed, half jokingly adding that he didn't know if he could ever sleep on a regular bed again. As if on cue, Jodi arose, winked at me and asked Jim whether the water bed wasn't big enough for three people. She then planted a wet kiss on his lips, kicked off her shoes and disappeared down the hall.

Grinning slyly at Jim, I told him we'd just been made an offer we couldn't refuse. With little further ado, we raced to the bedroom, burst through the door and immediately began shedding our clothes. Already gloriously nude, Jodi impatiently grabbed both our arms and pulled us down onto the undulating sheet. For the next six hours Jim and I massaged, licked, sucked and fucked Jodi into an altered state. My most erotic memory of that night was of Jodi being furiously doggie-fucked at one end while she deep-throated another cock at the other end. We bid Jim adieu at eleven o'clock in the morning.

Since that exciting night one and a half years ago, we haven't really pursued swinging as a life-style, but only as an occasional variation. We have swung once again with another guy, once with a young married couple, and another time we attended a wild orgy. The two latter experiences came about as a result of some visits we paid to an Atlanta swing club. At the moment we are planning to seduce a sexy female friend who has obliquely expressed an interest in a threeway.—*G.M., Macon, Georgia*

Jogging Sailors Perform Vigorous Laps on Their Lieutenant's Wife

My buddies and I are sailors stationed at the training center in Great Lakes, Illinois. We had recently started jogging, and last Wednesday night had run about a mile and a half when we spotted a woman jogging about seventy-five yards ahead of us. We quickened our pace and hung back at a distance of about ten yards. She appeared to be in her late twenties and was a real fox. She had gently waved sandy blond hair that cascaded down to the small of her back. Her body and legs were perfect—probably as a result of her jogging. She wore very short shorts that were fairly revealing. I could picture what they concealed.

We decided to move closer to get a better look. We were far from disappointed when we saw her from the front. Her face was really pretty, and her pendulous breasts were swinging freely since she obviously wasn't wearing a bra. Coming or going, this voluptuous beauty could turn on any man.

Steve gave a soft whistle of approval, and she responded with a dazzling smile and a very suggestive hello. We all introduced ourselves and jogged together for a few more minutes until she declared that it was time for a rest. Then we sat down in a small secluded grassy area amid some trees. After talking for a while, Cindy lay back and suddenly started stroking herself! My friends and I picked up the not-so-subtle hint and helped her disrobe. Needless to say, we were all naked in a matter of seconds. God, she was gorgeous! My friend Terry is hung like a horse—almost ten inches when erect. I run about eight, and Steve is a close third at seven and a half inches. Well, Cindy was hotter than hell with three big pricks wagging in her face, and sailors are *always* ready.

First, I kissed her luscious mouth while Terry and Steve caressed her beautiful body. Steve moved down to the sweet, moist cleft between her firm legs, and Terry licked and sucked her tits until the nipples were rock-hard. When Steve flicked his tongue over Cindy's clit, she ground her pussy against his mouth and let out the sexiest moan I have ever heard. She grabbed my tool and pulled it to her mouth while Steve and Terry switched positions. Terry slowly sank his hot ten inches into her waiting box as Steve straddled her chest and tit-fucked her. This was too much for

Cindy—she had her first orgasm, which was quickly followed by Terry's. Next I came, and as she swallowed, Steve sent his jets of come over her chest, throat and chin.

Next, she took Terry in her mouth—at least, she tried to. She couldn't take all of him, but she took enough to give him the best head he's ever had. Then Steve started up Hershey's alley. It was difficult, but with the aid of his saliva and love juices, he managed to get his sizable tool up her tight little anus. I then penetrated her pussy, and Cindy went wild. She bucked her hips frantically while she devoured Terry's cock. All four of us came almost simultaneously and then rested for a while.

We went on for almost three hours, until we were all so exhausted that further sex would have been impossible. I told her that it would be great to get together again, but she said that her husband didn't like her going out alone. He was afraid she'd be raped. She talked about her husband for a while and then lowered the boom. He was a lieutenant in the navy and was stationed at Great Lakes! She then kissed us all and walked away. Just think: Three enlisted men had been screwing the wife of an officer. My buddies and I now play basketball to stay fit.—*S.T., Great Lakes, Illinois*

Different Strokes

Couple's Marriage Improves As Husband Lets Wife Play Around

An affair that began for my wife in infidelity, as a statement of dissatisfaction and resentment, has evolved into a living fantasy of open sexuality for both of us. The first night that Leslie came home late from work, she confessed that she had been with another man. Leslie is a beautiful, seductive woman with an inner mystique that leaves even the casual male acquaintance yearning to touch her body.

Though I felt anger and rejection, I could not help getting a tremendous hard-on as she related the events of the evening. They drove to a bar for cocktails and then to a disco. As they enjoyed the sensual beat of the music, the liquor, the touching and kissing, their juices began to flow. At his apartment afterwards, they shed their clothes and ended up in bed.

I felt I was to blame for having ignored her needs, but I also wanted madly to fuck her. I wanted to rape her then and there, to eat her pussy and taste her and her lover's mingled juices, and then to fill her with my own. Unfortunately, I had to wait.

We solved our differences the next day when I agreed that we would spend more time together. I know Leslie expected me to reproach her for sleeping with another man. Instead, I shocked her by telling her that what she had done excited me. I told her that she could go on seeing her friend and even fuck him whenever she wished. That floored her, because Leslie expects total fidelity from me and she could not understand why I would allow her such freedom. Still, that inner fire burned from the touch of another man and she seriously considered my proposition. The only stipulation I made was that she would have to tell me every detail of her affair when she arrived home.

Several weeks passed and Leslie still had not returned to her lover. One morning, as we were dressing for work, she aroused me by mincing around the room in nothing more than panty hose. Her coy smile betrayed any hint of innocence. Grabbing her by the waist, I wrestled her to the bed and began kissing and fondling her. As I touched her mound and my fingers slid between her legs, she resisted me, objecting that there just was not enough time.

"How about a threesome tonight?" I cajoled as she finished dressing before the mirror. "Why not ask your friend over? You know you'd enjoy being ravaged by two men."

"Yes, I would," she agreed. "But I don't know if that's such a good idea. I think I'm becoming a nympho as it is. If you keep enticing me, I may go too far."

Somehow, I just could not imagine her going too far. I am as much a voyeur as she could hope to become a nympho.

At nine that night, Leslie called to tell me that she and some colleagues had gone out for drinks after work. I asked her teasingly, male or female? When she answered "both," I wished her luck in a sly, wistful way.

At two-thirty in the morning, she called again from a friend's house to tell me that she was stoned and still enjoying herself. I asked her if she was alone with her friend and she replied, "Not yet." Needless to say, my cock stiffened and my pulse quickened. I complimented her for following my instructions so well.

The night passed restlessly. I awoke every hour, fighting the urge to masturbate. At seven o'clock Leslie arrived, weary but with a very satisfied expression on her face. Her eyes were slits and, by the way she doffed her clothes, I could tell the night's excitements had exhausted her. The long, black, curly hairs of her pussy glistened.

"Sore?" I asked.

Leslie rolled her eyes and smiled. The details of her previous encounter had included a mention of just how well endowed her friend was. She estimated that his cock was at least eight inches long and so large around that even inserting it slowly had caused some initial pain.

As she slipped into my bed, I rolled up against her, my leg separating her thighs. I guided my cock into her and began massaging the walls of her cunt with it. As tired as she was, she related all the details of the evening. Her description rekindled the fire in her hole and soon she was coming explosively. Holding myself back, I withdrew my cock and plunged my tongue into her gaping hole, licking and swallowing the flow of come, hers and his. Her fingers plied at my arms and face as she came again. She was still pleading for more, and my balls were churning with the need for relief, so I remounted her and gave her my entire cock. It took only about a half-dozen in-and-out strokes to bring us both off simultaneously. Since then, Leslie has engaged in sex with several other men and women. Perhaps if other married couples allowed each other greater freedom to explore outside relationships, marriage would never seem like a dull, worn, lifeless arrangement.—*Name and address withheld*

GIRLS MANHANDLED WITH JUMP-ROPE GRIPS

My roommate, Steve, and I each have girlfriends who share a common interest with us—sex. We usually have mini-orgies for fun and exercise. The other night, however, we had a mini-orgy that was worth recounting in *Penthouse Letters*.

It all began when Steve and I took our girlfriends, Julie and

Fran, to a bar and proceeded to get drunk together. I must add that Julie and Fran are both gorgeous, and each has an outstanding feature worth mentioning. We call Julie A. for short, because her ass is so nice and firm. It's so firm, you could crack an egg on it and it would probably fry on those hot buns of hers. We call Fran T. for short, because her tits are so big that if they had presidents' faces on them, they would be mistaken for Mount Rushmore.

Well, getting back to the story, we all got drunk and went home at about one o'clock. We were all horny and anxious to get started; so we bolted the doors, shut the drapes, and practically tore our clothes off. We began our usual fingerin', lickin', suckin', and fuckin'. I just got done fucking Fran, but Julie was still barking as Steve was giving it to her doggy style. Then I saw a jump rope lying nearby, and I got a great idea. I grabbed it and shoved one handle into Fran's erotic tunnel of love. I stood up with the other end and started swinging it around. Fran went into a sudden frenzy, and she screamed in ecstasy. I started getting a hard-on just from watching her get off. I kept twirling while Fran squirmed like a fish on the floor.

Julie decided that she'd like to have some part of the fun when she saw Fran's pussy dripping with pleasure, and so she grabbed my end of the rope and shoved it into her sweet, muscular pussy. She began moving her lovely, smooth hips in every direction imaginable. Fran also got up; so they were both standing up, swinging the rope around as if they were possessed by the love demon himself. Steve and I were so turned on that we started whacking off on our Johnny Wadd juniors, turning the girls on even more. I noticed joy juice flowing rapidly down their long thighs. Then Steve stuck his jackhammer into Julie's ass, and she went mad with pleasure. So I went over to Fran and rammed her ass with my torpedo, causing her to explode with ecstasy. Now all four of us were going crazy all over the floor, with the rope swinging wildly, breaking a lamp that we ignored as we reached climax. It was the best orgy we ever had, and needless to say, we have been "jumping for joy" ever since.——*Name and address withheld*

Proud Husband Shares Wife's Charms

My wife and I are not swingers, but we recently found a harmless way to involve another person in our love games.

Sharon and I are in our late twenties. We have been married for five years and live in California. We have a wonderful sex life and really get off on each other and enjoy every imaginable way of getting mutual satisfaction.

Sharon is four-foot-eleven and weighs a hundred pounds; her measurements are 33-26-34. She has thick blond hair, perfectly shaped, full, firm tits (which spurt milk by the way), a broad firm ass, and her pride and joy—her cunt.

I have never seen even a *Penthouse* centerfold with a pussy as nice as Sharon's. She has handfuls of bushy blond pubic hair from her tummy to her pubic area. She wears a swimsuit or shorts most of the time. When she does, she gets lots of looks at her bulging crotch and stray fur hanging out. She enjoys going nude and letting the sun bleach her big pussy and tan her nice little titties and big ass. Sharon's outer cunt lips are huge and puffy. When she wears tight clothes, it looks like a pair of bananas are stuck side by side in her crotch. The inner lips are bright pink and get plump and red when she is turned on. She has great muscle control with her cunt and can wink and twitch at you at will. When she comes, her cunt milks you better than any hand or head job (which she is great at also). Her clit grows to about two inches when excited and gets so hard it shines like a little cock head.

We like turning other people on and vice versa, but we've been monogamous for the most part.

A situation presented itself this summer that we couldn't pass up, though. Sharon wears cutoffs when she isn't wearing a bathing suit, and she has a favorite pair. However, I didn't think they showed off her perky buns enough; so I cut the legs shorter. I overdid it and they turned out with just a strap of cloth up the crack of her ass and fluffs of pussy hair on either side when she sat down, stretching the shorts over her ample cunt. She wouldn't wear the shorts if she were going in public, but didn't hesitate to wear them around the house or with friends around.

This last Fourth of July we were sitting at home when Sharon's boss, Stan, dropped in. He is in his thirties and is very square and immature—no threat to either of us sexually. He never goes out with women. And he drinks a lot and was quite inebriated when he came over. I was in the mood for a smoke and lit up a bong. I asked Stan if he had ever tried one. He hadn't. I coaxed him, and soon he was stoned out of his mind. I get hornier than hell when I smoke, and Sharon turns into a real bitch in heat. After a few tokes her cunt is creaming.

Stan hates rock, but I figured he was too messed up to care. So I put on my best tape. Before I sat down, I went over to Sharon and suggested she put on her revealing cutoffs and a sexy top. I sat in a chair a few feet from Stan and watched anxiously. I about lost it when Sharon came out in her cutoffs, hiked up on her hips so her cunt bulged against the seams. She had on a flimsy, loose blouse with no bra. I could see her tan little nipples poking out excitedly from her bulging boobs. I didn't know what to expect, because she turns into a nympho when she's high. I was a little apprehensive at first, but I was excited and didn't care. She sat on the carpet with her knees together and her legs drawn up near her well-exposed ass cheeks. She had a few more tokes and soon had that buzzed, seductive look in her eyes. She stretched her shapely long tan legs out on the floor and leaned back on her hands and stared deeply into my eyes. I nodded my approval.

She bent her right leg up and placed her foot flat on the floor, revealing a big patch of pussy fluff on the inside of her thigh. Then, keeping her eyes glued to mine, she began to rock her leg back and forth in time to the music, exposing the hair outline of her engorged cunt. With each beat she showed more pussy hair.

Then both knees were drawn up and were spreading apart and back together again in time to the music. Now billows of shiny, fluffy pussy hair were hanging out for all to see. The hair disguised the meaty cunt lips bulging out on either side of the crotch of her shorts.

We glanced at Stan and saw him drilling a hole between my wife's bare cunt lips with dazed eyes. Although it doesn't sound like it, Sharon was being very nonchalant about the whole thing, and that, plus Stan's stupor, assured me he wasn't onto us.

I excused myself to take a piss, which I did loud enough to let Stan know I was out of the room. Then I came back into the living room and stood well behind his chair to get a ringside seat for the show.

She began to rock her legs back and forth to the beat again, and this time her cunt was well exposed. I was on the edge and wanted more. With my hands I signaled Sharon to really spread them, and as she did, her fuzzy outer lips blossomed like a pink rose. She shot a beaver that would make any man like to blow his wad.

She was really into it now, and I couldn't believe it when she reached down and pulled up her shorts so that the inch-wide crotch of the cutoffs was clear over on the inside of her thigh.

My beautiful little bride's pussy was spread completely open to the summer breeze drifting through the windows and her plump ass was swaying back and forth with the tune. I was really digging it and massaged my stiff prick through my bulging pants. Just then Stan started to stand up, and I dodged back into a bedroom. He took a piss, and when he came out, he said he wanted to run back to his apartment for more booze. I told Sharon to drive him because he was too stoned. As he followed her bouncing buns out to the car, I saw him reach in his pants and resituate his stiff little bulge.

When they came back, Sharon suggested we go to Stan's apartment to watch the fireworks being put on by the local community.

It was quite a show, especially inside the screened porch. This time my wife decided to show off her firm little tits. As she propped herself up on her elbow while stretched out beside Stan, her loose gauzelike blouse fell aside, revealing her beautiful right breast and swollen nipple.

As the fireworks exploded, she said, "Did you see it!"

She rolled over on the back and put her head on my knees so she was partially sitting up. Her bulging left tit stuck out like a spotlight in the semidarkness of the balcony. She turned to Stan and said, "Do you see that one?"

By now the poor bastard was letting out little groans as if he were coming. Sharon climbed up on my lap, and we melted in each other's arms and kissed deep and wet. My hand pushed aside the little strip of cloth covering her cunt, and my fingers were buried in steaming hot pussy. Her pubic hair was dripping with her juices.

Stan excused himself and headed for the bathroom. Sharon and I decided he was coming down from his high, and we agreed to split. We rushed home, and as she threw her clothes off, I dived into her pussy, eating and fucking all night.—*Name and address withheld*

Loving Wife Lays Others As Hubby Watches

My husband and I have one of the most unusual and successful sexual relationships imaginable, and I want to share our story with your readers. I am an extremely attractive woman in her early thirties—in fact, I am a well-paid model of high-fashion clothing—and my husband is a handsome, athletic man with a successful business organization.

During the last five of my seven years of marriage, I have been fucked by more than thirty different men, yet I have never once been unfaithful to my husband! You see, my husband's biggest turn-on is to watch me fuck other men—and my biggest turn-on is to let him watch me doing it.

If someone had told me five years ago that this life-style would be my key to sexual ecstasy, I would have thought that person to be a lunatic. I was brought up as a strict Catholic. Until I began fucking other men, I believed that sex was of minimal importance, except for making babies. Before I got married, I'd never masturbated and never had an orgasm. I'd had sex with only two men, on four occasions, and I'd hated every minute of it!

During the first two years of my marriage, I didn't come close to climaxing. Eventually, my doctor told me that my fallopian tubes had never completely developed, and that I couldn't have children. So, for the first time in my life, I had to regard sex as a mechanism for pure pleasure rather than for reproduction.

For more than a year, my husband and I tried desperately to find ways to bring me to a climax, but I couldn't reach it, no matter what we did. Soon, we both began to wonder if my problem stemmed from a lack of sexual compatibility with my husband. We discussed, and more often argued about, whether I could have orgasms with another man. Eventually, a marriage counselor suggested that I try it once, under very strict ground rules, in order to put the notion behind us and get on with our future.

Because of my good looks, I had very little trouble finding willing lovers, but I was uneasy about sleeping with anyone but my husband. I slept with three men in the next two months, but I just couldn't respond. I kept wishing that my husband were nearby, so that I could feel safe. When I told him of my feelings, he suggested that he should hide in the house when I was with my next lover. He also confessed to me that, during each of my liaisons, he had had a burning desire to be in the bedroom, watching me. It seemed a weird idea, but as soon as he mentioned it, I became very turned on and asked him to make love to me.

The next evening, my husband drilled a peephole in the wall between the bedroom and the study, and a little later, he watched me fuck another man. Lo and behold, the thought of fucking another man, with my husband watching, was so thrilling that I came for the first time in my life. Boy, what a difference! I couldn't wait for the man who was screwing me to leave, so that I could tell my husband that I had come. He was as turned on as I was! We talked about it all week.

In the following six months, I had four more lovers. Each time, my husband watched from the next room, and my pleasure increased. Moreover, having sex with my husband became marvelous. We shared a wonderful ritual. As soon as my lover left the house, my husband would come into the bedroom and seduce me. He would lick some of my lover's come from my vagina and then enter me so that he could feel another man's juices bathe his cock. Then, as he made beautiful love to me, he would ask me dozens of questions about my experience. The conversation was always the same:

"Did you come?"

"Yes."

"How many times?"

(I would tell him.)

"Was it good?"

"Very good."

"Better than me?"

"Yes, better, much better. I love fucking other men. They make me come again and again."

And on cue, with those very words, both my husband and I would erupt into intense orgasms. You see, sharing my infidelities with my husband so opened me up sexually that my orgasms with him became as good, if not better, than with other men. But his big turn-on was the thought that other men were better suited for bringing me to orgasm, and I let him enjoy his thrilling concepts.

Finally, I met a man who raised me to a new level of sexual

fulfillment. He was my tenth lover, and he was the first with an exceptionally large cock. My husband and my other lovers had average-size ones, perhaps six to seven inches long, while this man had an eight- or nine-inch-long cock that was also very thick. I was both impressed and intimidated when I first saw it. When he entered me, I immediately began feeling new sensations, and I had the ten best orgasms of my life during that first afternoon session with him. The size of his cock pushed my labia and clit down toward the opening of my vagina, and it was pure stimulation on every stroke. I couldn't remember the details of what happened because I was totally absorbed in the sensation of back-to-back orgasms, but my husband told me that I had laughed and cried uncontrollably, that I had trembled orgasmically every few minutes, and that I had been very relaxed and spacey. All I know is that I hadn't believed anything could be so good.

It was also the biggest turn-on my husband had ever had, and after my large-cocked lover had left, we enjoyed hours of climax-filled fucking and sucking. It was the best and most satisfying love my husband and I had ever made to each other. After several months, I discovered that sex with my husband had become better than with my liaisons. When I told my husband that he had really become the best of them all, he was overjoyed.

Armed with the knowledge that he was my best lover, my husband got up the courage to ask if I would make love to him and another man at the same time. After several months, when I met a man whom I felt would be compatible with us, I told my husband that I would try a threesome. To this day, I remain thankful that I did decide to go through with it. It was wonderful for all of us.

My husband and the other man were gentle, loving, and did everything to please me. The man said afterwards that he'd had the best lovemaking of his life, and my husband had had the chance to feel and listen to me as I climaxed with another man. Our ménage à trois took place every weekend for five months. They made love to me separately, together, and in every combination. I was fucked/sucked, fucked/ass-fucked, ass-fucked/ eaten, ass-fucked/sixty-nined, ad infinitum. Neither man had any inhibitions about eating me or fucking me after the other one had just come inside of me. And I received compliance to a request for the performance of one of my secret fantasies. I watched my husband being ass-fucked while he made love to me—and then I sucked both men clean.

My relationship with my husband has gotten better and better. It works because we each possess an incredible desire to do that which most pleases the other. And it only works when we do it together—for each other. I know this, because on the fifteen or twenty occasions when I've fucked other men without my husband's presence, I've been incapable of attaining a climax.

At last count, I have been fucked about five hundred times with my husband voyeuring or participating, and every time I've climaxed, I've done it for us.

Thank you, my darling husband. You've given me the happiest marriage on earth.—*Name and address withheld*

CAR FLIRTS HEAT UP TO A HORNY TIME

Let me offer your readers a pickup technique that was entirely new to me and that worked perfectly.

I was cruising home from work, thinking about my love life. My girlfriend had recently tossed me aside to marry a rich older man. In a way it was a relief to me to be rid of her, if that was what she was into, but I was feeling pretty horny.

I made a stop for a red light, and my attention was drawn by the very loud, very sexy disco music coming from the car to the right of mine. It was a cream-colored '64 Chevy convertible. It appeared to be in mint condition. It had a pink satin interior, and the top was down. Moreover, the driver was one of the tiniest, most beautiful women I've ever seen.

Her hair was tied up in a scarf, but I could see a few black curls peeping out. I thought her hair had to be very long. Her skin was smooth and creamy. Her lips were the same shiny, deep pink as her car's upholstery. She looked over at me, bouncing in time to the music, and winked one blue eye and licked her lips. Then she looked down at her left hand.

My eyes followed hers, and my cock rose to its full height. Her bare hand, with long, long fingers and rosy nails, was doing a lively dance on the outside of her car door. Always in time to the sensual music on the tape, she was miming foreplay.

She caressed an imaginary nipple with her middle finger. She rolled it in her palm and between her thumb and forefinger. Her pantomime was so accurate that there was no question what she was doing.

She stroked what I was coming to think of as my chest, tickling it with her nails. She inched her hand down, down, with little nips and pinches of her fingers. I could almost feel it. I had to open my fly before my cock was squeezed to death.

Suddenly, she grabbed the invisible thing she'd been reaching for, and jerked up and down, hard and quick, her hand tense with squeezing, her arm pumping. It was as close as I had ever been to coming without touching myself or being touched.

Then the light turned green, and she took off, but fast. I was so distracted with horniness that I almost lost her. Driving is very competitive on that road. But her Chevy, hot as it was, was no match for my Jaguar, and I was soon next to her again. She stared straight ahead, swaying and lip-synching the song "Lead Me On."

Soon she slowed down, and I kept pace. I realized she was stalling to catch the next light on red, which suited me fine. I was aching to see more of her act.

Stopping for the light, she lightly brushed her fingers up and down over "my" chest. I could still feel and respond directly to her motions. I was so horny that I could feel the skin on my balls crawling.

Then she began to tease that invisible cock that I imagined so vividly was my own. She bent her fingers and held them in a tube shape, sliding them up and down around the shaft. She raised her hand, placing her fingertips around the head and gently kneading it. She formed a circle with her thumb and forefinger, and slid the circle up and down, spiraling around the shaft. She stroked it lightly with the backs of her long, shiny, pink fingernails. She cupped the invisible balls, weighed them, toyed with them.

I was gripping my steering wheel, afraid to touch my rampant prick, lest I shoot come all over the windshield or onto my face. It was like being tied up by my own willpower. All the fun but no release. Besides, I was saving up my jism in the fervent hope that I could get a lot closer to this hot pussycat in the hot pussy car.

The light was almost ready to change. Her left hand again took on the shape of a filled fist, and she moved it up and down, twice slowly and then three times fast. The light changed, and she floored her gas pedal again. I was amazed that she could concentrate so well on driving while putting on a sex show at the same time.

We sailed through the next few lights. I stuck like glue to her, while she pretended to ignore me. A couple of times, though, I nearly caught her eye. I was sure she wanted to pick me up.

At the next red light, she maneuvered carefully so we would be first in line. As we pulled up and stopped, she took a candy bar from her handbag and quickly unwrapped it. It was a Sugar Daddy, caramel on a stick. Now her hand and her mouth were both very busy.

She started by licking on the long, narrow, hard sweet. Then she nibbled on the end of it. Soon she was pushing it in and out of her mouth, deep-throating it, stopping now and then to suck on the tip of it or to draw circles on it with her stiff, pointed tongue. It was the first phantom blow job I'd ever had, and I wanted it to go on forever. My cock and balls were so full of hot, heady jism that it was an effort of will for me not to shoot my load. I kept holding myself off, though, mostly so I wouldn't miss any of the show.

Her hand was a blur. In contrast to the smooth, even rhythm of the sweet stick in her mouth and the music coming from her car, her hand was moving in the fast, uneven tempo of a terrific orgasm.

Suddenly, the fistful got smaller and she dropped it. Then her hand rubbed make-believe jism all over the car door. Now, though, in my imagination, the door had big round tits with long nipples; I could see her playing with them as she massaged the door with her hand.

I looked at her face. She had shoved that Sugar Daddy clear down her throat and was gobbling and moaning. She jerked a few times on the candy and pulled it out of her mouth, slightly bent and much smaller than when it had gone in.

Then, still without looking at me, she tossed the half-eaten candy bar right into my lap. My cock throbbed and reared at the unexpected touch, and for the third time I had to concentrate to keep from coming. When I looked at her, she winked again, beckoned, and peeled out.

I stayed right beside her until she turned off onto a residential street. Then I followed her to a house set back among some trees. She parked her car and waited until I pulled in behind her and opened her door for her.

As for what we did in that house that night, and many nights since, perhaps more later.—*C.D., Langhorne, Pennsylvania*

FUCKING COUPLE SIGHTED—SEX SPREADS

I've always thought of fantasies as my way of "experiencing" things that are somewhat beyond the possible, of enjoying feelings that most people never really feel. What happened to me one recent Sunday morning has altered the threshold of reality so much that I'm afraid there is nothing left to fantasize about.

My wife, Julie, and I got up early to drive to a state park we had never visited before. It was a perfect early autumn morning,

crisp and clear. The prospects were good for spectacular fall fo-
liage, so we packed our camera and hit the road before seven.
Ours was the only car in the parking lot when we started hik-
ing down the main trail at about eight-thirty.

We spent the first hour of our hike so deeply absorbed in the
sights and sounds of the park that we hardly spoke, except to
whisper our delight at seeing a doe on the path ahead of us—
or to call attention to a spiderweb that glistened with dew in the
morning sunlight. By ten o'clock, I had shot my first roll of film
and was looking for a place to reload. Wandering along a deserted loop trail, we found a rough-hewn bench and sat down.

It soon became obvious that Julie's interest in nature had gone
beyond the picture-taking stage. As I reloaded the camera, I felt
her lips brushing my cheek and the side of my neck. The more
I concentrated on getting the new roll of film started, the more
insistent her needs became. When she started tickling the inside
of my ear with the tip of her tongue, I couldn't stand it any
longer. I put down my camera and told Julie that she was about
to get the fuck of her life.

We began to undress each other very slowly as if we wanted
to make every move last as long as possible. We stood there on
a cool, mossy carpet with only our underpants on. Julie slowly
pressed her tits against my chest. Her breasts are large and firm,
but they're also long and just pendulous enough so that they
swayed from side to side as she moved her slender body toward
me.

While she cupped the straining pouch of my jockey shorts in
her hand, I pressed one finger firmly against the bulge of her
panties, feeling her warm fluids soak through the thin material.
And she let me know how it felt, with a wonderful sigh of pleasure that echoed against the trees of our little clearing in the forest.

As if this perfect scene weren't enough, the real excitement
was just beginning. I caught a glimpse of movements as I looked
over her shoulder. There, no more than twenty yards down the

path, came an attractive couple, a little older than we are (probably in their mid-thirties) and a teenage girl. They were looking right at us. I instinctively averted my eyes. I'm sure Julie didn't notice a thing, because she kept saying how good my finger felt. The man walking toward us grabbed the arms of the two females and pulled them back around the turn in the path and out of sight.

After a minute or so, just as I was beginning to regain my composure, the three of them, all looking transfixed, appeared again and just stood there in the path. I couldn't believe that they didn't know I'd seen them. The woman stood behind and to the side of the girl, holding the girl's arm with both hands, as if to keep her from turning away, and the man stood behind both of them.

As the reality of the situation began to soak in, I got more and more excited about it. The better the show we could put on for them, the better I liked the idea, as long as I could keep Julie facing the other way, so she wouldn't know we were being observed.

I didn't seem to be having any trouble keeping her attention. When I knelt in front of her and pulled her soaked panties down, she immediately raised one foot to the bench and placed her hands behind my head, drawing my lips and tongue right into her gaping pussy. Her juices were streaming down the inside of her thighs in clear, slippery flows that soon inundated my cheeks and chin.

I ran my dripping tongue down her soft inner thigh, just to get another good look down the path. They were still there, and I don't think it was my imagination that all three of them looked more than a little hot and bothered. The young girl—I'd say a well-gifted fifteen-year-old—was rhythmically shifting her weight from one long slender leg to the other. If I'd been a little closer, I'm sure I could have seen a growing spot on her shorts between those well-shaped thighs. The woman kept glancing back at her husband, who looked transfixed, wishing his tongue were my tongue.

I went back to work on Julie's bottom again, and by the urging her hands conveyed to my head, I knew she was about to come. As I nipped and sucked at the tip of her big clit, her rhythmic sighs grew to unashamed cries of pleasure, which filled the forest around us for a minute or more. While I buried my face in Julie's sopping cunt, her secretions flooded down my neck and chest.

I abandoned all restraint and had Julie sit with her legs straddling the bench. I could feel the heaviness of my cock and balls swinging freely. Apparently, our spectators were impressed by the size of my hard-on, because I saw them all exchange incredulous glances.

Julie and I shifted position, and I whispered to her in detail what I was about to do to her. I made her lean back and then I sucked her luscious tits until her nipples were crimson shafts, almost three-fourths of an inch long.

We sat facing each other on the bench, and I helped her raise her gaping crotch up to the tense, purple head of my cock. I felt like a cannon about to go off! She kept telling me what a big boy I was (she always tells me that when I'm about to fuck her). Then she lowered herself slowly into my lap and, looking down to watch, impaled herself with several delicious squatting thrusts. I leaned back and watched, too, as inch by inch, her puckering inner lips engulfed my rigid staff. It had always been a pretty tight fit for Julie and me before, but this day she was so ripe that she could have taken a stud horse to the hilt.

Again, Julie's sweet cries carried in the cool air, and between her cries, I'm sure, our friends could hear the soft, wet, slopping sounds we were making.

Looking over Julie's shoulder, I could see the young girl was nearly beside herself. Her right hand was now buried inside her shorts. The woman's head rested back against her husband's chest, her eyes glued to us. Her pleasure was no secret, either, as he cupped her breasts in his hands. If I could have done it without Julie knowing, I would have invited them to come over and stand right next to us for the best possible view.

It seemed as if Julie's orgasm lasted several minutes this time. Her thighs pistoned her eager hips up high enough so that the huge blossom of my cock just rested between her lips, and then she would drop down to engulf its entire length again. Just as she seemed to be unwinding, she rose to her third climax—and over the next few minutes, she experienced yet another. She was absolutely insatiable. She just kept pumping and pumping, and our juices just kept pouring out, soaking our legs and the bench supporting us.

All the time, I feasted my eyes on the young girl, now trembling in the throes of her own orgasm. The couple didn't touch her at all, but they were sure interested. I don't think they knew whether to keep watching us or her. She had managed to lower her shorts and panties, but only to her knees. The poor thing looked as if she couldn't spread her legs far enough apart.

Meanwhile, Julie continued to come. This time, I was with her. I couldn't imagine how she had anything left to give, but it was the biggest climax yet. We were both screaming as we gushed our final release.

By the time we got up to get dressed, our spectators had ducked out of sight. I knew they'd eventually have to pass our bench to get back to the parking lot. As Julie and I walked slowly off, I looked back. All I could see was the bench, with a soaked spot right in the middle.

I would have given anything to hear what was said in their car as our friends rode home. I wouldn't be at all surprised if they had stopped to reenact the melodrama they had just seen.—*Name and address withheld*

BUSINESSMAN SHOWS OFF HIS COCK TO WOMEN, AND JERKS IT OFF, TOO

I am an attractive, successful, thirty-three-year-old businessman who, for the past fifteen years, has enjoyed showing my prick and balls to women. In this time, I have shown my privates to at least three hundred women. With looks ranging from quick glances to longing stares accompanied by full masturbation, women have viewed my dick in parks, libraries, college dorms, apartment buildings, theaters, cars, and on the street.

In college, I used to wear short cutoffs, torn up the sides, and no underwear. I'd go to the library and sit across from a sexy girl, letting her see my cock. Sometimes, I'd quietly masturbate while she watched. Whenever I was invited to a girl's room to study, I'd lie on the bed with my knees up and legs apart. When this happened, the only thing these girls studied was my penis. They always carefully positioned themselves to stare right at it.

After college, I rented a room across from a hospital. One night, I got so horny watching the nurses that I just had to let them see my erect penis. With the lights on and window shades up, I walked around nude until I'd caught the attention of two young nurses. When I saw them sneaking looks at me, I lay on the bed with a pillow on my chest, which I pretended was a girl, and masturbated.

The nurses stood at the window with big smiles, watching me as I slowly stroked my cock and shot my load into the air. The next night, the same nurses were staring out of the hospital window, waiting for me to repeat the performance, but I didn't oblige.

I've also lived across from female exhibitionists and frequently masturbated while they dressed or walked around nude. One woman loved to exercise in the nude and then to masturbate while lying belly-down on the bed, with her hands buried in her snatch. Many times, I jerked off wildly as I watched her.

My favorite episode occurred last spring. I was in my car, smoking a joint and reading *Penthouse Letters,* several blocks away from a local high school. I looked up, and saw three girls walking toward me. There was a brunet with large breasts, a sleek blonde with firm, medium breasts and a tight ass, and a beautiful Oriental girl with small breasts and long, straight hair. They all wore designer jeans and tight blouses.

I got out of the car and ducked behind a tree. As they passed my car and saw the open magazine on the seat, I heard them giggle. I was already stroking myself when they walked past the tree, all smiles and whispers. As they continued walking down the street, the sight of their swaying young asses was more than I could take. Without a second's hesitation, I dropped my pants and undershorts, fell to my knees, and started beating off like crazy, trying to come before they got too far away.

Suddenly, the blonde and the Oriental turned around and sat down, looking straight at me from only about thirty feet away. The brunet took a few more steps and then glanced back over her shoulder, giving me a profile of her luscious breasts. I continued pumping my pecker, somewhat more slowly, while they watched, fascinated. The brunet just gaped, while the blonde and Oriental talked and giggled, until I finally shot my load all over the grass in front of me.

The blonde then teasingly called down, "Did you get off OK?"—even though she knew I had. I said yes, and stood up to show them my full seven-and-a-half-incher, with its head still glistening with come. The brunet let out a little squeal. I couldn't tell if she was shocked or delighted. The three of them then continued on their way, laughing and glancing back at me as I pulled up my shorts. I can only wonder what they said about me.

I've had numerous other experiences, and I hope to have lots more. So, girls, stay alert. If you should see me, relax, have fun, and enjoy the show. And, needless to say, if you want something more, don't be too shy to ask. I'd love to fulfill your fantasies, too.—*Name and address withheld*

CINDI GETS BAWLED OUT—AND BALLED OUT, TOO

I am an assistant cook at a fairly large California restaurant. As an avid reader of *Penthouse Letters,* I would like to relate an experience that I had about a month ago.

It happened after I had spent the best part of three hours putting away new stock that had come in that morning. I had the place very tidy when Cindi, a waitress, came into the storeroom. The uniforms worn by the waitresses here are made to bring out the girls' best features, and Cindi is one of the most beautiful girls working in the place. Her beautifully shaped thighs lead up to a wonderful ass that is almost exposed whenever she bends over. Her tits are perfectly shaped, with large nipples that can be seen pressing against the thin fabric of her blouse. Her gorgeous face is complemented by her long blond hair.

As she walked into the storeroom, she asked where the salad oil was. I pointed to it and, as she picked up the five-gallon container, I copped a look at her lovely bottom. No sooner had she picked it up than she dropped it. Five gallons of salad oil spilled all over the floor. In my anger, I forgot her luscious ass and began to yell at her about the mess she'd made. After several minutes of my scolding her, she covered her face and began to cry.

At this, I stopped my ranting and went over to her. I told her that I was sorry I'd lost my temper. With a sudden smile on her tear-stained face, Cindi began to massage my cock through my pants with one hand and untie the top of her uniform with the other.

I was stunned. It was a fantasy come true. Thinking fast, and being sure not to slip on the oil, I went to the door and locked the dead bolt. I returned to find Cindi totally nude. After I quickly took off my pants, we grasped each other and went into a deep French kiss. She had her hands all over my cock while I inserted two fingers into her warm love hole.

Breaking off our kiss, we fell to the oil-slicked floor in a 69 position. It was hard to lie still in all that salad oil, but as I was slipping and sliding around, I knew I was going to come soon, and I managed to keep my tongue concentrated on her clit. We climaxed together, and Cindi gulped down every drop of my load. When we kissed again, she licked her juices from my smiling face. Playing with my limp rod, she soon had it at attention again. As I spread her legs, she scooped up some of the oil and lubricated my cock. I was about to enter her when she whispered, "Yell at me."

"What?"

"Fuck me, and yell at me like you did when I dropped the oil."

I shoved my rod into her hot twat and started to scold her and call her nasty names.

"Harder! Harder! Fuck me harder—and louder!" she gasped.

I slammed my balls against her cunt lips with exclamations of "You fucking bitch!" and "Stupid whore!" I lost my load—and my voice—when I soon experienced the best orgasm of my life.

Totally exhausted, I got a towel from one of the lockers and we quickly wiped the oil from our bodies before putting our clothes on. As we left the storeroom, we were met at the door by two other waitresses with curious looks on their faces.

Cindi later informed me that she had faked her crying in hopes that I would respond as I did. She told me that she had always wanted her husband to scream and talk dirty to her when they fucked, but that he wouldn't. Since the storeroom incident, I have masturbated Cindi in the employees' dining room while whispering dirty words to her. Next, she wants to try a fast fuck in the freezer! Has anybody else had any restaurant fun?—*Name and address withheld*

PUBIC-HAIR REMOVAL TURNS ON THEIR FRIENDS

I would like to share with your readers an adventure I had recently with my wife and her boyfriend. It all began when we had a talk about shaving her cunt, so we men could enjoy it more. She was, to put it mildly, reluctant as hell about letting us remove her pussy hair, which is very bushy. One day last month, however, she came to me with a proposition. She would let her boyfriend and me shave her cunt if she and he could first shave my entire body—and record the whole thing on film.

Needless to say, I got quite excited about making her pussy bald, but when it came to losing all my body hair, I thought twice. You see, I am an extremely hairy man, and everyone in our apartment complex has seen me in swimming trunks. What would they think if I showed up at the pool suddenly clean-shaven? Nevertheless, I decided to accept my wife's offer, but I insisted that a depilatory be used instead of a razor.

Unknown to me, when the appointed hour arrived, my wife had invited friends over to watch. I went into the bedroom, where I stripped and was then tied spread-eagle to the bed. Five naked couples were in the room, all eager to see their first de-pilated cock. My wife and her boyfriend applied the hair-removal spray carefully, being sure not to get any on the skin of my cock. About five minutes later they marched me off to the shower, from which I emerged as hairless as a babe. The effect of my new appearance on the audience was impressive. The women seemed especially fascinated by the sight of my unadorned cock. They proceeded to rub skin lotion all over my body.

After that, I had more sex than I have ever enjoyed in a single day. It was a dream come true. I had women sucking my cock, nipples and toes, while I ate the cunt of a friend's wife. For the next two days, women whom I barely knew were coming over and asking my wife if I could strip so they could see my hairless crotch. Word had gotten out, and for the next two weeks, almost everyone I knew mentioned something about my bald crotch.

Last weekend, after her boyfriend and I denuded my wife's pussy, we decided to have a party in the rec house by the pool. We invited fifteen couples over for drinks and a swim. The pool is located in the middle of the apartment complex, but at night, with the lights out, it is dark enough for nude swimming. When we finally got down to skinny-dipping, I discovered to my surprise that out of the fifteen couples, ten had hairless cocks and pussies. They said they had been inspired by my example.

I'm planning to keep any hair from growing out again around my penis, because I've been getting more sex—especially blow jobs—than ever before. I suggest that any man who is ready for something new should try the clean-shaven look. You will be amazed at how large your cock appears. Mine is only average (six and a half inches), but it looks much bigger now.—*J.F., Lansing, Michigan*

PTA Chairlady Gives Virgin Student a Hot Ride in Bottomless Chair

I admit my skepticism up to now, but I had an experience recently that has convinced me that your letters are true. I am a student at a local college, and am so shy that I've managed to get this far without having a single pleasant encounter with a member of the opposite sex. Every time a beautiful girl approaches me in a hallway, I break out into a cold sweat and become tongue-tied.

All that changed one day this summer. I was dressed only in my cutoffs and enjoying the sun at home in my backyard, when my mother announced she had a dentist's appointment but needed to deliver some papers to the chairlady of the PTA on the other side of town. She wanted to know if I could drop off the papers for her. My heart sank as I envisioned a wasted summer day.

The PTA chairlady had been to our house several times for committee meetings and I remembered her as a very curt, plainly dressed woman of about forty. She always wore her hair in a bun and spoke in clipped sentences. Although my mother and many of her friends seemed to like Mrs. Bartlett, with me she was all business.

When I arrived at the Bartletts', I noticed that Mr. Bartlett's pickup was nowhere to be seen, which is not that unusual since Mr. Bartlett has his own construction company and is often out of town. When nobody answered the doorbell, I went around the house to the pool to try to find Mrs. Bartlett. Imagine my surprise when I saw a voluptuous brunet in a white string bikini lying on her stomach, her skin glistening with suntan oil. At first I thought I had the wrong house, but when she sat up I realized that the heavenly body in front of me did indeed belong to Mrs. Bartlett. I broke out in my usual cold sweat, but I felt a distinct twinge in my groin. As she leaned forward to take the papers, she revealed the most beautiful set of tits I had ever seen.

Staring at the bulge in my pants, she thanked me and asked if I was enjoying my summer vacation. I stammered nervously that it was quite dull so far, and to my surprise she nodded her head in sympathy. With a suggestive smile she told me that sometimes people have to make their own fun and added that since her husband had been out of town for nearly two weeks, she herself was quite ready to do that. Without another word, she reached out and gently caressed my rock-hard nine-incher, which was beginning to peek out of the top of my cutoffs. I moaned in delight and just stared (one of her magnificent breasts had slipped out of her bikini). In a flash she had my shorts down around my ankles and had taken my entire penis into her warm, moist mouth. It was the first time I had ever experienced this pleasure, and I came almost immediately. I thought I would never stop, yet she greedily swallowed every last drop of my virgin love juice.

Now I was at a loss for what to do. But Mrs. Bartlett took charge. Still licking her lips, she instructed me to lie flat on my back on her beach towel. I did so, watching in amazement as she slipped out of her bikini to reveal a perfectly shaved pussy. Next, she straddled my face, and not knowing what to do but enjoying the scent, I decided to explore the treasure that had been presented to me. I felt her body shake as my tongue darted nervously into her steaming cunt, and I heard her gasp with delight when I found the love button that I'd previously only read about in textbooks. Now she began moving her hips violently and grinding her pussy lips into my hungry mouth. Before long she was crying, "Oh, my darling, eat me! Oh, yes! Yes! Faster!"

I sensed that she was on the verge of orgasm, so I ran my tongue rapidly across her clit, at which she let out a yell and fell off of me in complete exhaustion. As we lay there panting, I noticed to my delight that my cock was once again standing at attention. This time I knew exactly what to do. I knelt between her legs but, to my surprise, she told me to wait. Her fragrant juices running down her tan thighs, she took my hand and led me into the house.

As she led me up the stairs to the bedroom, she told me she had a special surprise for me, and in her bedroom I saw it right away: In the corner of the room a basketlike chair was suspended from the ceiling by pulleys. She told me coyly to lie underneath the odd-looking contraption, which I did. As she climbed into the seat, my anticipation grew, and with it the size of my tool. She instructed me to spin the basket and use the rope beside me to raise and lower it. I noticed then that her pussy was positioned directly over a hole in the bottom of the basket, and my curiosity was satisfied.

I gave the basket a spin and started to lower it slowly. When the head of my cock touched her spinning, dripping cunt, sending electric shocks through my body, she moaned. I spun the basket once more and lowered it further, watching the dark nipples on her heaving breasts swell in excitement. The sensation was beyond anything I had ever imagined. Feeling a surge in my groin, I gave the basket a final spin and lowered it all the way. That's when she begged me to fuck her like she had never been fucked before. I then pulled on the rope in short jerks, making her cunt engage and release my cock time and time again.

Her moans turned to short gasping yelps and my own climax

approached. I arched my back and had the greatest orgasm ever and she too lost control, her fingers gripping the side of the basket as she begged for more. I thought I would black out by the time my orgasm was over. Mrs. Bartlett was now screaming at the top of her lungs with animal-like abandon. The basket came slowly to a stop and my now withering cock slipped out of her. After we had recovered enough to stand on our feet, we took a slow sensuous shower together.

As a result of my initiation into the realm of fantastic sex, my mother has never had to worry about getting her reports delivered to Mrs. Bartlett on time.—*Name and address withheld*

SEX SHIFTS INTO HIGH AS WOMAN DISCOVERS NEW MODE OF "AUTO" EROTICISM

Almost three years ago my husband and I shared an experience that we both very much enjoyed and that we haven't ever read about in *Penthouse Letters*. At that time we'd just begun living together and I discovered that he really got off by watching me masturbate and by stimulating me with miscellaneous objects—candles, a dildo, even a large cucumber that he inserted into my cunt.

Because my husband is a construction worker, he often drives to company meetings. I've accompanied him on the tedious six-hour drive, which we find more enjoyable if it is alleviated with sex games.

For example, we were returning home one summer evening and he told me to take off my jeans. I quickly did, excited at the prospect of playtime. Then he instructed me to sit very close to him. As I moved over on the seat, he slipped his hand under me, fingered my clit and slipped his fingers inside. I was so turned on that I begged him to pull off the road, but he laughingly told me, "Not yet." Then he half-lifted me off the seat. I cooperated as he pressed my pubic bone and then my clit against the vibrating four-speed floor shift. I came almost immediately. It was great. The road was slightly bumpy, and the gearshift transmitted all the vibrations very pleasantly. I climaxed once more, and then he lifted my ass up higher. I felt his thick, strong fingers part my labia, slide deep inside me and then out again. He repositioned me slightly, and I felt the smooth, wide gearshift knob, dampened with my wetness, pressing against my labia and then sliding into me.

Still driving down the highway at a steady fifty-five miles per hour, he began rhythmically stroking my clit, and as my wetness increased, the gearshift knob slid further inside me. It was tremendous—the feel of his fingers on my clit, the size and pressure of the knob, the continuous vibrations. The sensation was so unbelievably wonderful that I had a stupendous wave of orgasms, peak after peak, each one more intense and lasting longer. I must have enjoyed twenty orgasms as he continued to drive and play with me. I was lost in waves of delight, moaning and writhing, screaming out my pleasure. I barely noticed as he turned off the highway down a dark country road. After helping me disengage myself, he parked the truck. I unzipped his pants and caressed his huge erection with my mouth. I felt it deep in my throat, but after a couple of strokes, he turned me away from him. I knelt on my hands and knees as he penetrated me with smooth, deep strokes, and I climaxed five or six times before he filled me with come.

Unfortunately, his company has now provided him with a more modern truck—one with an automatic transmission—which has taken some of the fun out of our trips. I hope that my husband will succeed in finding just what he's looking for—in time for our next vacation—an older, ratty jeep or four-speed pickup!— *L.R., Silver City, New Mexico*

Editors' note: Despite L.R.'s high praise of gearshift knobs as pussy stimulators, we would discourage women from doing what she says she's done. It can be dangerous, especially in a moving vehicle.

ONLY PANTY-CLAD COCKS GET NEAR HER BOX

I am a twenty-seven-year-old graduate student in my second year at a southern university. Moving here from Boston has been a big adjustment for me. However, I have found a small diversion that has made the adjustment much easier.

A while ago I discovered three things about myself: One, I don't get off from balling; two, I love cunnilingus—I would rather have a guy's tongue in me than his cock anytime; three, the one thing I do like about a man's cock is the way it feels through a silky, sexy fabric. I discovered this a couple of years ago with a boyfriend who wore nylon briefs.

After I was settled in my new home, I decided to take charge of my sex life—have it go my way. Some of the young under-graduate boys at the university are easy prey; I am pretty and have a nice figure, so I can turn these boys on like a lamp. I like to dress up and go out and find a nice-looking prospect to take back to my apartment.

After we have a few drinks, I remove my dress and stroll around in my slip, nylons and high heels. As soon as I have my boy panting for my bod, I sit down and prop my legs up so that my slip slides up, revealing my stockings, garter belt and bush. Needless to say, by this time I have my boy's undivided attention.

Next, I start masturbating myself until I am dripping wet with anticipation. The boy is almost going crazy at this point; I love to see his hard cock bulging in his pants, ready for action. I go to him, rub his cock through his pants and suggest that we go into the bedroom, where I tell him to strip.

The boy will almost always leap out of his clothes. I rub up against him and kiss him a few times. When he is almost frantic to get his meat in my oven, I take a pair of my panties out of a drawer and explain my fetish. Very few boys have refused to put them on.

Next, we get on the bed in a 69 position. I guide his head to my dripping bush and tell him to kiss it. I begin to rub his cock and balls through my panties, which really churns him up. Usually, he'll start eating pussy like it's going out of style. Now I am ready to cut loose, so I clamp my legs around his head, get a firm grip on his cock and balls, and start humping his sweet lips and tongue.

After I've come as many times as I can, I tell him that I'm too exhausted to ball and that I think he should leave and come back another time. Of course, sometimes the boy will come in my panties while I'm humping his face. I really like that because I love the feel of his squirting cock in my hand, and I particularly love the look on his face when I tell him he must wash out my panties before he leaves or he can't come back. I have never had anyone refuse this little request.

I have been getting off like this about twice a week now for nearly a year. What amazes me most is that I have several repeaters. I don't know what it is—maybe the fresh air—but the South certainly is number one when it comes to cunt-lappers. Little did I think when I came down here that things would work out so well.

Recently, I took in a roommate to cut down on expenses. I told her about my "hobby." She didn't believe me until she hid in my closet one evening and saw for herself. We're now planning to team up and get double duty from our catches.—*M.A.K., Jackson, Mississippi*

TWO GUYS GIVE SWEET BUTTERFLY SIPS OF THEIR LOVE NECTAR

My childhood sweetheart and I were married five years ago while still in our teens. So far we haven't had any children. Karen, who looks a lot like Marlo Thomas, is still a student at the University of Washington. She often wears boy's jeans or cords, with tennis shoes and a shirt, sweater or sweatshirt. When we are out together, however, she leans toward far more provocative apparel. Her favorite dress is a calf-length silk print with a very low, scooped neckline. When she moves in a certain manner, her neckline falls aside, totally exposing one or the other of her breasts. This often occurs while she casually studies a menu with the waiter looking on or while getting out of our car, or at a cocktail party. She has average-size breasts but they are round and high, with pointed tips that look too good to be real.

One day on the tennis court I noticed that she had an appreciative audience of four young guys seated on the ground behind her. While facing away from me, she bent down to retrieve a ball. Then I saw that under her short tennis dress she was wearing panties that consisted of only small triangles in front and back, with a seam that disappeared between the cheeks of her pert ass. That was the end of play for us, for I got such an erection that I was unable to continue.

We were both virgins when we first went to bed together, and only once have we ever thought it desirable to include another person in our sex life—our good friend Ron. Besides me and Ron, the only man ever to see Karen's naked crotch was a tattoo artist some years ago. As an anniversary present to me, she'd shaven her pubic hair and had a butterfly tattooed above her cunt. She admitted to having had two small climaxes while the artist worked on her, sitting between her legs with his mouth only inches from her slit. Gently he'd stretched and twisted her tenderest flesh to create the butterfly design. When he'd finished, as he was rubbing antiseptic lotion on her, he dipped one finger between her pussy lips and said he would waive his fee if she would have sex with him. With his finger still penetrating her, she had a shattering orgasm, then paid him and left. Her pubic hair has grown back, but it is so sparse and fine that you can see her pink lips and the butterfly through it.

The thing with Ron happened a few weeks ago when he and I returned from a three-day fishing trip and found Karen asleep. It was rather late. I have known Ron since we were children, and he and Karen are more like brother and sister than just friends. He was to spend the night sleeping on our couch. It only seemed natural, however, that he should follow me into my king-size bed. All Karen did was slide up next to me and rest her head on my chest.

A few minutes later, when Ron's breathing suggested he was asleep, Karen started nibbling my nipples and lightly stroked my cock. After a few minutes of this, I slipped her gown up above her breasts and positioned myself on top of her. I entered her in one long, well-lubricated stroke. She was moving very slowly and sleepily and making soft sighs and whimpering sounds. Ron was lying on his back when I placed Karen's hand on his large, soft cock. She left her hand there, motionless, and I placed my hand on top of hers. Intertwining my fingers with hers, I started making a slow circular motion. Ron's softness began to harden. He soon raised his hips to help as I rolled his bikini shorts down to just below his balls. I pulled my cock out of Karen and repositioned her on her side facing Ron before I entered her again, this time from the rear. I was moving slowly in and out of her as she pushed against me and gently stroked Ron's groin. I reached over her and encircled the base of his tumescent member with my thumb and forefinger, cradling his balls with the rest of my hand. Karen then leaned down and took his impressive hard-on in her mouth. Everything seemed to be happening in slow motion, as in a dream.

I felt Ron's penis throb and heave as he shot off in Karen's mouth. She followed immediately with her own orgasm, quickening her movements as I released into her. She turned to me with a long, wet kiss so she could share Ron's hot jism with me. Karen and I then fell asleep in each other's arms with her head tucked against my chest.

A few hours later I woke to the feel of her soft, wet lips sliding up and down my penis. There was also a very masculine hand rubbing me around my balls and a gentle rocking motion coming from behind Karen. I needn't detail our lovemaking further, except to say that I'll always be grateful for having such a sexy and adoring wife and a wonderful, loving friend.—*R.P., Tacoma, Washington*

IT WAS A LONG TIME COMING, BUT WOMAN FINALLY EXPERIENCES THE BIG O

I am an attractive twenty-six-year-old divorced woman who once told a friend that I would never write to *Penthouse Letters* until I'd had my first orgasm. Since I'm writing now, you already have an idea of what this letter is about!

Although I enjoyed an active sex life with my ex-husband while we were married, I never managed to have an orgasm. Since my divorce a year ago, I have shared my bed with several loving, handsome men, each of whom made it his personal mission to be the first to bring me off. While I certainly enjoyed their special attention and the pleasurable sensations it brought, they failed in their mission. I was beginning to think I was doomed to go through life that way. Until two weeks ago, that is.

That's when a friend, who manages an athletic club, invited me to a private party there. Although I was sure I wouldn't know anyone at the party, I decided to go. When I arrived, I saw that there were over one hundred guests—noisy, high, having a great time. We had the run of the place, which covers several blocks. Guests wandered about the tennis courts, racquetball courts and pool. I grabbed a drink at the open bar and started to mingle.

After I'd been at the party for over an hour and downed several drinks, I decided to explore the main building. I found that beyond the racquetball courts were several large weight-training rooms. The rooms appeared deserted. As I strolled into one of them to examine the equipment, I heard a deep, sexy voice say, "How much can you handle?" I whirled around and was startled to see a good-looking guy whom I'd noticed earlier at the bar. He was sitting cross-legged on a mat, flashing a charming grin at me. He stood up and came over to me. We began to talk while walking slowly around the room, sipping our drinks. When we passed a massage table, I noticed a rectangular object, about the size of a man's hand, and asked what it was.

He smiled and replied, "It's an athletic vibrator." Immediately, he slipped his hand under the strap, turned it on, and ran the humming machine across his face and neck. "It feels good," he said. "You ought to try it."

With that, he began to massage my shoulders and neck with the pulsing machine. My first inclination was to pull away, but it felt so good that I let him continue. He began to whisper soothingly to me as he moved the vibrator across my tired muscles. "Feel how it relaxes you?" he said. "I can see all the tension leaving your body. I can see your beautiful body relaxing—melting—relaxing." I felt like I was in a trance as I closed my eyes and leaned back against the massage table.

He began to move the vibrator up my arm, across my shoulders, and then to my breasts. I could feel my nipples pressing against my light sweater with an excitement I couldn't control. I felt a tingle between my legs, and suddenly realized that my panties were dripping with my own passion juices.

He slowly eased the vibrator from my throbbing breasts to my wet pussy. At his first touch there I let out a moan, and I heard him whisper, "Relax, let me massage you. I know all the right places." He pulled up my skirt, gently removed my soaked panties and placed me upon the massage table. With the vibrator he caressed my helpless, throbbing pussy while his free hand explored my breasts and he sucked and licked my erect nipples. My whole body was bursting with incredibly pleasant sensations.

Then, confident of my readiness, he put down the vibrator and inserted his throbbing dick into my eager pussy. His dick was so hard that it hurt me at first, but with each thrust I felt a more intense desire come over my body. I began to moan and toss my head from side to side. He grabbed my hair and pulled my face up to his and thrust his tongue into my open mouth.

He ran it across my teeth, along the roof of my mouth, and then he thrust his whole mouth against mine until our teeth clashed. His hand was on my breast, sometimes gentle, sometimes rougher. I became aware of a sustained wailing sound and was startled to realize it was coming from my own mouth!

His strokes became faster and faster, and he positioned himself so that each thrust sent a delicious wave through my trembling clit. I began to see colors behind my closed eyelids. All of a sudden I felt something strange rising in me. It was as if a powerful surge were rushing up through my body from my cunt. In panic I tried to pull away from him, but he shoved me back down. "You can't stop it now!" he snapped hoarsely. No sooner did these words leave his lips than the wave engulfed me—my body jerked and convulsed, and my arms went wild. I screamed and pulled at his hair, and then I felt him jerk and moan above me as he shot his wad deep into my cunt.

Since that wonderful night we have shared the same bed every evening. He thinks I am the sexiest, most responsive woman he has ever met. I haven't yet told him my secret—that he is the only man who's ever made me come—but I will sometime soon.—*Name and address withheld*

Domination & Discipline

Denial and Discipline Spice Up Sex

Even though we've been married fourteen years, my husband and I have a fantastic and ever-changing sex life. Let me share one of our favorite scenes.

We fantasize that I am his captured slave. First, we have a cleansing ritual. I'm not allowed to move as he soaps, rinses and roughly rubs me so that I am clean enough for my master. He is especially diligent toweling my crotch and clit. All the while, he tells me what a bitch I am, how I have failed him, and how my body belongs to him to do with what he wants.

"Isn't that right?" as he flicks my left nipple.

"No," I answer. So he squeezes, gently at first, then harder, harder until I'm on my knees whispering, "Yes, Master."

Then I am pulled and dragged to the bedroom where I stand naked in my shame. Taking an old tie from the closet, he binds my hands behind me. My master then takes out our special earrings. One earring is screwed on to each nipple, not too tightly at first, but then tighter and tighter. The delicious pinching brings me to my knees. Then he pushes my legs apart with his knee and shoves me backward, with my legs still bent at the knees behind me. He now separates my cunt lips and puts in place the third earring—tightening it on my clit. I squirm and writhe as he works my clit, now squeezing, now pressing and rotating. My complaints just make him screw the earrings tighter. Then, using his hard knuckles, he works in rhythmic circles toward my cunt lips. There, he manipulates two or three knuckles round and round and up into my hole—just enough to have me want to be filled—but never quite filling me. I want to pull my knees together and squeeze them, but he keeps them shoved apart and doesn't quite let me come.

Then he reaches over and grabs me by the hair, shoving his bare foot in my face. He makes me kiss his feet and suck his toes. I want him in my mouth so badly now, but he makes me beg first and tell him how much I want to suck him and lick his balls. Finally, I am allowed to suck and he forces his prick down my throat. I am on my knees now, with my ass in the air. He takes our paddle and rubs it on my ass, teasing, rotating, telling me what will come. He makes me beg to be hit. He prolongs my impatience by raising and lowering the paddle. Each time I shudder and cringe, anticipating the hard whacks. This makes him hotter. Finally, he smacks my ass several times, with each smack thrusting his cock down my gagging throat. Then, off come all the gadgets and we fuck like crazy.

We would love to hear from anyone else who enjoys a little bondage, a little female submission and just a little pain with their pleasure.—*Name and address withheld*

SLAVING FOR AN "A"

I'd like to tell you of a learning experience I had. I had to study for a big final exam which dealt with twelve chapters of vocabulary words and meanings. So I asked my girlfriend, Sandy, if she could help me study. When I told her I didn't know any of the words, she was mad at me for not going to class. But later in the evening, after she had been reading a *Penthouse* letter about "female rapists," she said she would help me. But I would have to agree to any rules she made. Being as desperate to pass as I was, I readily agreed.

She said that I would learn my vocabulary through a reward and punishment system. When she told me this, I was dying to fuck her right there and then. But she was more interested in my learning the words, so she told me not to change the subject, and that meant no fucking around. Besides, I knew she was planning something for the next evening, a lesson that I now know I would never forget.

The rest of the evening was just an appetizer. She grabbed my hand and led me to our bedroom, stripped me naked, tied me to the bed, and made me eat her out. I also had to sleep like that so I would be totally horny and up for the next evening's "lesson."

The next afternoon I picked her up from work and to my delight she was wearing a black shift, black seamed nylons and black high heels, which I love. She told me to move over and said that she was going to drive. She reminded me that I had agreed to go by all her rules. While she was driving, she told me to unzip my pants, which I promptly did. She then drove to a store to buy another pair of black seamed nylons because the others were ripped. As she left the car, she commanded me to pull my pants down to my ankles. She told me that I had better be like that when she came back because she wanted to humiliate me and embarrass me in case anyone should walk by the car. She told me that I would have to stay like that until we got to the motel. Naturally I obeyed.

When we got to the motel room, she said that I was a naughty boy, and would be taught a lesson. I was to do everything she ordered and be her slave. She gave me my notebook of vocabulary words and told me to study while she took a shower. I was going to be quizzed on them later. After she got out of the shower, she put on her seamed nylons (garter included), black five-inch spike-heeled shoes, and wide black belt. She also put on a black-laced bra. She then told me to remove my clothes.

She made me put on a pair of black panty hose. She had cut a
hole in them so part of my cock hung out. Then she tied long
pieces of cloth to my hands, and tied the cloth together. She ordered me to get down on my knees and kiss her high heels. She
knew how much I enjoy her feet. After I kissed every inch of
her feet and her spiked heels, she made me kiss my way up her
nylons—without touching her pussy. Then she bent over in front
of me and made me kiss her ass and tell her she had the nicest
ass I'd ever seen (which she does).

She stood up and said, "Now the lesson will begin, you naughty
student." She pushed me onto the bed, put my hands over my
head and tied them to the corner of the bed. I was lying faceup
so that she could tickle my ribs and chest with her long fingernails. She had also left the panty hose on me so that my
aching prick would be encased in its own type of bondage. Next,
she tied my feet together, making sure she touched the bottoms
of them with her fingernails, in order to show me that I had
lost all control. Another string was tied around my thighs and
yet another around my knees, so that I was completely at her
mercy.

Sandy told me she was now going to ask me vocabulary words,
but first she laid out some rules. For every three I got wrong I
would be punished. I would be either tickled on the ribs, get a
hard brush rubbed against my nipples, or if I pleaded and begged
enough, I only would have to lick her ass or pussy as punishment. She told me I would get a hard-on, but that if I was going
to come, I had better let her know. If at any time my hard-on
was to fall, she would lick it back up to attention. She added
that every time I got more than ten words in a row wrong she
would suck on my toes, as she knows I hate to be tickled that
way. Then she said that if I got five in a row right I would be
rewarded by getting my prick licked—but only the portions of
my prick that were not encased in her panty hose. The only way
I could take the panty hose off was either to get two chapters
correct, or to satisfy her with my tongue and drink all of her

pussy juices. In either case, the panty hose would only be removed an inch at a time. So, at best, it would take me twelve chapters or six of her orgasms, to get the panty hose off my aching prick. In either case I still wouldn't be able to come, even after I had finished the requirements, unless she let me. However, she told me that if I was very good about licking her ass and pussy in the way she liked, she would remove her panty hose from my cock at the rate of one inch per chapter, but that I would have to beg her appropriately and also that she would spank me until my whole ass was red. If I protested while I was being spanked, I would have to spend the whole night without coming.

Suddenly, she roughly ripped the panty hose off my body, tied my legs spread eagle to the corners of the bed and said that it was even better for her to play with my anus! By this time I was so horny that I begged her to let me have this new alternative. The whole time I was begging, she just laughed and tickled me with her nails. Finally she agreed, and let me lick her ass, which I did to the best of my ability.

The lesson finally began with her asking me questions and rewarding or punishing me appropriately. If she got really angry with me for not knowing the words, she flipped me over and spanked me without my being able to utter a complaint.

Well, I finally learned my words and Sandy had a hell of a time spilling her juices all over me and teasing my helpless prick. She loves to have me tied up and horny, totally obedient, answering to her every order. As you can guess, by the end of the night, I was doing everything that Sandy ordered to her specifications. Needless to say, I got an A on the test and another A in obedience from my newfound "Master Sandra."—*Name and address withheld*

PUNISHMENT WITHOUT MEASURE IS
HIS CONSTANT PLEASURE

I am a thirty-five-year-old male who has become the completely feminized slave of my mistress/wife. This morning, before she left for work, my mistress shackled me into my punishment chair (in the backyard utility shed) and ordered me to remain here until I wrote to you to tell the world of my enslavement and degradation.

I am, as I have been for the past six months, dressed as a woman. I'm wearing a bra, a waist-slimming corset, garters, stockings, painfully tight spike shoes, a slip, a frilly chiffon dress, a blond wig, earrings, and the chastity device I was fitted with five months ago. The chastity device, which is truly devilish in design, resulted from my mistress's noticing a semen stain on my panties.

My penis, which Mistress insists I refer to as my "pussy," is encased in an openended length of plastic hose and tucked back between my legs. The hose is attached to a molded-rubber support that is shaped like a vagina, and the entire assemblage is locked in place with quarter-inch steel cable. The tightness and smoothness of the plastic hose keeps me in a constant state of erotic arousal, although denying me fulfillment. I am required to wear a sanitary napkin to absorb any discharge of semen.

Mistress often squirts baby oil inside the tube (reducing all friction), and has me do deep-knee bends until my arousal makes me shake violently. Then she straps my head between her legs, keeping it there until I have brought her to satisfaction, which sometimes takes hours.

The chastity device requires me to sit down to urinate. Mistress controls my bowel movements by releasing the locked butt cable once every other morning for my enemas. This takes less than ten minutes and is closely supervised by her. I am not permitted to touch or even look at my "pussy," and Mistress has permitted me to ejaculate (which she detests as "unladylike") only seven times since my enslavement, and then only as a reward.

On these occasions, I am bound and blindfolded, and Mistress, administering a suction device, gives me only five minutes to climax. Failure at this results in my being required to wait several weeks before I am so favored again.

Besides my daily duties of housekeeping and cooking, I bathe and dress Mistress, do the grocery shopping (which is still acutely embarrassing because of my being six-one, though I am learning to move as a woman), and must pass her stringent inspection of my makeup, my wig (as soon as my own hair has grown more, I'll be required to perm and set it myself), nail polish and accessories. I shave my whole body every day, but my facial and pubic hair has been removed through electrolysis. I am also required to wear stockings and garters twenty-four hours a day, and to sleep in a locked leather slave helmet and leash, which denies me sight, sound, movement and speech. I have truly been reduced to insignificance and servitude.

My forced feminization and enslavement began on our vacation last winter. For years, I had secretly donned female attire for the deep sexual arousal it provided me. My first wife, discovering my secret playthings, divorced me because I would not admit my obsession to her. I let her believe that I had been unfaithful, and that she had found the clothing of an illicit lover. When I met my present wife (Mistress), I chanced hinting at "dressing up" as a sexual game. We also played at light bondage, and everything was wonderful.

Then, while vacationing, we were invited to a masquerade party by people we probably would never see again. I convinced my wife that it would be fun if she went as a "pimp," and I as a "hooker." We bought all the clothing necessary, and I ended up in a black satin dress, heels, blond wig, and some very sexy, very dainty underwear. She applied my makeup and, when I got a raging erection, promptly taped it up tight to my belly. This merely increased my excitement, but she was extremely businesslike about it. I should have noticed this early warning, but I was feeling too wonderful.

The party was a blast. We won second prize. I got drunk and passed out in our hotel room later. When I woke up the next day, still dressed as the "Happy Hooker," it took me a few minutes to realize that my wife was gone, as was all our baggage. I also realized that all the hair on my body had been removed during the night, and that I had been undressed and then dressed again. On the bathroom vanity was a note addressed to "Kathy" (my former name was Kevin), and there were two Polaroid photos. As I saw in the pictures, she had brought a man to our room while I was asleep. One photo graphically depicted me, in drag, being butt-fucked, while the other photo showed me, eyes closed, with someone's cock stuck in my mouth. (Unless I'd been drugged, I can't understand how this was done without my waking up.)

I was disgusted and terrified. The note told me that if I failed to follow her instructions, similar photos would be sent to many of my friends and associates. She said she had left me a bus ticket to San Diego, some makeup, and a coat (no money or ID). She would meet me at the San Diego terminal the next evening, she said, and she warned me that I had better arrive as "Kathy."

The next thirty hours were the most terrifying, humiliating, and deliciously erotic that I had ever experienced. My fear of embarrassment during the trip was intensely stimulating.

Well, I did make it to San Diego, and there she was, grinning as I had never seen her grin before. She greeted me as "Kathy" and advised me that, thenceforth, "Kathy" was to be my only name. In the car, she placed a silver collar about my neck (it is still in place). She told me that I was to call her "Mistress." I would go to my office as "Kathy," quit my job, retain an attorney to change my name legally from Kevin to Kathy, and sign over my real estate and other assets to her.

It was as if I had been hypnotized! Mesmerized!

Mistress had discarded all my male garments, providing me

instead with frilly female clothing. My life as a feminized slave had begun.

We moved to another town, where I am always introduced as my mistress's sister. She owns me, body and soul.

So far, my life as a slave has been wonderful. I would caution others, however, who are tempted to confess their secret fantasies to their spouses, that the consequences can go far beyond their expectations.—*K.S., Westminster, California*

Wife-Spanking Spreads House to House

I've seen many letters in your excellent publication about "spanking games" between husband and wife, but I feel my experience is slightly different. A couple of years ago, my wife appeared at breakfast wearing only a flimsy negligee and became rather teasing. I threatened her with a spanking, and she dared me. So, putting her over my knee and wedging her shoulders under the table, I slapped her bare buttocks until she asked to be let up. No sooner had she gotten up than she said she wasn't at all sorry, so I repeated the treatment, this time with a long-handled clothes brush.

That evening our neighbor, Joan, dropped in after my wife had gone to the cinema. Joan is a smart, attractive blonde and behind her back she held a polished willow stick. She was very friendly and said teasingly that my wife had told her about the spanking after I'd gone to work, and shown her the damage! We had a sherry and I asked why she had brought the stick. She was doe-eyed and said she had wanted a spanking but that her husband would not oblige. She explained that he was very placid and more interested in marine biology than love.

We kissed on the sofa and started petting. She gradually worked herself facedown across my lap, then opened my fly and caressed my penis into a major erection. I slipped down her silk panties and she opened her thighs, so I entered along her lips, and she started pleading for a spanking. She was very moist and with each spank her vagina slipped up and down my penis. From a few gentle starting slaps I progressed to harder and harder blows, which made her sob in ecstasy, till we both came together. After another sherry, she knelt on the end of the sofa, bending over the arm, and asked, begged, for the cane. I gave her twelve quick medium cuts on the same spot and she writhed and sobbed. "Harder, harder!" After six more, as hard as I could apply them, she rose and kissed me all over and, taking the cane, gave me two dozen as hard as she possibly could. Then, with me on my back on the floor, she bestrode me and performed like a veritable Bathsheba.

Pretty well every week after that, for a year, we had our little evenings. "Turn me over and turn me on" is Joan's motto.— *K.R., Devon, England*

BALLING, BONDAGE AND BABY OIL ARE THIS LADY'S FAVORITE THINGS

I'd like to share the wonderful evening my husband and I experienced last night. I was in the bathroom, washing up, when my dear man came in and said, "Get undressed, totally. That's an order!" He is a military man and used to giving orders, but I'm not used to receiving them. However, I finally decided, "What the hell! It could make the night rather interesting." I stripped and joined him in the living room, where he'd gone to watch TV. The look on his face was priceless. We had never made a habit of living in the raw except in bed and, as I nestled up to him, he whispered, "I guess I should undress, too." I quickly agreed.

In no time we were in the bedroom with only the light of two candles to love by. I suggested reading a bit from *Penthouse Letters* (which we recommend as a great incentive for lovemaking), so my husband reached under the bed, but he wasn't reaching for the magazine. I realized this when I felt my left hand being securely bound with one of the cords we keep fastened to each corner of the bed for just that purpose. Soon all four of my limbs were tied down. I lay spread-eagle, totally at my husband's mercy. Then he blindfolded me, which heightened my sense of helplessness.

Not knowing what to expect next drove me wild! He began caressing my body with his mouth—my neck, face, breasts, thighs, everywhere but my pussy, where I was aching most to feel him. To my horror, suddenly he got up and left me alone. I don't think anything can make you feel more vulnerable than to be tied up, blindfolded, naked and horny, and then left alone. When I heard my husband moving around in the adjoining bathroom, I assumed he was looking for his shaving cream and that he intended to shave my pussy, which he loves to do every once in a while. (He says that the little-girl look of a hairless cunt is a real turn-on for him.) However, when he came back, it wasn't shaving cream he spread on me, but baby oil! He oiled every inch of me from my neck on down. The way my body glistened in the flickering candlelight, my husband said, made me look extra sexy and alluring. I didn't think the delicious sensation could get any better, but he proved me wrong when he laid his body on top of mine and started fucking me. Usually I am unable to come without direct stimulation of my clit with his tongue, fingers, or a vibrator. But the luscious combination of our oilslicked bodies sliding together, and the sensation of having that nice hard penis inside me, did the trick. It was wonderful to have such a tremendous orgasm with my lover's cock filling my cunt.

My message for those who feel, as I used to, that baby oil just creates an oily mess: Try it! The shower together afterwards is a lot of fun, too!—*Name and address withheld*

Spanking Spells Relief to Hardworking Exec

I have been reading *Penthouse Letters* for about a year, and the readers' letters have encouraged me to write this. At one time I thought I was alone in my predilections. I have been married three years now (I am thirty-one) to a woman four years my senior. She is the sexual aggressor and I find this extremely pleasurable. About a year ago I confided to her my most personal sexual desires. Since my boyhood I have always had thoughts and dreams of being spanked by an attractive woman. My wife wasn't overly surprised because, during our courtship, I had occasionally played some sort of spanking games with her. She gladly agreed to fulfill my desires.

Often now she takes me over her knee after taking down my pants and underwear and, as my penis gets extremely rigid, locks it helplessly between her thighs. While I am in this embarrassing position, she usually lectures or scolds me for being a naughty boy and repeatedly mentions that she is going to give me a good spanking. And let me tell you, the tingling sensation of my bare behind in this vulnerable position is fantastic! She then proceeds to spank me lightly until I ejaculate. After my ejaculation, she keeps me over her lap and lightly rubs my bottom with her open hand in a circular motion that sends chills up my spine.

I am an executive and this little ritual relieves the strains and tensions of a hectic day at the office. It works far, far better than any amount of alcohol could. Sometimes we will play a game while I am being spanked over her lap. If I can hold off from coming until she releases me, we can have sex. Occasionally, if I am tense or keyed up, she will give me both a spanking and then an enema with a rectal syringe, and during the course of one or the other I will ejaculate. The feeling of being on her knee and given a sound going-over is out of this world, coming from a responsive, attractive, big-busted woman.—*C.E., Huntington, New York*

Humiliated By Sis and Her Girlfriends, He Gets Dressed Down and Cross-Dressed Up

Recently I began to read your magazine, and I think it is great. My favorite letters are those about female domination. I would like to share an experience of mine that I shall never forget.

I was a freshman in college at the time. When I decided to visit home one Friday night, I arrived to find that my parents were gone for the weekend. But my kid sister, Kathy, was there with four of her friends from high school. They were having a slumber party.

At first the girls were worried that the arrival of Kathy's older brother would spoil their plans, but I went out and bought some beer, which helped everyone relax and enjoy. After a while, we somehow got to talking about wrestling. I reminded Kathy how angry it had made her when I pinned her down. She retorted that there had been a few times when she had almost beaten me, and that I was not nearly as good at wrestling as I thought.

The situation escalated from there, and I found myself challenged to a wrestling match by all five of the girls. It was agreed that I would wrestle each girl, one at a time, and if I won all five matches the girls would be mine to punish. However, if any of the girls pinned me down, I'd have to submit to their punishment.

What a deal! Just thinking about all that body contact made my cock start to twitch.

The first two girls I wrestled were easy to beat, but the third girl, Colleen, surprised me. As we began to wrestle, she used a quick move to flip me on my back. Before I knew what was happening, Colleen was on top of me, trying to hold my shoulders to the floor. For a few seconds it looked like I would lose, but I finally managed to push her off of me. It took almost ten minutes for me to pin her. One reason why it took so long was that I was afraid she might have another trick to pull on me and so I was extra careful. Also, she was much stronger than she looked.

By this time I was very tired. The fourth girl, Sharon, took advantage of my weariness and quickly had me on the floor. I struggled as hard as I could to keep her from flipping me on my back. I knew if she managed to do that, I would be finished. The other girls were cheering Sharon on, and she was using all her considerable strength in trying to turn me over.

Finally, out of desperation, I stopped resisting Sharon and let her flip me over. Before she managed to pin me down, however, I wrapped my legs around hers and tripped her to the floor. Moving quickly, I sat on Sharon's chest and pinned her before she realized what was happening.

This left only my sister to beat. If I had not been so tired, I would have had no trouble defeating her, but I barely had enough strength left to stay on my feet. After maneuvering awhile for position, Kathy ducked behind me and twisted one of my arms behind my back. I struggled to escape, but my exhaustion left me too weak to resist any longer. As the other girls applauded, Kathy reached around my waist, unbuckled my belt, opened my jeans, and pulled them to my knees. I felt totally humiliated by my sister, because I had developed an erection from all the physical contact during the wrestling, and it now poked out from my underpants.

Kathy finally decided to end the combat and pushed me roughly to the floor. I could offer no resistance as she rolled me on my back, straddled my chest, planted her knees on my forearms, and pinned me down. I was completely helpless. Looking up at the cruel smile on my sister's lips, I knew I was in for trouble.

The other girls sat down next to me, laughing and teasing me about having been beaten at wrestling by my little sister. My face flushed red from embarrassment. Then one of the girls pulled down my underpants and uncovered my erection. "What do you think of my *big* brother?" Kathy asked her friends.

"I bet we can make him even bigger," one of them replied. I felt the girls teasing my prick and balls, rubbing their hands over my crotch until I thought I would go crazy. The whole time this was going on, Kathy looked down at me with satisfaction and amusement. Finally, my cock could take no more teasing, and I came all over myself. The five girls applauded.

Kathy and her friends were far from finished with me. After talking among themselves for a few moments, they stripped off my clothes and dragged me to the bathroom, where they cleaned me up and, to my complete chagrin, shaved all the hair from my legs. After that, they led me to Kathy's bedroom and forced me to dress up in my sister's clothing.

At first I refused to cooperate, but the girls insisted that this was a girls-only slumber party. They added that if I did not do as they ordered, they would spank me. I had no choice but to give in to their demands. I was forced to put on panties, a bra (which they padded with some of my sister's socks), a pair of thigh-high white stockings, a white blouse, short blue skirt, and ankle boots with high heels. (Sharon donated the boots, because my feet were too big to fit into Kathy's shoes.)

After I was dressed, the girls manicured my nails, made up my face, clipped on earrings, and fitted me with one of my mother's wigs. When they were finished, they forced me to stand in front of a full-length mirror and gaze at myself. I couldn't believe my eyes! I had been completely transformed! I looked exactly like a girl! I was even pretty!

During the rest of the night, the girls did everything they could think of to humiliate me further. I was forced to wait on each of them hand and foot, and to endure their endless pinches and squeezes. They made me pose while they took pictures of me. At one point, two of the girls escorted me around the block. As we walked I was actually trembling, afraid that one of my friends or neighbors would see me in my feminine garb.

Finally, as the ultimate humiliation, one of the girls pulled me across her lap, lifted my skirt, pulled down my panties, and spanked me until I was begging for mercy. Following that, I was forced to stand in the corner for an hour with my panties down around my ankles, holding my skirt above my waist so that all the girls could took at my red fanny.

At last the girls decided it was time to go to bed. I had to undress each one and help her into her nightclothes. The girls then undressed me, put me into a babydoll nightie and panties, and sent me to bed. Before I fell asleep, they all came into my room, one at a time, to kiss me good-night. The last one to come in was Sharon, and she gave me a great blow job.

That experience was at the same time the most humiliating of my life and the most sexually exciting thing that has ever happened to me. Since that night I have been an avid fan of female domination, and have often wished that I could find a woman willing to dominate me. Until I do, I guess I'll have to be satisfied with my memories.—*Name and address withheld*

TEACHER EDUCATES BARE-ASSED COEDS OVER HIS KNEE

I am an avid reader of *Penthouse Letters* and am particularly interested in the letters about spanking. I think your readers will find my experiences interesting.

I am a teaching assistant at a large Midwest university. About a month ago I left some books in my office and had to return late at night to get them. When I got there I found two of my female students copying a test. After surprising them I told them that either I would have to report them or arrive at some other form of punishment. They didn't want to be expelled, so they agreed to accept whatever punishment I prescribed. I decided on spanking. At first they protested, but they eventually accepted my terms. The terms were that they would be spanked in three installments on weekends when the office building was empty.

Linda decided to go first, leaving Susan with a whole week of anticipation.

I got to the office early that Saturday and Linda was waiting for me. She seemed too much at ease for someone in her position; I couldn't figure it out. I got the hairbrush (which I procured just for the occasion) from my desk. She was all smiles as she crawled over my knees. Then I found out why she was so confident. I could see the faint outline of a magazine under her jeans! I pulled her off my lap and she immediately knew I was onto her. I told her that for such a trick she would receive all her spankings on the bare behind. She pleaded with me, but eventually submitted. She blushed from head to toe as she removed her panties. She was very careful not to expose anything as she once again crawled over my knees. I lectured her for five minutes on the evils of cheating, the whole time enjoying the view of her plump behind. Then I began spanking. I took my time, leaving four to five seconds between each swat. She maintained her composure for the first ten swats, then she broke down, lost all modesty and began kicking and crying wildly. Each time the paddle landed, her behind jiggled and she let out a loud yelp. As she wiggled and squirmed to try to avoid the blows, I saw everything she had tried so hard to conceal. When I finished the forty strokes her rear was a deep crimson. I stood her in a corner until she stopped crying. As she was putting her clothes on, she said that she was sorry and had deserved everything she got.

The next week, Susan showed up fifteen minutes late. I used her tardiness as an excuse to spank her on the bare bottom, too. When I told her to take off her dress I found that she didn't have on a bra. As she stood there naked, Susan was even more embarrassed than Linda had been. I had her fetch the hairbrush from the desk and then bend over my knees. Her behind turned red fast, and she seemed to be suffering more than Linda had, so I set the brush aside and finished with a hand spanking. The difference was phenomenal. The hand spanking was much more sensual. I could feel the warmth and the quivering of her behind as I landed each spank. When it was over, I couldn't resist rubbing her bottom. I continued until she stopped crying. After she was dressed, she kissed me passionately on the mouth and then ran out.

Since then, I have spanked each girl again and they each have once more to go. I begin with the brush and then use my hand. I am looking for ways to get more of my students over my knee in the future. Overall, I think spanking is fairer than expulsion for first-time cheating.—*Name and address withheld*

A Bare-Ass Paddling and an Earnest Fuck Get Her Initiated

I never thought it could happen to me, but it did. I am a student at a very small private college in the San Francisco Bay Area and a member of a small but close-knit professional fraternity that has been predominantly male in the past. This semester, however, we decided to initiate some female members and were surprised by the number of responses we got. The frat brothers were delighted with the upcoming initiation ritual, and one pledge in particular.

Julie was a newly elected cheerleader, with the body to prove it. Her silken spun-gold curls cascaded lightly to her beautiful tan shoulders. Her smile revealed gorgeous, full lips and gleaming white teeth. As you watched her speak, it was hard not to envision how it would feel to taste that mouth. Her limbs were long and firm and slightly muscular, due to the exercise she got as a cheerleader. Her breasts, enormous but firm, jiggled slightly as she walked. Her pretty ass fetchingly filled out the gym shorts she always wore to tantalize the guys. When she was wearing bikini shorts, you could see her tan lines and imagine the luscious, creamy-smooth skin underneath the nylon fabric. Just watching her was a sexual experience.

As pledge-master I planned special activities for her just so I could spend more time with her. When the big week rolled around, I summoned Julie to my room late one night and informed her (falsely) that she might not make it to the final ceremony, due to some seldom-used fraternity bylaws. I made it clear to her that the decision rested in my hands. She begged and pleaded for me to reconsider, whereupon I told her that there might be something she could do. My manhood swelled in anticipation as I explained the task. She considered the proposition, and then, coming to a decision, began to unbutton her thin silk tunic. Sliding it from her golden limbs, she revealed her magnificent white breasts with their hard, brown nipples. She beckoned to me, and I approached, my desire obliterating all other thoughts from my mind. Her trembling fingers lightly unbuckled my belt and slid my jeans to the floor. Some of her nervousness rubbed off on me and I trembled as I placed her hands on my erect warrior.

After she'd stroked it for several moments, I felt a rising excitement and tore her skirt away from her hips. Quivering, she pulled her panties down and kicked them away with her perfectly formed feet. She had revealed a neatly trimmed bush with a slight glistening wetness visible on her pussy's lips. I gestured toward the pledge paddle hanging above the bookshelf, and her eyes grew wide. After she'd handed it to me, I made her bend over and hold her ankles, and then I gave her one stroke for every demerit she had accumulated. She cried out in painful pleasure with each whack, and her cheeks turned a shade closer to our fraternity colors of purple and red.

Upon completion of my disciplinary duties, I saw the erotic love juices flowing freely down Julie's legs. Still bending over her, I thrust the handle of the paddle between her wet cunt-lips. She dropped to her knees, moaning with pleasure. She herself worked the handle deeper and deeper into herself, twisting and turning it to suit her enjoyment. Turned on by this, I dropped to my knees and thrust my tongue as deeply into her asshole as

I could. She yelped to indicate her satisfaction and breathed very heavily so that her enormous chest expanded and contracted seductively. She was still unsatisfied, though, and turned around to face me. Then, with incredible strength, she made me lie on my back so she could straddle my hips. In this position, she guided my cock into her love crevice, rotating her hips and pelvis in rhythm to a song that only she heard.

With her eyes closed tight in ecstasy and her head thrown back, Julie came in a powerful rush. She gripped my ass with her clawlike fingernails and I came immediately after her. Our juices mingled in her steaming cauldron, and we fell to the floor in each other's arms. We made love again the next morning, missing all our early classes.

In my opinion, Julie had passed the fraternity initiation with flying colors. The official ceremony a few days later was a breeze for her, and we have since relived our own private ceremony several times. We take our fraternal bond very seriously.—*Name and address withheld*

Flying Solo

He Sucks His Own Cock While Under the Kitchen Sink

The *Penthouse Letters* articles I enjoy the most are about autofellatio. For other readers who enjoy this subject, I would like to describe how I go about getting into position and relate some of the feelings I get doing myself.

First off, there are two positions I can get into to suck my cock. The one I prefer is to lie naked in front of my kitchen sink and take a small pillow and put it underneath my neck. Then I bring my legs up over my head and place my feet under the bottom of the sink. This brings my cock so it is right up over my head and not very far from my mouth. Then I take hold of my cock and bring it to my mouth and lick the head of it so it gets all wet and slippery. Soon I have a good hard-on. This permits my cock to slide easily into my mouth. By this time my cock is so hard and so hot, it is touching my lips. Now I place both of my hands on the back of my hips and pull them forward, sliding my dick into my waiting mouth. I am able to get the head all the way into my mouth so my lips are around the neck of my cock. Also, I am able to move my hips back and forth, all the while moving my cock in and out of my mouth. While I am thrusting my cock, I move my stomach muscles just right, and come begins oozing into my mouth. It does not take me long to get real hot and ready to shoot a load of come. But since I don't like to come right away, when I feel myself starting to come, I let my cock slip out of my mouth and rest for a while. I like to suck on it for about half an hour or until I get so hot I can't hold back anymore. Then I let myself go, filling my mouth with my delicious come. And I swallow it as it flows into my mouth.

The second position is to lie on my back and put my arms down between my legs. Then I roll on my back and bring both legs up and put them behind my head. With a good hard-on, my cock meets my mouth so I can suck it. This is very hard, so I don't do it this way very much.

I don't in any way feel that I am doing wrong by sucking my own cock. I have been doing this for about fifteen years now. When I first started, I couldn't get my cock far enough into my mouth so that I could really enjoy it. But I really wanted to suck myself off. I knew if I kept trying, someday I would be able to get the head of my cock all the way into my mouth. When I did get it in all the way the first time, it was a very wonderful feeling.

The reason why it is so easy for me to suck my own cock is that it measures seven-and-a-half inches with a good hard-on. When I first started sucking my cock, it measured only five-and-a-half inches. I knew I would have to make it longer. I know people have said you cannot make your prick longer, but that is a bunch of bullshit. The way I made mine longer was that every chance I got to be alone I would take it out of my pants and play with it. I would put my fingers at the base of it and draw the foreskin back as far as it would go and pull on the shaft.

I love the taste my cock leaves in my mouth. Also, I like the smell of it. Sometimes I won't wash my cock for a couple of days so it will smell real nice. When I suck it, the smell really turns me on. I like to masturbate and not wash the come off my cock. Then the next day I will suck it again. I get the taste of the old come in my mouth.

Even when I masturbate, I don't waste it. If I am lying on the bed masturbating, I let the come gush onto my belly; then I take my finger, wipe the come off, and put it into my mouth or catch it in something and pour it into my mouth. I have masturbated into a rubber and saved the come until the next time I sucked myself off. I would pour the old come out of the condom into my mouth for lubrication. The previous come didn't taste too bad, and it really helped me to suck my prick. I have found that if my mouth and cock are wet and slippery, it is easier to get it in.

Also, I take a mirror sometimes and tape it to the inside of my leg so I can watch myself sucking my cock. I have also taken pictures of myself while I had my prick in my mouth. I was able to get the head of my cock two-and-a-half inches into my mouth with each thrust. One other thing I like to do is to stick the head partway up my asshole, then put the head into my mouth. But when I do this, I make sure there is no shit on my cock. I just like the smell and taste it provides. Many times I have lain naked in the bathtub, brought my legs up over my head so my prick was close to my mouth, and then pissed into my mouth. When I am in the shower, I take hold of my cock and point it toward my mouth, and the piss goes into my mouth, then runs down my body. I like the feeling of the hot piss running down my chest and my abdomen. I enjoy everything I do. More of you guys should try this. You might like it. Don't get me wrong, I like to fuck women, too. But I will keep on sucking as long as I can.—*Name and address withheld*

FOR HER, SEX IS ALWAYS AT HAND

I am a twenty-four-year-old female and very sexy. It's not just because of my looks, although I measure thirty-nine around the boobs, twenty-four at the waist, and thirty-eight around the ass. The reason why I say I am sexy is that I fantasize and masturbate constantly. Because of my looks I can get all the cock—or cunt, for that matter—that I need or want, but I prefer to play with myself.

I have masturbated to orgasm twenty-three times in one day, and I come never less than a dozen times a day. Sundays are my hottest days. Usually I am a little hung over from drinking wine and playing with myself on Saturday night and I wake up horny as hell. My hand is always on my cunt when I wake up. I quickly put it to good use—and away I go!

Today is a Sunday, and I came four times before getting out of bed. It's ten o'clock now and I've had four more orgasms since breakfast. I intend to have a real jerking afternoon. My favorite position is lying on my back on the fur rug in my living room. I have a ceiling mirror so I can watch myself fuck. My fantasies while I fuck myself (I prefer this term better than saying masturbating) swing all over the full spectrum. I see hands jerking big, thick cocks, girls taking it up the ass, a couple of husky blond guys sucking each other off, two redheads in a 69 and me joining them. My fantasies of eating pussy always seem to be with redheads. My most orgasmic fantasy is imagining a young redhead about sixteen going at herself with her fingers. She changes hands and licks her juice from her fingers. And when she comes, she shoots out of her cunt the way a guy goes off. Loads of it. I love sucking and licking my nipples when I masturbate (sorry, I mean fuck myself). Being well hung in the tit department, I can do this easily. I guess I have fucked myself with just about everything: vibrators, dildos, candles, carrots, cucumbers, corn on the cob (which is a really good fuck), perfume bottles, hairbrush handles, broom handles—you name it, I've tried it. But nothing beats my fingers.

I am writing so that others who are in the self-fucking group will also write. I would love to hear of others like myself, whether men or women. I am sure there are millions who prefer fucking themselves to having a relationship with another person.

I have stopped writing this letter twice already in order to have a go at myself. It's going to be a great afternoon. I've just opened a bottle of wine, and the more wine I drink, the wetter I get. There is only one thing I wish I could do, and that is to be able to suck my own cunt. I have been eaten by men and women and have even sucked several women (I mean, young ones). To me that would be the ultimate in self-fucking.

Can you female readers just imagine going at yourself with your tongue? Wow! I can't imagine people saying they are not getting enough sex. Sex does not have to be between two or more persons. It's between your legs, believe me. With a cunt or cock between your legs, sex is always at hand. Add a little fantasy or some sexy reading, some good porno movies, or even explicit pictures. Who needs another body? I've jerked my clit to every centerfold in *Penthouse* for the last three years, and I still go back to some of my favorites (redheads). I could go on, but I don't want to make my letter too long. Besides, something is at hand (something wet and juicy).—*G.G., Toronto, Ont., Canada*

THREE FEMALE VOYEURS WATCH NEIGHBOR JERK OFF

We are foxy eighteen-year-old girls with at least a normal interest in sex. We live in a small midwestern suburb. Now that we are high-school seniors, we are getting our quota of fucking, but a few years ago we limited ourselves to oral sex and finger work with boys and with each other. We want to share with other *Penthouse Letters* readers an activity that greatly helped our education and still manages to keep us hot and has given us much pleasure during the past two or so years.

We have a marvelous neighbor. He's a widower and about forty-five years old, and he's still very sexy looking. He spends a lot of time working outside around his house. When it is warm enough, he usually wears loose nylon running shorts. It is not difficult to see the outline of his prick and his balls as they flop around inside the shorts. As kids, we used to enjoy this sight very much. Then we learned that if he knew we were looking at him, the flopping would stop and the bulging would start. We'd encourage this by wearing revealing clothes and doing some whispering and giggling while we ogled his barely concealed equipment.

Having enjoyed these furtive erections for a while, we decided we'd try to see the real thing. Ours is a pleasant community of homes, and no one cares who wanders around from yard to yard. This man has a big patio door behind his house. It's private back there because of trees and shrubs. One spring evening at about ten o'clock when my two closest friends were sleeping over, the three of us went quietly into his backyard. The light was on in the room with the patio door, and the drapes were pulled open. There was our guy, sitting on a couch, stark naked. He was looking at pictures in a copy of *Penthouse*. His cock was long and limp, and we were delighted to see that it was uncircumcised. This was the first time we'd ever seen one with a foreskin. While poring over the pictures, he used his free hand to rub his cock and his balls. The prick naturally began to lengthen and harden up. It was thrilling to see for real what we had seen only in outline. It was a really neat piece of meat.

Soon his staff was standing at attention. He spread the magazine on the couch so he could study an especially sexy picture, knelt on the couch, and placed a large pillow between his legs. He took his tool in his hand and began humping the pillow. He worked slowly at first, fucking his hand. Then, as he got ready to come, he started pumping away with his hand, faster and faster. He pulled back his foreskin, and we saw the come spurt out of the little eye in the ruby-colored head. He shot his load into a towel he had ready, wiped the surplus off his prick with his fingers, and sucked them dry.

We waited around to watch his peter soften down and then, with dripping panties, went to my house, where we had our own jack-off session while we discussed what we had observed.

We'd go over to his backyard at night about twice a week from that night on. We think he jacks off just about every night, but sometimes we'd be there and there'd be no show. When it's warm enough, and the patio door is open with just a screen to keep insects out, we get the impression that he knows we're there. We giggle and squeal some, which he must hear, but he just keeps banging away. He seems to position himself to give us the clearest possible view and puts on a particularly good performance.

Now and then he shows X-rated movies, which we appreciate because the screen is located where we can see it. He sits on the couch, playing with his peter and timing his climax to those in the movie. When his cock goes limp, he strokes it hard again and gets up and walks around with his hard-on bouncing up and down. Then he does the pillow bit. It always takes longer the second time, but we don't mind. He fixes the pillow so that one corner pushes into his asshole, and that seems to help him get it up and off again.

We enjoy our nighttime peep show and our daytime fun. When he's out there in the yard working in his shorts, we sometimes watch from my bedroom window, using binoculars and making sure he knows what we're doing. Or we just sit around out front, whispering, giggling and staring. Without fail, his prick hardens up and sometimes makes such a tent out of his shorts that he gets embarrassed and has to go in the house before it pops out and waves in the breeze. When he comes back out, he's got it down to the dangle stage, and we're betting it's because he's pumped it dry. We're also betting a lot of other foxes like us could enjoy similar excitement if they'd only look around at the men and boys in their neighborhoods. Let them know you're interested.—*Name and address withheld*

HE PRACTICES YOGA FOR SELF-FULFILLMENT

I have read *Penthouse Letters* a lot, and I believe that I have something really good to share with your male readers (and female, too; in fact, with anyone who looks with dread upon advancing years). My story has a comic twist to it, but, believe me, it's true!

My puritanical upbringing resulted in a wrecked first marriage, and I became an alcoholic. In my mid-forties, I was a total wreck; however, a series of happy events resulted in my getting this monkey off my back. As my health improved with abstinence, my sex life also improved.

Don't let anyone tell you that alcohol improves your drive. Quite the opposite is true. In any event, it wasn't until my second, and sober, marriage that I began to understand what sex is all about: making one woman happy and sharing all aspects of her life has been much more rewarding than my several thousand alcoholic encounters before this.

In my line of work, I often find myself alone. I was lying on my cot in a "YMCA-type" atmosphere in New York City, thinking about home, and I got the biggest hard-on I had experienced in months. I had been swimming and had just finished a sauna, and I felt in excellent shape. I wondered how it would feel to suck myself off. Try as I would, I couldn't do it. The closest I could come to making contact was about two inches. However, since I was to be alone for a whole month yet, I began yoga exercises to limber my back. I practiced each night until one day, about a week after trying this exercise, I could reach the tip of my dick with my tongue. A few days later and the whole head was in.

There is no way to describe the feeling of sucking yourself off. I even managed to massage my asshole without losing my balance. I came all over my mouth, chin, beard, and even swallowed some. (Warning: Be careful if you try this not to get any up your nostrils. It has a self-propelling mechanism to climb up and up any small tube and can cause some discomfort.) The next day I experienced that wonderful feeling that I have had only a few times in my life, after a night of continuous fucking. I did have a few muscular pains around my shoulder blades, but they soon went away.

My questions are: Is this practice common? Is there anything homosexual about it? It doesn't seem to have affected my relations with my wife; in fact, I am trying to figure out how to tell her so she can help out and enjoy it, too. So far I have hesitated to mention it to her because it sounds so comical, but believe me it is true.

Now here is the good part. I am sixty-two years old. Yet by keeping young in spirit, I have discovered new things about sex and am enjoying it more and more. I hope this will encourage any of your readers who may fear growing old. Nonsense. The older one gets, the better things get. Don't be afraid to try something new.—*W.R.R., San Francisco, California*

MASTER MANIPULATOR PUTS VIBRATOR IN HIS ASS, OIL ON HIS COCK

I'm a reasonably attractive, twenty-eight-year-old man, married to a wonderful girl who just happens not to like sex. For years—at least twelve—like most men, I assume, I have been masturbating, but never with the dexterity, intensity and interest that I have developed in the past year or so. I used to make a point of coming once or twice, sometimes three times, a day. Now I like to hold off for three or four days because my orgasm is more intense that way.

When my wife is out of the house for a while, I go upstairs to our bedroom, turn up the thermostat and remove my clothes. I go to the bathroom to get a couple of hand towels, some baby oil, and my vibrator. Returning to the bedroom, I place one towel on the bed where my hips will be. Then I lie down on my back. The light from the table lamp is low and my head is propped with pillows so I can comfortably read *Penthouse Letters* or look down at myself.

After pouring baby oil on the tip of my vibrator, I lift and spread my legs and run it around my anus to ease the entry. By this time, my penis is hard and throbbing against my flat, tan, firm stomach. I insert the vibrator four or five inches into my rectum, then relax my legs and my whole body for a few seconds until the pleasurable pain of entry ebbs. I never turn the vibrator on because I want only to be aware of the feeling of my rectum being full and the stretching sensation at my anus.

I place the second towel on my stomach to catch my come when it spurts from my penis. Holding my erect penis in my left hand, I take the bottle of oil and place several drops on the tip of the head near my peehole. Gently and slowly, I massage the head until it feels silky and glistens in the dim light. Moving my hand down to the shaft, I add more oil and ever so slowly begin an up-and-down stroking.

The vibrator inserted in my rectum causes the muscles behind my balls to tighten so that my penis is as rigid as possible. The tightness prevents the foreskin from moving, so only my oiled hand near the tip of the head provides the friction necessary to make me come.

After a short while of easy stroking, the clear salty fluid begins to ooze out of my peehole, mixing with the oil to make my penis even smoother and more slippery. This sight excites me even more and I tighten my stomach muscles, causing my anus to contract around the vibrator. With the constriction of all these muscles, my peehole opens wide and more of the sticky, clear juice seeps out.

As my excitement increases, the veins running along the seven-inch length of my shaft swell and stand out in blue contrast to the shiny pinkness of my balls and penis, and the head of my cock becomes a crimson red.

I'm aware I'm about to come when the muscles between my balls and anus begin to tighten and release. I place my right hand there to massage the little ridge in rhythm with my left-hand strokes. A little pressure behind my balls helps bring me to climax.

When I start to come, the entire area behind my balls seems to become rigid and then to contract spasmodically. My thick white come squirts out hard at first, often shooting as far as my shoulders. After several squirts, my semen comes forth in globs, spilling over my hand and running down to my balls and onto the towel. As I feel my climax fading to an end, I withdraw the vibrator from my rectum. The relaxing of the muscles around my anus causes a few more intense spasms, and still more come slips out of my peehole.

After several moments of rest, I exert a last firm stroke or two on my penis, which cleans out the leftover juice. The come and oil are mixed all over my hands, balls, penis and anus, as well as the towels, and I love it. What a turn-on! I think I'll do it again right now.—*Name and address withheld*

GUYS ENJOY JERK-OFF NOONERS WITH EACH OTHER IN THE JOHN

My name is Charlie, and I'm the manager of a department store. The story I want to share with you and your readers is rather comical as well as erotic.

I used to work at a company that was only a ten-minute walk from my house. At lunch I would come home and have a noontime quickie. The minute I walked through the door, I'd tell my gorgeous blond wife (38-25-37) to strip. We'd go right to it for about five minutes. (At night we take *much* more time to set the mood, to enjoy some delicious foreplay, and to leisurely and lovingly screw each other.)

Recently, we moved to a new town and our new house is too far away from the big shopping center where I work for me to have those daytime quickies, so I have to relieve myself by masturbating in the public bathrooms.

I usually wait until no one is around, go into one of the toilets (which are protected from anyone's sight by swinging doors), unfasten my belt, unzip my zipper, pull my pants down and sit on the toilet. I go to it, fantasizing about the many ways I'd be fucking my lady's pussy, getting sucked off, etc.

One day I was hornier than usual, and when my lunch hour came around, I rushed to the bathroom to beat my seven-inch dong. No one seemed to be there, so I went up to one of the stalls, but when I swung open the door, my eyes nearly popped out. One of my associates at the store was jacking off his own peter (it was about nine inches long)! He was handsome, to say the least, with curly blond hair and a hairy body. I couldn't help but laugh as his face turned beet red. I reassured him, saying, "You too, huh!" We both laughed as he pulled his jockey shorts on over his still-hard prick. I apologized, and he said it was OK.

I found out later, while we shared lunch, that he was in the same position as I, with a house and a wife too far away. I sympathized and confessed my own goings-on in the bathroom, and we shared a few other laughs as well. Ever since we've been buddies.

Sometimes we'll go to the bathroom at the same time and watch each other whack off (you can see into the next stall through a small, lengthwise opening at the back). My friend is more of a performer: He puts his sport jacket on the hanger, unbuttons his shirt, and pulls his pants all the way down to his ankles. Then he plays with his balls and feels his hairy chest, his other hand pumping first in a slow rhythm, then faster and faster until his hammer spurts out his come. I just pull my pants down and go right at it.

I hope you don't think that our "doors open both ways"—it's just that once in a while we get off watching each other jerk off.—*Name and address withheld*

JELLO-JERKING STUDENT AROUSES COED PEEPING TOM

I am a female student at a small, liberal arts college located in the middle of a cornfield. There is not much nightlife here, so we have to create our own amusements after classes. Dave is mine.

He is blond, with big hazel eyes, broad shoulders, and muscular arms. He is exactly my height, which really turns me on (I hate having to look up at my men). He seems to be a serious student, but I discovered that there is a delicious decadent streak in him.

One day, after dinner, I had to go back to the dining room to retrieve a book I had left behind. The room is spacious, with floor-to-ceiling windows forming three of its walls. On this spring evening it was lit only by the golden-white sunset, and empty, except for Dave, who was eating a big bowl of lime Jell-O topped with whipped cream. I stood in the shadows, watching him.

Dave put down his spoon and started picking up the slippery gelatin with his broad, strong fingers. He wet his lips with his tongue while slowly and thoughtfully spreading the dessert over his fingers. Without looking to make sure he was alone, he kicked off his shoes and tossed off his jeans and shorts. Clothed only in a T-shirt and denim jacket, he perched on the edge of the table.

To my surprise, Dave dipped his hands into the Jell-O, smearing them quite thoroughly, and started to play with his cock. He arched his back, showing off a flat, furry belly and a patch of fine, dark pubic hair. Dave wrapped one hand tightly around his thick shaft and stroked it firmly and slowly, the cool, green Jell-O oozing out between his fingers. He shut his eyes, flung back his head, and grinned from ear to ear.

When he started stroking his throbbing cock with both hands, his grin got even wider. I was really turned on by the time he got close to climaxing and started moving his hands up and down his huge prick incredibly fast. Pieces of Jell-O flew to the floor as he shuddered and twitched, topping them off with his own sweet cream.

Dave sighed contentedly as he retrieved his pants, but the fun wasn't over yet. He slowly licked his hands clean, lapping up every trace of the luscious leftovers. I couldn't help moaning as I watched that juicy tongue at work. He looked at me, still lapping at his palms, and I knew he had been aware of my presence the whole time.

Without a word Dave picked up his shoes and left, pausing at the door to wink at me. But don't think I was upset at being left by myself in that empty dining room. There was one more bowl of green Jell-O, and, believe me, it didn't go to waste.—*Name and address withheld*

She Loves a Man Who Makes a Lasting Impression—Of His Erect Cock

My current lover is a dental student, and we have enjoyed an extremely satisfying and uninhibited sex life together. Last summer, however, I was exasperated to learn that he had to leave the city for three weeks. I knew I would miss him. He has the most beautiful penis I have ever seen—it measures ten inches when fully erect. I just could not bear the thought of not being able to suck his penis or feel that wonderful monster deep inside my hot pussy. Then my lover got a brilliant idea and brought home some powder from school one day. He called it alginate. After I had thoroughly aroused him with my tongue, lips and nimble fingers, he quickly mixed the alginate powder with water and put the puttylike mixture into a very tall glass. Then he pushed my mouth away from his throbbing penis and inserted his hot organ all the way into the alginate paste. After letting the paste set for a few minutes, he pulled his penis out of the glass, leaving a very detailed impression of his erect organ in the alginate. He then mixed up some dental stone and poured this into the impression in the paste. After letting it harden, he removed the magnificent plaster model from the glass. It was an exact model of his beautiful monster—which he gave to me so I would remember him while he was away.

During his absence, I used the model to bring myself to orgasm every night. I used it in every way imaginable, and it brought me great pleasure. It was the perfect way to remember my lover while he was gone. And when it was not being used, the "statue" occupied a prominent place on my living-room coffee table.

Since his return, I haven't needed the model because I can fill my love tunnel with the real thing, which is much better. But my lover has found another use for it. While we are making love and he is eating my pussy, he inserts the statue into my anus and gives me double pleasure.—*N.S., Buffalo, New York*

SELF-SERVICE IS HIS ANSWER TO GIVING AND GETTING ORAL PLEASURE

I enjoy reading *Penthouse Letters* so much that I have to reread it several times. Now and then I've noticed a few articles in which men have said that they fellate themselves. I've been sucking my own cock for the past thirty-two years and have some how-to advice for other men who'd like to do it themselves. Now if you're fat, forget it. I have a thirty-two-inch waist and am about five feet six inches tall. My cock is five and a half inches long, and I'm not double-jointed.

Years ago, when I was walking down the street with one of my friends, he mentioned that he wished that he could suck his own cock. Until that time I had never given the matter a thought and, in fact, had been taught that this activity was unthinkable. (Today when I suck my cock, I feel that it is the cleanest part of my body. I even wash my hands before I touch it.)

At the time of my friend's confession, we used to attend live shows in two local theaters. One consisted of a group that would walk around the stage on their hands, with their heads held between their legs. I used to wonder if they sucked their own cocks. In this position they could very easily reach their cocks with their mouths. One evening I heard one of these persons being interviewed on the radio. The performer was asked if he and the other members of the group were double-jointed. He answered that they weren't and said that many people could do the same trick after the right exercises.

When World War II ended, I was in Europe and had lots of free time on my hands. I decided to begin my experimentation. I would lie on my back with my head on a roll of toilet paper and raise my feet up above me until they rested on the wall behind me. Then I would put my arms around my legs and gradually pull my cock down toward my mouth. Finally I would switch the position by sitting on the floor, wrapping my arms around my upper thighs, arching my back and pressing my neck and head forward as I slowly reached my mouth down toward my cock. It seemed almost impossible to do, but each time I tried, my mouth would get closer and closer to my cock. After weeks of trying, I was able to lick up and down the shaft, tasting the sweet juice that starts to run when you get hot. Then I opened my mouth and moved it down slowly over the head of my cock until it was about a third of the way down the shaft. I started rolling my tongue around the head and soon brought myself to a climax that sent gushes of come down my throat.

One of these days I may get up the nerve to suck another guy's cock. I remember how, in my younger years, when I was going to high school, I was with one of my classmates during lunch. At one point he pulled out his cock and took a leak behind some bushes. I remember that his cock was large and beautiful. He asked me to suck it. I wanted to very much, but refused. To this very day I still think about that near encounter.

I would love to stand up and shout to the world that I love to suck cock, but there are far too many narrow-minded people out there.—*A.B., Washington, D.C.*

DAUGHTER TEACHES WIDOWED MOM TO DIDDLE HERSELF TO HAPPINESS

I am a thirty-eight-year-old widow and mother of two. Since the death of my husband, Jim, three years ago, my sex life has been nonexistent. I simply haven't had the inclination to date anyone.

Jim always kept me very happy and satisfied sexually. After I lost him I was too busy working to notice my increasing sexual tension. During my second year of widowhood, however, I became aware of a yearning between my legs as I lay in bed at night. My upbringing had taught me that touching myself "down there" was wrong, and though the need for relief became more urgent as time wore on, I just couldn't bring myself to explore the flesh between my thighs.

Then, about eight months ago, I was cleaning the house while the kids were at school. As I was rounding up the laundry in my daughter Terri's room, I found a small stack of *Penthouse* and *Penthouse Letters* magazines under her bed. At first, I was aghast and quite angry at my daughter for having all of those "dirty" magazines. But my curiosity got the best of me and I started leafing through a few copies. I read one letter from a woman who masturbated regularly and who taught her friends how to do the same. I also read an editorial on masturbation in *Penthouse Letters* that, to my amazement and frustration, made my vagina grow damp with excitement.

My arousal and my inability to deal with it only made me more angry at my daughter. I put the two magazines back and decided to give Terri hell when she got home that evening. My nerve failed me at the last moment, however, and I said nothing to her.

As I lay in bed that night, too frustrated and horny to sleep, visions from the letters I'd read were dancing in my mind. A torrent of emotions flowed through me—lust, loneliness, anger, and somewhere in there, jealousy of my daughter's apparent ability to gratify herself sexually, which I lacked.

Finally I decided to try touching myself. As soon as I touched my pubic hair with my fingers, though, I felt an overwhelming rush of shame and embarrassment, as if I'd been caught fucking in my mother's bed. Through some strange convolution of reasoning, I suddenly decided that my current state was my daughter's fault. I rose from my bed, threw on my robe and stormed down the hall, determined to confront my daughter about her magazine collection.

I opened the door of her bedroom and received the shock of my life. Terri, my sixteen-year-old daughter, was lying totally nude on her bed. She didn't hear me enter because she was wearing headphones and listening to music from her Walkman radio. She didn't see me, either, because her attention was thoroughly involved in an issue of *Penthouse* she was looking at. As I watched, speechless, she turned a page and placed one hand at her crotch. She rubbed her pubic mound in slow circles and, after a moment, her shapely hips began moving slightly in time with her roving fingers.

Another page was turned and, when her hand returned between her legs, her fingers sought her clitoris and stroked it leisurely. At this, the nipples of her small young breasts grew and stiffened.

And still she hadn't noticed me.

I stood completely transfixed by the spectacle before me. In spite of my inhibitions, I felt my vagina lubricating as I watched Terri play with herself.

For a while longer, she continued stroking her clit. As her excitement grew, she spread her legs wider and wider, until they were as far apart as they could go. Glistening with her fragrant love juices, her open pussy was now spread before me. Terri then did something that surprised me still further.

The magazine now forgotten, she reached behind her pillow and withdrew a dildo-shaped vibrator and switched it on. The soft buzzing of the device filled the room, as did the musky scent of Terri's pussy. She closed her eyes and guided the vibrator to her clitoris. As it touched her pink little knob, she arched her back and gasped with pleasure. Then she pushed the vibrator between her sopping-wet labia. Her hips bucked upward as she sank the whole length of the vibrator slowly into her cunt. Her face was suffused with a look of rapture. I saw a trickle of creamy fluid ooze from her cunt and down between her buttocks.

As Terri began fucking herself with the vibrator, thrusting it in and out, I suddenly became aware of how lustfully I craved orgasm. With that thought, my earlier anger returned, strengthened now by jealousy of my daughter's ability to masturbate so shamelessly. Speaking loud enough for her to hear me over the music in the headphones, I asked her, "Just what the hell do you think you're doing?"

Terri's eyes popped open in alarm. Seeing me standing over her, she let out a yelp of surprise and sat up on the bed, pulling the vibrator out of her cunt.

As I tore into her verbally, ranting as if mad, I noticed that her mortification was mixed with arousal. Her inner thighs twitched rhythmically, hungry for the orgasm I had interrupted. I suddenly realized that my words of anger had a hollow sound, and I knew that nothing I could say would make her stop. My emotions swirled within me and I started crying at the unfairness of it all.

"Don't *you* ever masturbate, Mom?" Terri asked meekly.

I admitted that I didn't know how. Then, of all things, my daughter offered to teach me how! Stranger still, I nodded my consent. Terri smiled and ordered me out of my robe and nightgown. I joined her in bed and she told me to watch her. Lying back against her pillows, she opened her legs to me again and returned to her masturbation, rolling her thumb and forefinger over her clitoris again and again. She placed her other hand under her ass and slid her fingers into her cunt.

"Just do like I do, Mom," Terri said, her hips starting their bucking motion again. As if in a dream, I parted my legs and opened my wet twat to my daughter's gaze. I felt separated from reality as I touched my clitoris, but the jolt of pleasure overrode any guilt or inhibition I was feeling. I thrust one finger into my wet pussy and moaned with pleasure. Then I inserted two fingers, then three, and finally I had all four fingers buried in my quivering vagina, stretching its walls and completely filling me.

Terri was squealing and bucking as she came, her fingers dancing furiously at her cunt. Seeing her come so beautifully set me off. As I fucked myself with one hand, I rubbed my clit rapidly with the other, urging myself toward that cliff of supreme pleasure that had eluded me for so long. Finally I reached the edge, and I drove myself greedily over it. My fingers made squishy noises as they worked inside me, and nothing existed for me except my spasming vagina.

Finally, sanity returned and I realized I had drooled all over myself in my moments of ecstasy. My fingers still lay at my pussy, and I knew I had to come again in order to be truly satisfied.

Terri, recovered from her own climax, recognized my need. She picked up the vibrator and switched it on again. Then she placed it in my hand and guided it to my waiting cunt. The moment it touched my throbbing clit, another orgasm began to rise. I hurriedly slid the vibrator all the way into my pussy and my mind was instantly dissolved by wave after wave of rapture. I lost track of time as I came and came. Finally, sated, I pulled the vibrator out and turned it off.

Terri was coming on her fingers one more time as I just lay there next to her, watching. She was incredibly beautiful as she writhed on the bed in orgasmic bliss. After her climax was over, I embraced my daughter. As I stroked her hair, I told her how grateful I was for what she'd done and for the precious gift she'd given me. I told her that I loved her and kissed her good night.

After retiring to my own bed, I felt the urge again—and then again and again—and I masturbated the whole night away. After getting the kids off to school the next morning, I slept all day and woke happier and more relaxed than I'd ever been since losing Jim.

Now *Penthouse* and *Penthouse Letters* are regular reading in my bedroom. I have a collection of vibrators and other toys that I use on myself every night. Terri has graduated from high school and lives in a dorm across town, where she attends college. She still finds time to visit her old mom once in a while, and we masturbate together whenever she's at the house.

My guilt and inhibition have been swept away by a tidal wave of self-stimulation. I am happier than ever now that I diddle myself, and I never intend to stop. My advice to people who don't masturbate but who get tense and horny is: Drop your pants and do it! If you're horny and frustrated, there's no one to blame but yourself. The solution is right in your own hands.—*K.H., San Jose, California*

Girls & Girls/
Boys & Boys

Avon Lady's Cream Soothes, Smooths and Seduces

One recent Saturday, my husband, Bud, and I were lounging by our pool in the buff (the children were visiting my mother for the weekend). Bud was sitting in the Jacuzzi, sipping margaritas (his specialty), while reading *Penthouse Letters* out loud to me as I lay on the chaise. The combination of the sun baking on my naked breasts, the margaritas and Bud's gentle voice reading about other people's erotic adventures made me feel extremely sexy. I was so engrossed that I totally forgot to roll over. Since this was the first real sunning I've had this year, my breasts were still sensitive and I'm afraid I scorched my nipples pretty badly. I told Bud and he suggested gentle massage as a remedy. He climbed out of the Jacuzzi sporting a giant hard-on that made me moan even before he touched me.

Happily, our backyard affords us all the privacy we need. He began by sucking on my toes, making me squirm and pant. "Give me your cock," I begged. "I want it in my mouth." Bud's cock has always turned me on. It's not very long, but it's very thick, with the head about the size of a small fist. He obliged me by swinging his leg over my face, which brought his cock into full view. I began nibbling, licking the fat tip and under the head with rapid tongue movements. He groaned and lowered his face onto my pussy, which felt like someone had doused it with hot water. As he got closer, his stomach brushed against my nipples, causing me extreme pain. Just as I pushed him off me, the doorbell rang.

I didn't want to answer the door, figuring it was probably one of the children's friends. But when the bell sounded for the third time, I slipped on my short terry robe, wincing as the fabric rubbed against my sore nipples, and went to answer it. I saw Bud climb back into the Jacuzzi, disappointed and deflated. When I opened the door and looked down (expecting a child), I saw a pair of long, lovely legs. I raised my eyes and saw that our visitor was a gorgeous, redhaired Amazon. She was so well built in her white tennis outfit, and she was so beautiful, that I gasped audibly when I looked into her green cat-eyes.

"Hi," she said. "I'm Mary. I just moved into the neighborhood." She paused, then explained, "I'm your new Avon Lady." I couldn't take my eyes off her face and, since I was still feeling unfulfilled, her body turned me on like crazy. I'd never had sex with a woman, but I love to look at all those tantalizing *Penthouse* Pets.

I invited her in so I could look through her brochure, asking her to join us in our backyard for margaritas. She accepted, following me out there. She sat down under the umbrella and I poured her a large drink while introducing her to Bud, who was as taken with her as I was. As we chatted, Bud stayed in the Jacuzzi, joking about the fact that he was naked. She countered that she had seen many nude men, having grown up with four brothers and been married for five years before her divorce. It sounded as though she were daring him to step out.

As I flipped through the brochure, I kept pulling the robe away from my body. Mary asked what was wrong and I told her about my sunburn. Without hesitation, she reached over and pulled the robe away from my chest to check out my nipples. She said she had a cream that she was sure would give me instant relief, then got up and went out to her car to get it. Bud just looked at me and grinned, like a smug Cheshire cat. When she came back, instead of giving me the tube, she offered to rub it in herself. She assured me several times that it would be quite clinical. I couldn't even look at Bud.

I lay back on the chaise and lowered my robe. She commented on how nice my breasts were (even though I'm thirty-eight, I maintain a smooth 36-25-36 figure). When she rubbed the cream on, I told her how much it hurt. She soothed me, all the while taking large gulps from her drink. Bud asked if she would like another drink, which she accepted. He climbed out and I could see he was at half mast. Mary said nothing but continued rubbing. My nipples began to tingle with odd sensations—at first hot, then cold, which in turn caused my pussy to pulsate like a rapid heartbeat.

Mary took another long drink and asked if I'd like to be rubbed all over. My God, I thought, I must be dreaming. These things don't happen in real life! I nodded shyly, unable to speak. She began working on my shoulders and I closed my eyes. Suddenly I felt hands on my feet (which are sensitive, too) and looked up to see Bud kneeling in front of me, a sexy grin on his face as he worked on my lower half, using some of Mary's "magic" cream. I began to squirm as Mary circled my breasts again with her long fingers, avoiding my nipples, while Bud's hands moved up and down my legs, gently kneading them.

After a while, Bud asked Mary if she'd like to smoke a joint with us. She said she never had before but was game to try everything at least once. This she said with a knowing glance toward me. I blushed, still unable to speak. Bud went quickly to our bedroom, where we store our joints in plastic sandwich wrap to keep them fresh. He came out and explained to her how to inhale. Then, like a proper host, he offered her the first hit. She choked for a while but gradually got the hang of it. We went through two joints because much of the first had been wasted. The combination of the marijuana and the margaritas began to give me a terrific high.

Then a strange thing happened. My nipples felt as though they were on fire—not in a painful way, mind you, but the best feeling I've ever had there. Mary watched me as I grabbed for them and she held my hands away and blew gently, first on my left nipple, then on my right. I couldn't stand it. I began moaning loudly. Then she bent down over me and placed her lips over my left nipple, while Bud took my right one into his mouth. I finally found my breath to speak and exclaimed, "I think I died and went to heaven!" They both laughed, then continued giving my breasts "first aid." Bud's mustached lips felt hard and demanding, while Mary's felt soft and delicate. It was like being tickled by sandpaper and a feather. What a sensation! After what seemed like ages, we all decided we were thirsty and made our way indoors.

Bud poured us each a glass of ice water, put some in a pitcher, and Mary and I followed him to our bedroom. We have a king-size water bed and one wall completely mirrored. My head was spinning and I quickly made my way to the center of the bed. Bud, flashing his thick erect cock, followed to my left. Mary stood in front of us and began a striptease that would have made any exotic dancer jealous, and I got to see the front as well as the back of her because of the mirror's reflection. When she stood naked before us, the pulse in my pussy began pounding so strongly that I had to grab myself just to ease the ache. Mary's breasts were large, yet they didn't sag. Her nipples were so pale that you had to look closely to see that they were there. I guess that's from her redhead's complexion. When I looked at her bush, a moan escaped me as I discovered she was completely shaved.

"Please," I begged her as I spread my legs. She crawled slowly onto the bed and eased her face teasingly toward my aching crotch. When her lips finally touched me there, I was so worked up that I began to come. She gently encircled my clit with her lips, took a deep breath and began to swirl it around, using her lips and tongue. I felt a stronger orgasm begin. Bud, idle until now, climbed over and sat on my chest, forcing his cock into my mouth. I had totally forgotten my sore nipples by then as I began to munch and chew and lick.

In the mirror I watched as Mary reached down between her legs and began to pump away at her naked pussy, and in seconds I felt the strongest orgasm I had ever had. First, my pussy pumped open and shut as usual, but then the pressure rose higher and I felt my stomach muscles tense and relax in rapid succession. My legs stiffened, my back stiffened, and my head was thrown forward, making me take in more of Bud than usual. Bud pushed toward me, his hands holding on to the headboard. As he came, he shouted so loud that I thought the neighbors might hear. Mary's mouth didn't stop working until I felt her shudder as she came seconds after I did.

We lay there for a while, panting, kissing and rubbing each other. When I regained my strength, I crawled between Mary's legs and did something I had wanted to do since first seeing her. I placed my lips gently over her naked sweet cunt and began to lick deeply, sticking my tongue in and out rapidly. I could tell by her sounds that she liked it. As I was doing this, I suddenly felt Bud's hands on my behind. He had found Mary's "magic" lotion and was spreading it over my little dark hole. This made me move my tongue even faster, which drove Mary crazy with pleasure. I felt the head of Bud's large cock at my anus and tried to relax while he thrust himself deep into my ass.

After about twenty thrusts, I reached down between my legs, grabbed my clit and began to pull and tug. The sensation of Mary's cunt in my mouth and Bud's cock filling my rectum was mindblowing and I soon had another incredible orgasm. Afterwards, Bud told me that when I came, my asshole got so tight that he'd thought he'd be locked inside forever.

We placed Mary between us, covered ourselves with a sheet, and fell happily asleep. Hours later, I awoke with a gnawing sensation of hunger. Pot does that to me. I quietly got out of bed, trying not to disturb Bud and Mary, and went into the kitchen to fix us some snacks. I cut up apples and cheese and opened a box of sesame crackers, arranging them on a tray as if I did this sort of thing every day—entertain a woman lover along with my husband of eighteen years.

I woke them up and while we sat and ate, Mary told us that she had been divorced for over a year and hadn't had sex during that whole time. She'd tried going to singles places but men had been intimidated either by her size (she's six feet tall) or by her looks. That was the first time I realized that being beautiful could be a hindrance. She said she'd decided to sell Avon products in order to meet her new neighbors and that she had been attracted to us immediately, finding our house and the way we lived very enviable. "Besides," she added with a sexy leer, "you and Bud really turned me on!"

With that she reached across to Bud, and began stroking his cock, which jumped to life again. I stared with strange fascination as I watched her make love to my favorite tool. I didn't feel jealous at all; in fact, it turned me on. I took the tray off the bed, sat down in the easy chair and watched as Mary and Bud fondled each other, using their hands and their tongues. I had never seen another couple make love, except in X-rated films. I could see Bud and Mary from all angles because of the mirror, and it was fantastic.

First, they deep-tongued each other, their hands moving all over. Then they got into a 69 position and, after a few minutes of this, Bud looked up and said to me, "Lady, from now on you're going to shave!" Of course, I knew what he was tasting because I had been there before, and I knew what he meant. Having it bare like that, all exposed and vulnerable, was thrilling.

By his groaning, I knew Bud was ready to fuck. He maneuvered Mary under him and she wrapped her long legs over his shoulders. He held her by her buttocks. When he entered her, she gasped and kept screaming, "Oh, my God! Oh, my God!" (I don't call Bud "Mr. Fat Dick" for nothing.) Then an idea struck me. I ran for some more of Mary's "magic" cream and rubbed it on my hands. I carefully climbed onto the bed and rubbed some of the cream on both Bud's and Mary's assholes, making them jump with delight. Then I slowly inserted a finger into each of their holes. Now, let me tell you, they really started squirming and jumping, but the more they moved, the deeper my fingers went. My heart pounded as I watched the finger of my left hand disappear into Bud's ass, then the finger of my right into Mary's.

I could feel Bud's orgasm begin because of the pulsating in his rectum, but I wasn't prepared for what I felt in Mary. It was like my finger was being chewed off! Her muscles grabbed, let go, grabbed, let go. First Bud exploded, then Mary, and we all started shouting together. Suddenly, Mary's legs stiffened and she straightened them on either side of Bud's head, catching him in an orgasmic headlock. I watched as her eyes rolled and her mouth worked in what looked like painful contortions. Seconds later, it was over. They fell apart from each other, covered with sweat, totally exhausted.

Needless to say, Mary never finished her rounds. In fact, she stayed the weekend. We wound up in all imaginable and unimaginable positions, and we counted at least fifty orgasms among us. We promised each other that this relationship wouldn't end and have even planned a week away at a cabin. I've shaved, too, and I've purchased a lifetime supply of that cream.—*Name and address withheld*

LONELY GAY MAKES A FRIEND

Having come out of the closet, so to speak, I would like to share a recent experience of mine at a small, male-dominated western college. Since I am gay and most of the other guys are straight, I was feeling very lonely as I watched the girlfriends of fellow students come and go. I was feeling isolated and rejected, and I was seriously considering going elsewhere to fulfill my sexual needs. That is, until I met Arthur.

We met at a school party where I was doing my best to act

straight amongst the guys. Then Arthur walked in. He seemed to be acting very freely, and was soon drinking and talking with some of the other students. I worked my way over to him, and we were soon engaged in a conversation about school life. As we talked, I realized that he was like me in many respects, and I had a deep yearning to get to know him better. He must have sensed something because he soon asked if I wanted to go to his room for a few brews. I almost creamed in my pants at the suggestion, and immediately said yes.

When we arrived at his room, he opened a couple of beers and calmly asked if I was gay. My immediate reaction was very defensive. When he said that he was gay, however, the ice seemed to break. I explained that indeed I was gay, and that I was feeling very lonely—and horny—because I could not find anyone else in the same predicament. He told me that he felt the same way and he had been overwhelmed with joy, when he had noticed the bulge in my pants at the party.

After what seemed an eternity, he began to rub my back and play with my crotch. I was getting very aroused, and before I could say "Let's fuck," we were tearing each other's clothes off. He then placed me on my stomach and thrust his six-inch cock deep into my waiting anus. I bucked to meet him, and almost immediately I could feel his warm come filling my insides. He collapsed on the bed and I mounted him, shoving my small-but-adequate five inches into his asshole. I felt like I was going to explode as I pumped and quickly shot gallons of my jism into him. Finally, I was relieved of my horniness!

We eventually settled down to more sensual play that night, and we continued sucking, fucking, and playing until dawn. I left his room feeling very happy and content, knowing that I had at last found a "friend" in a very straight school.

Although we don't love each other, Arthur and I have continued our loving relationship. I now feel more at ease with my fellow students, for I am no longer merely a frustrated onlooker.

And I know that the two years I have until graduation will be filled with pleasure and contentment.—*Name and address withheld*

HE DIDNT MAKE THE TEAM— BUT HE DID MAKE THE QUARTERBACK

I'm a junior in high school and just moved to Philly from the Midwest.

Last school year (my sophomore year) was so exciting. The first kid in school I got to know was a fellow named Joe, the star quarterback of our football team, and everyone knew him. By the end of the first semester we were best friends. We hung out together with his crowd.

One night we were at a party when Joe asked me whether I wanted to leave because I looked bored. I said I'd like to, and we drove to his house. All the lights were out, and I asked where everyone was, and he said, "Down at the shore."

After we were inside, he asked me to call my parents and tell them I was staying the night because in the morning we were going to go to the shore, too.

We went up to his bedroom and listened to records and drank sloe gin. He gave me a pair of pajamas to wear. Later that evening he asked to comb my hair. I thought that he was drunk and jokingly agreed. "Get up here on the bed, between my legs," he said. I did. About a half hour later he was still combing my hair. Suddenly he stopped and got off the bed and knelt in front of me. He said he wanted to talk seriously. I said, "All right."

He went on, "Your answer doesn't have to be yes, and don't let me pressure you into anything. I will understand if you say no." There was a long silence.

"Would you have sex with me? I've always wanted to try it. And since I met you, I've had a special feeling for you. I think you're very attractive, and we're close friends. If it doesn't work out, we could still be friends."

I'm not gay, and at first I was hesitant, but when Joe's big masculine hands went to work, I couldn't resist.

He rubbed my chest and then stopped. "Do you want me to stop?" he asked.

"No," I answered.

He undressed. I stared at him. He had a very handsome face and was clean shaven, with an extremely hairy chest for a seventeen-year-old. His arms and legs were hairy, and he had a lot of pubic hair. His cock had to have been at least ten inches. All these features on a very muscular body. I couldn't stand it.

He walked to the bed, unbuttoned my pajama shirt, and took it off. Then he pulled down my pajama pants and threw them on the floor. He stared at my dick as it began to extend to a full eight inches. He brought his face down between my legs and gave me the best blow job I've ever known. After I came, he sat beside me. He reached over to the night table and got some Vaseline. He began to grease my cock up. Then he knelt on the bed and told me to stick my dick up his ass. Slowly I entered him. It was so tight, and it felt great. I started pumping my jism in his hole as soon as he began groaning. I went to the bathroom to clean myself off. When I returned, Joe asked me to grease up. Gladly I greased my hand and started to jerk him off. Then I knelt on the bed, Joe kneeling behind me. He told me to lower myself slowly on him. I was scared but soon relaxed when I felt his cockhead touch my hole. When he got his whole ten inches in there, he bucked and rammed and in no time he spilled his load. He cleaned off, and when he came back, it was still hard. After he got in bed, with no word said, I sucked his cock. I wanted it so bad. I sucked the head, then deep-throated him, and then swallowed his come.

I was exhausted and lay on the bed. He got in next to me and rolled on top of me and started to kiss me full on the lips, and we began Frenching. His lips were so soft. I just gave in and began kissing him. Joe and I converted from that experience on, and the two of us often have sex with some of the other guys at school.

If you have the urge for gay sex, try it with a friend. If it doesn't work out, you can still be friends, and if it does, you get double pleasure.—*O.R., Philadelphia, Pennsylvania*

LEAVES WIFE, RUNS OFF WITH BEST FRIEND—HIS

Boy, am I surprised! I have been reading *Penthouse Letters* regularly and never thought that I would have anything of importance to write to you.

I'm a six-foot-two-inch stud. Most people say, because of my blond sun-bleached hair, that I look like Robert Redford. I am happy with my eight-inch cock and firm build.

Brad, my best friend, and I are both twenty-four. We lived next door to one another as kids, and we later went off to a swanky college together. We were always roommates, so I had seen Brad's beautiful body mature into that of a man. He has one of the largest cocks I've ever seen in any shower room. It's nearly ten inches long and bigger around than my wrist. Brad stands five-foot-ten, with a firm swimmer's body, jet-black hair—which he still wears long—and flashing green eyes. He has no hair on his body except around his cock. His smile could warm the coldest heart.

In college and up until I married thirteen months ago, Brad and I got more pussy than should be allowed by law. We were the college jocks and willing women were everywhere—shit, we are both handsome and frankly aware of it. As kids, we used to jack off together—but he always stayed in his bed and I remained in mine. I would hug him good-bye when he left to go home for a visit without me, but that's as close as we ever came to affectionate displays for one another—other than playing around in the showers, when we would pop wet towels on each other's ass.

We did meet some gay guys in high school and college. Some

of them became our friends, yet nothing sexual ever happened with them and us.

When I married Nancy Ann, a beautiful doll with jet-black hair like Brad's, he was my best man. Her family provided one of the largest weddings ever seen in the state. Nancy Ann had sixteen bridesmaids, and over two thousand people attended the ceremony and reception. The first ten months of married life were super great. Nancy Ann and I often fucked and sucked each other off three times a day during those first wonderful months. I suppose that it's pointless to say that Brad was at our penthouse (paid for by Nancy Ann's parents) at least six days a week. When Brad had a date, the four of us would go out on the town—and this occurred at least twice a week. After a while, Nancy Ann started getting on my ass about Brad being around so much. She started screaming at me, "You're gay! You're in love with Brad!" I slapped her around once for calling Brad "queer." As a result, my marital sex life became nothing. I was so pissed off at the way Nancy Ann was treating Brad that I just couldn't have cared less about making it with her.

About six weeks ago, Nancy Ann came up with the idea that she wanted to tie me to the bed. She wanted to have her way with my body, she said. I agreed to let her do it, thinking that it might save our marriage, for I really believed that I still loved her. So we talked it out in detail—and my cock got damn hard, too, as I listened to all the good things that she had planned for our evening of bondage.

We smoked a couple of joints before she had me lie on my back. She first tied my hands to the posts of the headboard. Then she tied my feet to my hands, leaving my ass wide open, up and ready for her hot tongue, which she loved to use. Man, she gave me a tongue bath from head to toe such as I had never had before. I wanted to blow my cream, but she wouldn't let me. Then, somehow, she worked herself between my tied-up arms and legs, placing her pussy right on my open mouth!

She was wet all over by then, and I was busily eating her out.

I couldn't understand how she was doing it, as my head was buried deep between her legs, but I felt something warm nudging at my asshole. The weight on the mattress shifted and I knew that someone else was in bed with us. I didn't know what to do as I felt first one finger, then two, working deep within my ass. Hell, it felt super—until I realized that a cock had entered my butt opening. I couldn't shout as Nancy Ann was pressing her pussy hard against my mouth. Soon the entire cock was inside of me, very slowly being worked in and out. After a brief shock of pain, it became the wildest sex I had ever dreamed of. To my astonishment, I realized that I wanted that cock inside of me.

Then I felt Nancy Ann being pulled away from me with such force that she fell against the wall across the room, and I heard Brad shout, "Okay, bitch, you set this up and now he's mine!" I raised my head to see Brad's beautiful mouth coming towards mine and he kissed me like I've never been kissed by any woman. As he returned to ass-fucking me, Brad somehow untied me. I wrapped my long legs around him and held him in my arms as he continued his long, deep, slow fucking of my ass. If ever two people were one, we surely were then. Brad told me when he was ready to come and we both shot off at the same time. He fell on top of me. His cock stayed deep inside me as we held one another.

By then, Nancy Ann was simply going crazy. She had talked Brad into what she thought would be "fun and games" for her, but her plan had backfired. Brad whispered into my ear that he had always loved me and no one else. I rubbed the come off my chest and onto my cock and slowly raised up Brad until he sat on top of me and I felt my cock enter his hot virgin ass. He and I must have fucked for more than an hour, neither of us wanting it to end, as Nancy Ann tore about the penthouse screaming, "Queers!"

Later, Brad and I showered together. Before we dressed, I walked naked to the bar and mixed us a couple of drinks, never saying a word to Nancy Ann, who was dressed by then. Brad and

I dressed slowly, never taking our eyes off each other. He reached into my closet and began packing an overnight bag for me. He never asked if I was going home with him; he just knew that I was and that I was leaving my wife forever for him.

As we left the penthouse that night, I held Brad's hand firmly in mine. When she saw Brad with my overnight bag, Nancy Ann really went nuts. She began screaming at us, but we could not have cared less by then. We departed without saying a word to her.

Brad and I are still deeply in love with one another. We have bought a ranch and are building a house just for the two of us. My divorce will be settled soon and that will be that. You might say that this was one time a lady overplayed her cards! Otherwise, I doubt that Brad and I could ever have been as totally happy as we are now. So, ladies, think twice before you offer your husband's body to his best friend!—*Name and address withheld*

SHE SEEKS SOLACE WITH BOYFRIEND'S SISTER; STAYS FOR SEX

My boyfriend likes to buy *Penthouse* and share it with me. He gets a particular thrill out of hearing me say how beautiful some girl's breasts are or how inviting her pussy looks. Scott also gets excited when I see a girl in the street and tell him how sexy I find her. Although I couldn't call myself bisexual, I feel I'm sufficiently liberated not to feel ashamed or guilty about acting like this to please Scott.

This little game goes on whenever we get together with his sister, Janice. Janice and I enjoy going along with the game, but we know if anything serious started, Scott would start feeling jealous and no longer be titillated by the whole thing.

Scott is in his last year of professional school and was scheduled to take a late flight to Chicago for a job interview. Janice,

Scott and I went to a pub near campus and had ourselves a few beers. I don't usually drink that much, but this was a special occasion and we were trying to make Scott more sure of himself for this interview. By the end of the evening, he was saying things like, "I know you'll be up to something when I'm gone." Naturally Janice and I caressed each other's hair and held hands. It was not serious, however. Around ten, Scott caught a cab and headed for the airport. He had told us to check his mailbox while he was gone. We wandered over to the law building and went to his box on the second floor. Both of us were slightly tipsy and my bladder was about to burst. The closest place to go was a men's room. Janice dared me to go in and suddenly I felt sexy and daring. We went in and I went over to the urinal as she guarded the door. I pulled my jeans to my ankles, pulled down my panties and stradled the urinal. As I held on to the separation and as Janice excitedly watched, I let a warm stream gush out of me. Some went down my thighs, but most of it flowed into the urinal, making a thunderous noise. Between the sound and feeling I closed my eyes and instinctively my hand went to my pussy to rub my throbbing clit. It didn't bother me that Janice was watching me do this. In fact, I was all the more excited by her presence. As the stream stopped, I took the hand that I had parted my labia with and extended it to Janice. Without a word she came over and we embraced. She opened her coat and her blouse, under which her breasts were bare. I had never seen them before. They were on the small side, with large, brown, pointed nipples. I hugged her and took her hand and placed it on my bush. Janice continued to rub me with her soft hands until after a few more minutes of heavy moaning, I came, my whole body shaking from the power of the orgasm.

Janice held me for a few silent moments until I began to half-laugh and half-cry. Then, as I held on to the sink nearby, Janice bent down, kissing as she went, to pull up my panties and jeans. We straightened ourselves up and exited, heading for her apartment. Janice drew a bath for me, which we both got into, and for the first time I saw Janice completely naked. She had a warm and inviting body, her skin was smooth and almost motherly. Her hips were full, and, my God, her pussy was incredibly hairy, covered in black silky curls. Needless to say we made love all that night, during which I, without any compunction, brought Janice to orgasm after orgasm with my fingers, my mouth, my tongue. She also excited me to higher heights, with, particularly, her tongue. None, however, was as powerful as that first orgasm. Janice's fingers on my blond triangle have never duplicated themselves.—*Name and address withheld*

HE CAN'T RESIST THE BIG WHOPPER

Last Saturday evening one of the greatest experiences of my life happened, and I want to share it with you.

My sister Nancy, and her husband, David, my wife, Susan, and I went out to dinner at this really great restaurant in Malibu that we had all been wanting to try. The food was terrific, but David and I had a little too much wine. By the time we finally got home, David couldn't even walk. So I had to almost carry him into the house, while Susan and Nancy drove the babysitter home.

We finally made it to the bedroom, and I just let him fall on the bed. As I began to take his shoes off, I decided to play a little joke on him and take off everything before the women got back. David was now completely out of it, and I started in. We had taken showers at the gym together before, but this really seemed different. I really started to get turned on.

I managed to get his shirt off without much trouble. His chest was really big, with dark-black hair all over it running down his abdomen and into his jeans. Once I got them off, I noticed he was wearing the bikini briefs Nancy had bought him last Christmas. They bore a message on the fly: Home of the Big Whopper.

At first I was afraid he would wake up. So I moved his legs

around to make sure. Then I just laid my hand on top of his cock. It felt so neat to touch another man. I had really never given it much thought before. While I slowly removed the briefs, his cock sprang alive. He was always teasing Nancy about how big his cock was, but he wasn't lying; he had at least eight-and-a-half or nine inches buried in black hair. His balls looked so perfect, I cupped them in my hands and gave each one a kiss.

I was so hot by now, my own cock was almost bursting out of my pants. I carefully put his cock in my mouth and just whirled my tongue around the huge shaft. What a great sensation! He started to move around. So I stopped and headed for the door. Then he said, "Tony, I'm really sick. Help me to the bathroom." So I walked back into the room, helped him up, and started for the bathroom. He noticed he was naked and still had a hard-on with my saliva still glistening all around his shaft. He only laughed and said the damn thing would never stay down and hoped that I wouldn't get too turned on. Little did he know.

We have since played racquetball at the gym twice, and I still can't look at his cock without thinking of that night. Maybe we can switch off some evening. Susan is always telling me she would like to try something different. She and Nancy, David and I, but I doubt that will happen soon. However, I am surely looking forward to it. The best of both worlds. Everyone should at least try it!—*P.T., Los Angeles, California*

SEX-CRAZED STUDENTS IN ALL-NIGHT LIBRARY ORGY

I'm a student at a large midwestern university, but I have often wished I attended a school where all those wild sexcapades are said to take place. Or that's what I thought until one night last semester.

Having a history midterm on a Monday morning, I decided to go to the library and cram for my test all day Sunday. I had been studying nonstop since early afternoon and had apparently dropped off to sleep at one of the corner tables on the second floor. When I suddenly jerked awake, I realized that it was eleven at night and the library was closed. Drowsily looking up, I saw three library aides staring at me, two guys and a girl. The girl's name was Sue; the guys were Tim and Keith. They all just stared at me for a moment, then looked at one another and began laughing, too.

Keith stepped forward and said that this happened all the time, and that I needn't worry about it. Then he asked if I would like to party with them. I said sure and asked them where the party would be. They answered in unison, "Right here." We walked downstairs to the employees' lounge. Tim opened up a small refrigerator and took out a case of beer, while Sue pulled out a bag of weed from one of the drawers. The three of them escorted me to the periodicals section, where we drank and smoked all there was. Everyone was really buzzed, and Sue was nuzzling up to me, driving me wild by nibbling on my ear, while Tim and Keith just sat and watched with big grins on their faces.

Sue and I were soon into some pretty heavy petting. After a while, I saw that Tim and Keith were making out, too. I must have had a pretty strange look on my face, because Sue began laughing at me, and then took my hand and led me over to where the boys were. Deftly, she unzipped Tim's pants, pulled out his ten-inch cock and began sucking on it. I really enjoyed watching her tongue slide up and down the long shaft. Suddenly, she stopped. As if by cue, everyone stood up and stripped in record time.

We all got comfortable again, and Sue started sucking Keith's eight-incher. I just sat on a lounge chair, watching the proceedings and wondering if this was actually happening. Sue looked up and said, "I think you ought to finish what I started," pointing to Tim's considerable cock. Tim approached me and, before I had a chance to protest, he began slipping his cock into my mouth. I was scared shitless. I mean, I'd occasionally thought about making it with another guy before, and I'd had plenty of chances but always chickened out at the last minute.

If I hadn't been so stoned, I probably would have run out now, but what the hell, I thought, and began to suck him off, getting as much of his cock as I could deep down my open throat. Still, I managed to get only about seven inches of it past my lips. I was truly amazed at how easy it was, especially since I gag even when I brush my teeth.

It wasn't long before Tim started moaning and pumping his ass, furiously driving his banana all the way down my throat. His huge balls slapped against my chin with each lunge. I didn't really know what was going on when he started gushing in my mouth. Then, before I had a chance to do anything, Tim pulled me up and started Frenching me, stirring his semen around in my mouth with his expert tongue.

Apparently, we had made quite an impression, because Sue and Keith were sitting bolt upright, watching us. Before I knew what had hit me, Keith began ramming *his* eight-inch cock down my throat, and Sue was eagerly attacking my own eight inches. Tim was at the end of the line, happily munching on Sue's delicious twat, which I was to taste many times that night. I couldn't believe that I was sitting there, letting some guy I hardly knew ram his dick down my throat, and that I was actually enjoying it. Keith spouted his load in my mouth; this time, I swallowed it and found that it wasn't bad-tasting at all. A few seconds later, I discharged into Sue's mouth.

We all lay on the floor, and Sue looked over at me. We both had come dripping down our chins. She let out a big sigh and started laughing again. Tim and Keith joined in.

We stayed in the library till after five o'clock that morning, doing everything we could think of to each other. I am now the greatest of friends with them and plan to move in with Tim this coming semester. I also plan to submit an application to become a library aide, for I've come to realize that the bookworm is something to be reckoned with.—*T.F., Rolla, Missouri*

AMERICAN GOES GAY IN GERMANY

I am a twenty-one-year-old guy who'd never ever dreamed of having anything to do sexually with some other guy, but now it's happened. Here's my story.

I am an American living in West Germany, and recently I met a middle-aged gentleman here. Let's say Tom is his name. A married man with three kids, he looks very good despite his age. He has a mixture of black and white hair. Except for his prick, he has hair on every part of his body, especially his chest. His prick is a thick and beautiful nine-incher, and his balls—gee whiz!—they can drive a person crazy. Everything put together, he is "sextastic." By the way, Tom is forty-two years old.

Well, it all began at a supper while his wife and kids were away in Austria. When I arrived at his place, we sat down and had a drink and some chitchat. After about half an hour, he excused himself and went to his bedroom, explaining that he wanted to make himself comfortable. He returned a few minutes later with a robe on. I didn't know yet that he was naked under the robe.

Well, then he asked me whether I was interested in porno movies. I said, "Yeah, sure I am," which was the truth. I love watching porno movies.

Anyway, we watched two movies and I could feel my prick getting naughty. The third film showed three guys doing all sorts of gay things to each other. It was most instructional and I got so horny that I wanted to jack off. I excused myself and went looking for the loo. I couldn't find it, so I went into Tom's bedroom and started jacking away. In less than a minute, I came all over my clothes and the bed, and I tried to cool down.

I went back to the sitting room and found Tom sitting with his huge dick in his hands, watching another gay film. He asked me to sit down and watch him, for he wanted to teach me a new jerk-off technique. Again my dick was hard as steel and I had to let it out of my pants. When I asked him if I could, he looked at me and started stripping off my clothes very slowly. Before I knew it, his mouth was on my mouth. His tongue caressed my tongue. Within two minutes I was out of my clothes, standing in front of him in my birthday suit. That was when he took my prick in his hand and started stroking it. Then he was on his knees with my whole seven-inch prick in his mouth and his hand stroking my balls. It was fantastic!

The porno film soon ended, but not our fun and games. We lay on the carpet and engaged in a fantastic 69. We both came at almost the same time in each other's mouth. His wad was huge and hot as hell. I just couldn't swallow it fast enough. It was trickling out the corners of my mouth. I also came a lot, but not as much as he did.

Tom and I took a little rest, but soon his prick was standing tall again. This time he led me into the bathroom. He left me alone for a few minutes and then came back with two bottles of wine. After we got into the bathtub, he opened the bottles, poured the wine over my body and started licking it off me. Never before had I experienced anything so wonderfully kinky.

After licking all the wine off of me, Tom greased up his cock and fucked me to glory. In the beginning it hurt, but then it was fantastic. I was sitting on his prick, which was completely inside me, and I was humping away wildly. When he had come in my ass, he said, "Fuck me! Please fuck me!" When I did, I discovered for the first time that a man's ass can be as pleasure-giving as a woman's vagina.

Tom and I retired to bed for more fucking and sucking. The next morning, I admired his prick while he was still asleep. I woke him up with my prick inside him, and we spent that whole day in and out of each other's mouth and ass. It was great!

Tom and I are still having our wild affair. His wife wants a divorce because of me. Tom has told her that he loves me and wants only me. I feel the same about him. We are very happy together.—*P.G., Stuttgart, West Germany*

TELEPHONE INSTALLER GETS CONNECTED—IN THE ASS!

I hate to sound like a broken record, but until recently, I'd always thought that a great many of the experiences related in *Penthouse Letters* were mere fantasies. Recently, however, I had one of the most erotic experiences of my life. Since it changed my mind about the veracity of the letters you publish, I've decided to share it with your other readers.

I am a happily married man who has always had a satisfying sexual relationship with my wife, but she is old-fashioned and doesn't care for many deviations from what she considers proper. Before we were married, I'd had my share of sex with guys as well as gals. I do enjoy a good romp with a healthy, sexy guy, but I couldn't live without pussy.

My wife and I have been designing and building our own house on the beach for over a year now. When it was almost complete, I asked the telephone company to come and install phone jacks. When the phone man came, I happened to be at home alone. I had been working and was all sweaty, so I had gone into the house to take a shower. No sooner was I in the shower than I heard someone calling out, "Hello! Is anyone home?"

I parted the shower curtain, and there stood this guy—six feet four inches, blond and tanned—grinning sheepishly. He was very embarrassed. After telling him that I would be right with him, I got out of the shower and threw on a robe. I walked out to the foyer, where he was bent over, fumbling with his phone equipment, and I couldn't help but admire his ass. I cleared my throat to get his attention. He stood and turned around, asking where I wanted the jacks installed. My eyes went to his crotch, which was bulging so much that I thought his jeans would split.

Well, that did it for me. My dick shot straight out of my robe. His eyes went from my eyes to my cock, and before I could say anything, he was on his knees and my cock was down his throat. His beard was doing wild things to my balls, and all I could do was moan. To avoid coming too soon, I had to push him away.

This being the first sexual contact that I'd had with another male in ten years, I wanted it to last.

When I'd gotten his mouth off my meat, he began removing his clothes. When he stripped down to the nitty-gritty, I could see that he was hung with about eight inches. My cock is the same length, but his was thicker.

We fell on the floor and started to explore each other's body. Before I knew what was happening, he had me on my back and was sitting on my face! That really threw me for a loop, mainly because I had never done anything like that before. I had eaten my share of pussies, but had never tasted a hairy asshole before. He kept grinding his backside down on my tongue. The harder he did it, the more I loved it. His balls were riding up and down my chin, and his tool was making a slippery trail on my chest. I was going nuts. I could tell that he was really hot and almost ready to shoot his load.

All of a sudden, he put his head down and took my hot tool in his mouth. He pumped up and down on it a couple of times. Then he got on his knees, resting his head on his arms, and arched his ass in the air. All he said was "Fuck me hard."

At this point, I was so hot that I would have done anything he asked. I just slid up behind him, positioned my tool, and shoved it into his hole. His ass was so wet from my saliva that my eight-incher slid all the way in, and he began grinding his ass against me. Just as I was really beginning to enjoy myself, he flipped over on his back, giving me much better access. He then wrapped his legs around my waist and went crazy. Until then, I'd thought that I was the one who was doing most of the work, but I realized now that he was providing most of the motion. I was getting the screwing of my life. That man had better muscle control of his ass than any woman—any whom I have ever screwed, at least—has had with her pussy. Needless to say, he brought me off in a matter of minutes. At the same time, he squirted his big load all over me.

We made plans to meet again soon. Next time, he is going to

bring along his girlfriend, because he has always fantasized about screwing her while he is being butt-fucked by a guy.—*Name and address withheld*

COCKS NEVER PLEASED HER, SO SHE GOES FOR PUSSIES

My name is Samantha. I'm one of those tall, leggy, seemingly aloof gals that most guys go gaga about, but which few know how to handle.

The aloof part goes with my upswept brunet hair and a Ph.D. in what is called TESL—Teaching English as a Second Language. My job here, at a West Coast university, has brought me into contact with a lot of African men who have exaggerated ideas about their dongs.

Well, I took a lot of bragging from this one guy for about three weeks. He was given to wearing colorful Nigerian dress on campus and around town, and it was a kick to be seen with him. After an evening out, heading for my place, he'd nibble my ear and tell me just how many times he was going to get hard for me. He made a believer out of me—for a few hours, anyway. But then, damn it—well, there's a helluva lot more to lovemaking than a stiff prick.

After that, I started dating some of the tennis clones on campus. I play tennis a lot, and they seemed to breed on center court. Most of them are virile and handsome, but those I bedded were lousy lovers. I mean, I like to dive between the sheets as much as the next lady, but I prefer to be sweet-talked along the way—and, afterwards, I hate being left abruptly, with only the moon going down on me.

Things were looking pretty drab as far as my personal life was concerned, although I enjoyed my work immensely. So much so that my good friend, Carol, who is the school dean and my boss, gave me a promotion and a raise, and named me as hostess to foreign visitors on campus. Carol, I should add, is a shapely brunet with a perfect rear end.

My first charges in my new capacity were two flaxen-haired charmers from Sweden. Their names were Inga and Lili. Both were rosy-checked, blue-eyed, and naturally, gloriously, blond!

On our first outing with them, Carol and I were obligated to take them to a faculty gathering. They circulated charmingly and furthered the whole foreign-exchange program with their sparkling presence. Once, Inga squeezed my knee under the table while a pompous professor babbled his admiration. I patted hers in return.

The next night, the four of us slipped away to an off-campus cocktail lounge. We introduced the girls to two or three presentable guys, but Lili seemed distracted, and Inga suggested that we four women just find a quiet table and talk. "We see guys all the time," she explained. "It's such a bore!" Thinking of my disappointing experiences, I nodded sympathetically. We moved to a dark corner table, where we sat down for a delightful conversation.

The girls from Sweden had traveled extensively, representing a prominent European university. I mentioned to Inga that my former husband was in Kenya.

"Then you're not married, Samantha?" she mused.

"Not any longer," I said. "He was like a little boy in a man's body."

"Well, maybe he'll grow up in Kenya," Lili laughed. "The natives really *do* get restless there." She had her arm over Carol's shoulder and impulsively kissed her cheek in amusement. Carol blushed and squeezed Lili's hand. It excited me to see their contrasting blond and brunet heads so close together.

When the time came for Carol and me to get our visitors back to the VIP dorm, we invited them to play tennis in the morning. Lili said she had a tennis outfit with her, but that Inga's had been lost in transit. "No problem," I said to Inga. "You can borrow one of mine."

"Weren't they great?" Carol enthused as we drove home after dropping them at the dorm.

"Great!" I affirmed, remembering the heave of Inga's breasts as she had laughed and talked so joyously. And I could still feel the warmth of her hand on my knee. Later, as I undressed for bed I discovered a wetness between my thighs and went to sleep feeling curiously more happy than I had been in years.

When we all met on the tennis courts the next morning, both the girls looked stunning, although it was obvious that Inga's outfit wasn't her own. She wanted to be my partner. Although flattered, I had strangely mixed emotions about this—maybe because, from the other side of the net, I would have been better able to feast my eyes upon her. I realized that I had some kind of a silly crush on her.

We played three sets, and when Inga and I won, she came over and hugged me. Her firm breasts pressed against mine, and one of her lovely legs ventured up between my thighs. I almost fainted. Probably I would have, except for Inga's sudden scream of pain as she stepped back and clutched her crotch. I knew what was wrong instantly.

"Don't worry," I said to the others. "I know what to do. I'll take her to the faculty locker room. I have something there that'll take care of it." I urged Lili and Carol to play another set, promising that we'd meet them later.

What had happened to Inga had once happened to me. She had borrowed a one-piece tennis outfit that I'd bought with more regard to fashion than comfort. The fabric was rough and the fit was tight. If you didn't wear a pair of panties underneath, and if you were very active and perspired a lot, a friction developed in the crotch that caused a sharp burning sensation. Inga could hardly walk as I led her into the empty locker room and sat her down on one of the long benches. While explaining what had happened, I removed her shoes and socks, and got her out of the tennis dress. Then I went to get a towel and a pan of hot water. When I returned and knelt at her feet to give her first aid, I couldn't help gasping as I looked up at her beauty. Inga wasn't wearing a bra, and her nipples were hard, probably from the pain.

I gently spread her legs and patted her vulva with the warm, damp towel. She stifled her moans of pain and reached out and pulled my head close to her smooth, tight little tummy, where I could catch the scent wafting up from her reddened cunt. Although I was trembling, I had to use the towel very carefully to keep from hurting her.

"Does that feel better?" I asked softly, still kneeling between her legs. She didn't reply, but her gasps of pain eased off into moans and sighs of pleasure as my movements became more rhythmic. Finally, she reached out and brought my face to hers. Our mouths opened to each other, and our tongues touched and intertwined as our saliva mixed and flowed. I moved my head tenderly down to her breasts, first kissing, then licking, then sucking, then nibbling, and when she sighed that she wanted me to bite them, I did, and she groaned with delight.

All this time, I was lightly fingering her vulva. Now I gradually increased the pressure on her clitoris, but I didn't get the wild reaction that I expected. She reached down and pulled my head up. "You know what's happened?" she said. "The pain must have dulled my senses down there."

"Well, we can't have that, can we?" I said.

"I was about to come as never before, and I want you to finish me off," she said.

Inga got up gingerly and led me by the hand into the shower. After turning on the cold water, she gently washed and massaged her tender area for about three minutes. Then she shut off the shower, held her lips to mine, and said, "Now I think I'm ready."

She hugged me tight as we kissed and breathed in the aromas of each other's womanhood. Dreamily, I knelt and continued with my tongue and lips what I had begun earlier with my finger. "When you're through," I heard her whisper, "I will make love to you, my dear, as you've never been made love to before." The next half hour with Inga was the closest I've ever been to paradise.

The following day, as Carol and I were returning from the airport, where we had dropped the girls, I noticed a fresh bloom and vibrancy about her. She caught me staring.

"You're looking very well," I said.

"Thank you." She smiled.

"I'm going to miss the girls very much." As I said this, I caught myself practically gushing like a schoolgirl. We both laughed. "You, too?" I asked.

"Oh, indeed," she said fervently, "I'll miss Lili very much!"

I knew what Carol was really telling me, and it confirmed a long-held suspicion. I reached over and ran my hand along her smooth thigh. "Maybe we don't have to be lonely," I said.

Carol smiled and pressed her hand on mine. "Let's find out!" she said urgently. "Let's stop at my place right now and find out."—*S.A. Tucson, Arizona*

SEXY WIFE SEEKS SATISFACTION WITH GAY LOVER

I am a horny twenty-two-year-old who works full-time and attends college part-time. I am fortunate enough to have a husband who understands my highly sexed nature. Recently, I took advantage of my freedom to try something different and exciting. It was so fabulous that I just had to share it with your readers.

I have always harbored a secret desire to make love to another woman. When I spotted an encouraging ad from a bisexual woman in a local swingers' magazine, I decided to make my move. We met at my house and had a few drinks to get acquainted. She was young, well-built, and almost as anxious as I to begin our passionate encounter. Staring longingly at each other's bodies, we agreed to retire to the bedroom. After eagerly shedding our clothes, we slowly began caressing one another.

I found myself fascinated by the incredible softness of another woman's body. Soon the air was filled with the sounds of passionate sighs and moans. This lady turned me on as no man ever had before. She gently sucked my nipples and caressed the soft contours of my tingling breasts. With exquisite skill and tenderness, she kissed her way down to my cunt, which was steaming by the time she reached it. She licked, sucked and kissed every inch of my pussy. Her soft lips felt terrific on my hot cunt. She brought me to the brink of orgasm again and again. When she finally made me come, I was screaming for more!

Then it was her turn to enjoy the pleasure of a warm tonguing. I loved sucking her firm tits. Then I finger-fucked her and sucked on her clitoris. We both had very powerful orgasms several times that night, and we were bathed in sensual sweat when at last we lay resting in each other's arms, exhausted but content. It was an award-winning show, and I'm sure there will be many repeat performances.—*D.F.S., Nashville, Tennessee*

IT'S PUSSY TO PUSS—AND THEN SOME COCK

I enjoy letters from other women and I would like to tell your readers a little story about something that happened to me last summer.

A friend of mine came to visit for the week. She had just been divorced. Over cocktails and lunch we discussed, among other things, the sexual merits of our respective husbands. Hers, she complained, had very few. We then decided to take a nude sunbath on the upstairs porch. When we got undressed, she was fascinated that my pussy was shaved. She could not take her eyes off my crotch. After a few minutes on the porch, she offered to put body oil on me, and I accepted. She rubbed it all over me, particularly on my behind, and I found myself becoming very aroused. She asked me to roll over so she could do the front, and I gladly did. She started on my stomach, then went up to my breasts and started playing with my nipples. I couldn't help but moan and open my legs a little. I was old enough to know what was going to happen next, and it did. She started kissing my breasts and put her finger on my clit and began to rub it. I pushed her head down, and she went willingly. I never had a woman do that to me before, but it was great. While she was doing it, I knew that I wanted to do the same to her.

After I had a wonderful orgasm and relaxed for a few minutes, I started the same rubdown on her. What a delight it was to suck her breasts (now I know why men enjoy it so much). Finally I went down on her, and it was wonderful. I had never done this before and, while I won't make a habit of it, I will do it again. After this we decided to shave her pussy, which I did. We then decided to have some fun with my husband when he came home. We both put on miniskirts and see-through blouses and fixed him drinks. We also went out of our way to bend over in front of him and we were soon telling him about the delights we'd enjoyed that afternoon.

As it was hot when he got home, he had changed into shorts. I could see his erection growing. Finally we told him to shut his eyes because we had a surprise for him. With that, we both took off our clothes and sat on the coffee table with our legs open. Then we told him to open his eyes and look. He got really hard and my friend and I started playing with him as well as playing with each other. We then both went down, trading his cock back and forth. When he came in my mouth, my friend kissed me so that she could taste his jism. We kept this up the whole week, with many more things that are too involved to describe. There were no inhibitions on anyone's part.—*Name and address withheld*

COLLEGE GALS LOVE EACH OTHER'S STUDENT BODY

I am a nineteen-year-old coed who was introduced to the glories of female love by an older friend when I was sixteen. We still get together occasionally, but she is married now with two small children, so our relationship has cooled considerably over the past few years.

When I first came to school I was very apprehensive about a lot of things: grades, friends, guys, but most of all, my lesbian love life. I was afraid that I wouldn't be able to find any willing partners for myself. How wrong I was.

I moved into a dorm during New Student Week. I was all moved in by the afternoon; however, my roommate had not shown up. Then there was a knock on the door and in walked the most beautiful blonde I had ever seen in my life. She said, "Hi! You must be Jan." I said, "That's right." She told me her name was Lynn, and I helped her move her things in.

I couldn't keep my eyes off her. She was gorgeous! She was wearing the shortest cutoffs I had ever seen, and they served to accent her perfectly formed legs, which she kept slightly separated during our conversation. My eyes kept wandering to her crotch. She was also wearing a tiny pink halter, which barely contained the fullness of her breasts. Her nipples showed plainly through the material. We finally decided to go out for some dinner, but I couldn't wait for nightfall so I could have her alone again.

By the time we arrived back in our room, it was getting to be pretty late, and I was getting hot! I told her I was going to take a shower and get ready for bed. I hurried through it as quickly as I could and returned to the room in my robe. I found that Lynn had also undressed and was wrapped in a towel that barely reached below her pubic area.

I must say that I consider myself a good-looking girl. I have a good figure with full breasts and shapely legs. I noticed that she seemed as interested in looking at me as I was in looking at her. I sat on my bed and started to apply baby powder to my shoulders. Suddenly Lynn came over and took the bottle out of my hand. She said, "Here, let me do that for you. Why don't you slip your robe down?" I slipped the robe from my shoulders and lay on my stomach on the bed. She started to smooth the baby powder on my back. My heart was racing from the soft touch of her delicate fingers. Slowly she pulled the robe completely away to reveal my smooth buttocks. She delicately squeezed them with her fingers. She ran her fingers down the insides of my legs and I thought a flood was going to pour from my pussy.

"Turn over," she whispered, and I did. She gasped as she saw for the first time my beautiful breasts. First she massaged them. Then, in a flash, her mouth was all over them, kissing, sucking, licking, biting. She slid out of her towel and it was my turn to gasp. Her creamy breasts were tipped by two rosy nipples that stood out like little pebbles, just waiting to be sucked. I nearly lost my breath when I saw her silky blond pubic hair. Her hands sank to my thighs and she gently separated them. She plunged her middle finger into me, and I grabbed for her breasts with all the passion in me. Finally, she lowered her head to my vaginal lips, and her licking drove me into ecstasy. I knew I wanted to do the same for her, and I pulled her crotch to my face. We made passionate love throughout the night and we have been tight ever since.

I am gratified to see that your magazine appreciates the tender relationship that two women can have with each other. I have read your letters from other women saying that they were turned on by the thought of making it with another gorgeous girl, and I also think that most men enjoy viewing two beautiful women making it. So here's a vote of confidence from someone who thinks you're the greatest.—*Name and address withheld*

IT'S A DREAM COME TRUE WHEN HE WATCHES WIFE MAKE HER BEST FRIEND

My wife, Liz, and I have been married for nineteen years. We have a good sex life together: We do everything in bed that we possibly can. I have even told my wife the two fantasies that I have about her: One is to see her suck another guy's cock, and the other is to see her make it with another beautiful woman. Well, neither of these sexual fantasies appeal to her, she says, so we have left it at that.

Well, my wife has a good friend, Patricia, whom she's known all her life. And I've always wanted to fuck her since I first met my wife. Pat has a nice pair of tits on her—big and hard. I know because I used to grab on to them every once in a while when my wife wasn't around. Pat was married for a short while and then she got divorced.

Now, my wife likes to make all her own clothes, and a few months ago Pat wanted her to make a dress for her. Well, this one night Pat was coming over for a fitting, and I said to my wife—just kidding—"Can I hide in the closet and watch Pat undress?" Much to my surprise, she said, "Whatever turns you on—but you'd better be ready to give me a good fucking after!" I assured her I would. When Pat came over and asked where I was, Liz told her I was out with the boys. I had actually gotten in the closet about five minutes before she arrived.

I had the sliding door open about two inches so I could see the whole room. Pat had on a blue denim shirt and shorts. Liz told her she'd better take off her shirt so the dress would fit right. Well, Pat started to unbutton her shirt, and I started to shake all over. She had no bra on, and her tits stood out real nice, with nipples the size of silver dollars. I had a hard-on instantly and noticed my wife gazing at those big tits for a few seconds while Pat was putting on the dress.

After my wife made the fitting, she told Pat to take the dress off carefully so as not to stick herself with the pins. As Pat stood there with just her short shorts on, I got the shock of my life. All of a sudden my wife reached up and put her hands on Pat's tits. Pat never moved; all she did was close her eyes and moan lustily. My wife quietly told her what a nice pair of tits she had, and then she started playing with her nipples. She put her mouth on one of Pat's nipples and started to suck it greedily. After about a minute she went to the other one, and Pat was really starting to get hot by now, which was when my wife reached down and ran her hands all over Pat's thighs.

It wasn't long before Liz unzipped Pat's shorts and pulled them down, revealing to both of us that Pat didn't have on any panties. Liz played with Pat's nice brown hairy cunt and soon stuck a finger in. This really started Pat going. They began kissing each other and sucking each other's tongue, and Pat reached around behind and undid my wife's halter and started sucking her tits. By this time I had already shot a full load without even having to touch my cock. The next thing I knew they were on the bed sucking each other's cunt.

After Pat left, my wife asked if I was happy now. I said I sure was and asked her how she had liked sucking her best friend. She said it was great. Pat and my wife get together about once a week now, and I hide in the closet to watch.—*Name and address withheld*

Two Glee Club Members Make Each Other's Member Sing

I remember, when I was at college, that every spring our men's glee club gave concerts in many small towns in our region of the Southwest. We spent two weeks on the road and stayed at private homes of individuals who sponsored the concerts. It was a very enjoyable break from routine—and sometimes something more, as the following story will reveal.

The glee club professor usually assigned two students to a home. In most cases we stayed with well-to-do families, so each student had his own room. Every now and then, we would bunk in a more modest place, where we would have to share a room or a bed. That is what happened on the occasion that I'm writing about.

My roommate this particular time was Fred, a very good-looking, tall, blond fellow with lips as sensuous and full as a girl's. When we went to bed, he asked if I minded that he slept in the nude. It was his custom, he explained. I said that it was OK with me. I put on my pajamas and got into the double bed. Fred began to undress from the bottom up—first his shoes, then his socks, pants and shorts. As he stood on his side of the bed stretching, I couldn't keep myself from staring at his genitals.

Now you should know that at eighteen I had already had a number of pleasant homosexual experiences with my neighbor back home, as well as with my older brother. But so far, there had been no action at all at college. I was too interested in football and girls. Nonetheless, I am a true bisexual, and this close-up view of Fred's nice long dong, surrounded by a bed of curly blond hair and two rather formidable-looking testicles, was getting to me. I decided that his sex organ was as beautiful as any I had seen, and my libido started to get in gear.

I kept sneaking looks at his naked cock and balls, but I wasn't sure whether he noticed me looking. He finished undressing slowly—very slowly, it seemed to me—sort of showing off his sex equipment while the light was on. But my sense of caution at that moment was stronger than my curiosity, so I shook all thoughts of sex from my mind, rolled over and soon fell asleep. Fred got in bed, said good night and stayed on his side of the bed at first. It was about eleven o'clock.

Now, nobody sleeps in one spot all night long. Fred didn't and I didn't, either. It wasn't long before our bodies were touching, seemingly at random and without meaning to. Vaguely, at one point, I had the feeling that Fred's thigh was against my buttock. It felt warm and comfortable, so I simply relaxed in my half-sleep and didn't move. A bit later, I had a dreamy feeling that a hand was on my thigh. It didn't bother me or awaken me entirely, but the next thing I felt was the hand under my pajama top, lightly resting on the back of my neck, and this couldn't be ignored or mistaken. Fred was making overtures.

I didn't mind. When his hand reached around my waist, I quietly put my hand over it and squeezed a little. Fred's response was immediate. He shifted his body so that his groin was directly against my buttocks and began to unbutton my pajama top. I could feel his gorgeous prick hardening fast, so I thrust backward with my rear end. He met the challenge and pressed his now-erect penis against my pajama-clad anus. My own prick had risen by now. I was hot and horny and knew I was in for a fun night. While Fred was removing my top, I started to slip out of the bottoms. In seconds I was as naked as he.

I turned over on my left side to face him, put my arms around his neck and kissed his delicious, softly feminine lips. He responded warmly, his tongue seeking mine. With his hand, he now brought our pricks together so that they touched and slowly began to stroke. My God, what an electric feeling! I kissed him again and again, never getting enough of his wonderful lips and mouth. The good feelings from my prick were now running throughout my body. I reached down and caressed his balls, which felt like plump peaches. I thought: peaches now, cream in a little while. Oh Christ! I was in a heaven of ecstasy. But I wanted to see him better. I wanted to look at, kiss and suck that cock of his, which, when erect, must be the most exciting piece of manhood I'd ever seen. So I said, "Let's lock the door and turn on the light, so we can really enjoy this." He let go of my prick, got up and secured the bolt on the door, then turned on the bed lamp.

He was beautiful, standing and holding his prick so that it pointed in my direction. I haven't mentioned that his prick was circumcised, which was something new to me. For sucking, I thought, a totally exposed penis head looks really inviting, and it puts the lips and tongue in direct contact with the most sensitive areas. As I sat on the edge of the bed, my organ fully engorged, he came nearer. "Suck me," he said. And I did, gladly. His was a cock I could suck forever. I licked the tip and under the glans. I kissed and sucked the tip. Then I put the whole wonderful thing in my mouth. He rubbed my hair and soon moved to the bed and lay on his back. I knelt over his prick and shoved my own cock in his willing mouth.

I was in heaven. Imagine, here I was with a casual acquaintance, in a strange house, performing the most intimate and sensuous sex acts. Just thinking about it caused me to come in a great big way, which, in turn, set Fred off. After jerking violently several times, his rigid cock ejected rich, delicious cream into my receptive and greedy mouth. My own formidable weapon shot loads of steaming love fluid past his hot red lips, every drop of which he swallowed.

We had been making love for about thirty minutes before we climaxed. Now came the difficult part. How would we act and what would we say?

"Well," said Fred, standing up, his prick soft but still swollen, "I never thought that this would happen with you. Sure hope you'll keep this to yourself."

"Don't worry about me," I said as I started to put on my pajamas. "I'm a believer in free love and good fun between friends of any sex. But I do believe in privacy, and I count on you for the same."

So, being in agreement about that, we decided to go back to sleep. But Fred asked me not to wear my pajamas. "I want to hold you naked throughout the night," he explained.

He turned out the light and we got into bed. For some reason, I now felt full of desire again. Rarely did my sex urge come back to life so soon. What the hell, I said to myself, melting into his arms. He offered me his lips, which I kissed again with no diminution of feeling. Naturally, my prick rose, and I could feel his stiffening as well.

He whispered in my ear that we should jerk off together. We felt for each other's prick and began stroking slowly and deliciously until I knew, by the hardness and throbbing of his cock, that he was close to exploding. I grabbed my pajama bottom and told him to come into it. We pumped faster and faster. First I blew thick wads of come. Then he came immediately afterward.

I heaved the soaking pajamas on the floor. Realizing that we'd better not let our come stain the sheets, we sucked, milked and squeezed the last drop of sperm from each other's cock, then finally fell asleep.

I awoke the next morning to find Fred's face on my thigh, his mouth open, breathing on my balls, my cock near his beautiful red lips. What a lover! We decided it was too late for another round of lovemaking, so we took a shower together. We washed each other's balls, cock, anus and armpits, and you can guess what happened. Our pricks were once again hard as rocks, so Fred grabbed both in one hand and brought us to our third satisfying orgasm together.

Did we ever get together again? No. It was risky at college, and I was too involved in my regular activities to try to figure out how to continue the contact. Anyway, Fred left at the end of the semester. But what a memorable night that was!—*Name and address withheld*

INCREDULOUS NEIGHBOR SPIES A PENIS ON ONE OF THE "GIRLS-NEXT-DOOR"

Can you believe that a forty-year-old woman is writing this? Admittedly, it will seem that I'm either naive or just plain dumb, but my curiosity over a certain recent incident is still driving me up a wall.

About a year ago two very attractive girls in their early twenties moved into the apartment immediately next to mine. They're both awfully nice, and over the months we have become quite good friends, to the point where our apartments are pretty well open to one another. At first I thought they were lesbians because of their apparent devotion to each other and the obvious lack of male visitors. But now I'm not at all sure. Also, a few months ago, one of them made an obvious but thinly disguised sexual overture, and although I gracefully declined at the time, now I could just kick myself in the fanny for not responding. Because since then I saw something strange that really aroused my curiosity.

To shorten a long story, about a month ago I came home from work early one day and, hearing noises next door, decided to go over for a little neighborly chitchat. Every pair of apartments in our complex shares a common balcony or patio, and it's a simple matter, and convenient, to step over the low iron railing between the patios to get back and forth from each apartment. Anyway, that afternoon I went over as usual and, to my surprise, immediately saw what was causing the noise.

Through the sliding glass door, I could see to the far side of the living room, and there on the couch were my neighbors— one flat on her back, the other astride her and between her spread legs. And both were quite obviously enjoying an act of passionate and satisfying coitus! Heterosexual intercourse, at that!

They saw me at the very instant I saw them, and in a twinkling they were up and dashing for the bedroom door, their backs toward me so that I couldn't discern who was who. They are both about the same height and shape, with long hair of almost identical color.

However, I *did* see a fairly good-sized and erect male organ on one of them. Not a dildo either. Of that I am absolutely certain. To resolve any doubts on that score, let me also add that my arrival on their balcony apparently either coincided with, or triggered, an orgasm, for as they arose and fled, the penis was obviously spurting its ejaculate.

Embarrassed, I froze and turned to leave when one of them called out for me to stay and said that they'd be right out. Well, what could I do? I was already there; so I thought I might just as well stick it out. And besides I was truly interested in the whitish liquid on the carpet and couch. I looked at it while I was waiting, and it was semen all right.

Sure enough, barely five minutes later they emerged, glowy of face, from the bedroom, and the three of us chatted politely for quite some time, carefully avoiding any reference to the episode. I'm sure they must have thought that what I had seen would merely make me think that they were lesbians.

How it's done, I don't know, and I'm certainly dying of curiosity to find out. There is nothing in either's voice to indicate masculinity, and although I'm not absolutely positive that I saw female breasts on both of them that day (I was looking more at the erect penis), they do wear skimpy sleeveless blouses and low-cut bras, and the underarm area appears decidedly feminine. And how is the male lump disguised? They wear tight pants frequently, neither bothering to keep her legs together. Also, the curve of the rounded hip and fanny line on both is obviously female. You can't disguise that in tight pants. Hips, breasts, legs, arms, shoulders and face—nothing seems other than female. Could they be taking hormones? If so, doesn't a male's libido diminish or cease altogether with an overbalance of estrogen? All I can say is, I'd give almost anything for the opportunity to have the sexual encounter I refused earlier. Then I'd know, or would I?—*P.C., San Francisco, California*

Head & Tail

Showbiz Lady Wowed in Weekend Body Blitz

I'm a twenty-five-year-old comedienne with a good body, but my best asset is my face. Being from a small town in Canada, I had to move away to pursue my career, but I normally go back during the summer to see my relatives and friends.

This summer, after a two-year absence, I went back and called up my old girlfriends. We hit the bars in town looking for some men, when suddenly my eyes made contact with a guy I had known for a long time. When I left two years ago, he was married and was running a small business. Back then he was quiet, on the serious side, but now he looks like a high roller.

I asked the girls about him and they told me he divorced last year and since then he's become a much sought-after man for peculiar reasons. Some of the girls admitted that they had a few nights with him and would "récidive" anytime. I decided to discover for myself what the attraction was.

I went up to him and asked him if he remembered me. He appeared to be delighted even if we had only been acquaintances before. We talked and drank together for the rest of the evening. I hoped he would make the move but he didn't. Instead he invited me for dinner the next night at his place.

The following evening I was at his place around seven o'clock. It was nice and very well turned out, amazingly so for a man's apartment. Anyhow, he served me a dry martini and went back to his kitchen while I looked around. The place was a perfect love nest. I was already turned on just by taste; then he came up with the feast. A great chef couldn't have done better. We ate and chatted happily. I felt excited and giddy. The contact of his knees under the table made me weak. There was so much anticipation in the air, that he knew I was hooked. Still, he took his time.

After the meal, we sat in the living room and that's where it all started. He caressed my thighs so gently that it sent electricity through my whole body. I searched for his mouth and he grabbed my ass with both hands forcefully. Shivers were running up and down my spine and I grabbed his crotch with shaking hands. The petting couldn't last long in the state I was in.

He started undressing me methodically, kissing every part he uncovered. I was stark naked in no time. Then he pulled me by the hand into the bathroom. He ran water in the Victorian bath and continued to kiss me all over. He was still fully dressed and I wanted him naked like me. I grabbed his organ but he told me to wait and he started a striptease. I would have never believed that a man undressing could be so exciting. I was sex-starved. Once undressed, he closed the tap and told me to get in the bath. He washed me thoroughly, lingering over my breasts, clitoris and ass, bringing me to a shattering orgasm.

After this, he dried me lovingly. I felt like a queen and his slave at the same time. We went to his bedroom and he made me lie on my stomach and started kissing me from neck to toes. Then he parted my cheeks and started giving me a rim job. Nobody had ever done that to me before—and I wasn't about to stop him.

It felt so great that I was on the brink of another orgasm. Seeing me so high-voltaged, he moved down to my cunt and clit, always keeping me on the edge of orgasm. I was going crazy but couldn't do anything about it. I started begging him to fuck me, almost crying.

He then stopped and went away to get some vibrators, a tiny one and a large one. I'd never used one before, but anything would do as long as I could come. He put his cock in my cunt slowly and put the lubricated small vibrator up my ass. I couldn't believe it. I was going insane, feeling his cock in my cunt and that vibrator up my ass. He wasn't moving inside me but just using small muscles in his cock to titillate my cunt. That was another world premiere for me. All the while he was still pressing the vibrator inside my ass, against the base of his penis on the other side of the thin wall. In this way, I came again and again, as did he.

I was spent but madly in love with such a magnificent lover. He pulled out, turned around and sat on my face and started licking me. I had his asshole right in front of my eyes. I used to think it was filthy and disgusting, but I was so madly in love that I didn't care anymore and he was doing the same thing to me. I started licking his asshole, even pushing my tongue all the way up like I couldn't get enough of him. He came all over my breasts moaning like a beast and I came too.

I spent the weekend with him. He fucked me in every possible way: butt fuck, tit fuck—name it, he did it. Aside from that, he cooked, he washed the dishes, cleaned the house, treated me like a queen, and I wasn't allowed to help him in any way.

He explained that he's the only member of his men's lib movement. He's independent and self-sufficient. If he seeks a relationship with a woman, it's not because he needs somebody to cook for him or do the laundry. All this came about after his divorce and I can tell you, he is better at it than any woman I know. He is also a better lover than any man I know.—*Name and address withheld*

HUSBAND ENJOYS ANNIVERSARY EAT-IN
WITH HOT WIFE

My wife, Adrian, and I have come up with what we think is a new and exciting variation of oral sex. So, although I never thought we'd be writing to *Penthouse Letters,* we just want to let your readers have a taste of this for themselves.

For a long time, I'd wanted Adrian to buy one of those sexy G-string pajama sets. On a recent anniversary, she surprised me by obliging. When I got home from work, she was sitting on the couch with an afghan over her. Not really thinking about it, I assumed she was nude and waiting to "celebrate" our anniversary. As she sometimes does when she's horny, Adrian was reading the latest copy of *Penthouse Letters.* So I hurriedly undressed and snuggled under the afghan with her. I soon realized that she wasn't nude after all. I pulled off the afghan and saw that she was wearing a sexy black G-string outfit. With her long blond hair and small muscular body, she looked fantastic.

I started reading some *Penthouse Letters* to her, which is always a great turn-on for both of us (especially for Adrian, who was not very experienced when we got married). As I read, we felt and kissed each other. Since she still had on the G-string, I could feel only the bulge of her swollen labia through the thin material.

Before long, as I was reading a letter to her about two guys and one girl (always very arousing to Adrian), I felt the G-string getting wet with her creamy come. By now, being very turned on myself (I had already dampened Adrian's hand with my pre-seminal lubrication), I decided to have a "snack" between her smooth, muscular thighs. Being eaten must have been just what she wanted, because the creaminess had not only soaked through the G-string but was actually dripping and running down the fabric. Not wanting to waste any of her tastiness, I kissed and licked it all away, which made her rush toward orgasm. Her rippling body and hard breathing told me that she was close, so I decided not to bother with removing her sexy G-string. For some reason, maybe because there was no hair to get in the way, her wet pussy tasted better and flowed with more creamy come than ever. It was so good that, after she had exploded into one orgasm, I continued eating her until she was ready to come again. Then I pulled the material of her G-string back to expose her very hard clitoris, and I kissed it until she went into the throes of her second orgasm.

By now, unable to wait any longer, I took off her G-string and put my rock-hard cock into her beautiful pussy. We screwed with her legs around me, and I felt her ass and clitoris while I knelt on the floor in front of the couch. We both had great orgasms and we were exhausted when we were finished. Adrian had gotten so wet that, while we fucked, her dripping juices made a small wet spot in front of the couch.

Since then, I've often gone down on her this way, and just talking about that first time is always another fantastic turn-on for us.—*Name and address withheld*

"Y" Worker Loves Cock—Student's, Not Husband's

I am a twenty-three-year-old male attending college in New England. I am an avid *Penthouse Letters* reader and have been turned on many a time by these cock-raising experiences. Now I'd like to relate to you an ongoing adventure of my own.

A few months back, I moved into the Y.M.C.A. here because the dorms were full. I noticed after a while a young girl at the desk who works nights. At first she did not appear to be that attractive, but as time wore on she began dressing more unusually. Sometimes she'd wear a thin dress or pants which would accentuate her very small, yet perfect ass. All these clothes were tight and well-fitted. This caught my eye when I came in, and I'd stop and talk with her. Her name, I learned, was Janie. She's five-foot-seven but her figure is tiny, about one hundred pounds with 32A tits.

One night I came in and saw she was wearing a low-cut blouse with thin white pants. Occasionally, she'd bend forward at the desk and I'd just "happen" to peer down her top. She always managed to look up and catch me. She'd just smile or wink. Then she'd walk around and bend over to pick something off the floor. This gave me a super boner because I could clearly see the outline of her bright pink bikini panties. We both knew we were turning each other on. This type of teasing continued for about a week. One day she wore a green silk dress (with a slit up the front and back) and real sexy high heels. I had come in from class about eleven o'clock. I had been in a super horny mood all day. I complimented her on her dress and that started the ball rolling. Janie started playing sexual word games with me, asking me what I liked a girl to do on a date, and so on. One thing led to another and we got to the topic of oral sex. Janie said she liked it but couldn't do it as often as she liked because her husband didn't care for it—although he had asked her to suck him off during their honeymoon.

I jokingly mentioned that she might enjoy my "mammoth mauler" and that I could be gentle. She didn't answer. By now it was time to leave and I walked her to her car. At the car I again mentioned my "mammoth mauler." Janie smiled wanly and said it was getting late. So I said that it looked like I'd just have to go to bed defeated and jerk off. That must have done the trick, because she told me to jump in the car and we'd go somewhere where she'd "toss" me off.

We drove to a parking lot near the pier and I hastily removed my Levi's. Once she saw my fat eight-inch cock she put a lingering lip lock on it. Her mouth was like a vacuum and I held off coming as long as I possibly could. Then I let loose hot and fast. She swallowed every drop.

She sat up and removed her dress so as not to get any come on it. All she now had on were stockings (not panty hose) and a white bra. With enthusiasm she started in on me again. Her tiny tongue and mouth were excellent. I put my thumb and index finger in her ass and twat. This drove her wild. Her head drove me apeshit and I thrust like a mule. Come was shooting all over her face, chest and back in her mouth. After what seemed like two minutes of coming, I calmed down and cleaned up. En route back to the "Y" she blew me a third time!

That was five months ago. Now we go to peep shows and drive-ins. Last week, we went to the mall and picked up a young black dude. We went to a motel where we fucked and sucked for almost five or six hours. His dong had to have been a full twelve inches long and six inches round. Janie's mouth just fit over the head and while she worked on him, I jacked off onto her face and hair. He pumped away, sending loads down her throat with the excess running in streams out her mouth. It was so impressive, I took some Polaroid close-ups. The best shot showed his cock in her mouth and my come dripping off her face.

I hope this fine arrangement keeps up forever.—*Name and address withheld*

BLACK READER HAS A DREAM AND IT'S FULL OF GOOD GRACE

I love your magazine, especially the letters. I rarely see any letters from black people who want to tell about their sexual experiences. It has occurred to me that I should let you know what we blacks are doing sexually.

I am twenty-four years old, male, with a slender build (I weigh one hundred sixty-five pounds). I have an eight-inch cock that gets pretty hard when I read in your magazine about all the sucking and fucking that is going on. Sometimes, I fantasize about having encounters like those I read about, but I already have a fantasy of my own, and her name is Grace. Grace is my ex-wife, and I still love her very much. She is five-six and weighs about one hundred forty pounds. She has the smoothest skin I have ever touched, and the roundest, softest ass in the world. Her breasts are small and firm, and her body is always warm. Grace's skin is the color of a Hershey bar—in fact, she always smells sweet.

Occasionally, we still get together, and I can enjoy that dynamite sex that only she can give me. What I love most about her is that she has the juiciest pussy I've ever known. Once her pussy juices begin to flow, everything is wet and wild.

Some people believe that black men don't eat pussy. Well, let me say just one thing about any of my brothers who aren't into cunnilingus: they haven't eaten a pussy like my Grace's. Her juices taste like nectar from the heavens. Whenever I'm eating her wet snatch, I hope that she'll scream, "I'm coming. I love you. Eat me. Drink me. Love me!" I yearn for her to drench my face with her wet sexiness. I love eating her and hearing her moan in ecstasy.

Here's my favorite fantasy about Grace. It begins with her calling me to come over to her place. "Hurry, honey," she pleads. "I'm all alone and really hot." When she greets me at her door, she is wearing a black knit dress that really shows off her curves, and I develop a hard-on before I can even get inside. We drink some wine and smoke a joint. She is wearing very red lipstick, and her nails are painted the same color.

Then she remarks about the bulge in my jeans, "Oh, isn't that big fellow too cramped in there?" She unzips my fly and pulls out my swollen cock. "Yum-yum," she says, and licks her lips hungrily. She puts her mouth around my cock and begins to lick and suck it sensuously, up and down. I moan in ecstasy as she lovingly keeps blowing me until I come. She takes as much of my hot sperm in her mouth as she can without swallowing. Then she kisses me and delivers my sperm into my mouth, and our tongues play with the salty juice. We break away and I lie down on the floor, smiling up at her. I say, "Oh, baby, that was good. I'd like to return the favor."

Grace straddles my face and says, "I thought you'd never ask." She isn't wearing any panties, of course, and she lowers her wet snatch to my lips. I can smell her musky bush as she is coming down, and I get another hard-on.

At last, I am sucking on her swollen pussy lips, tasting the sweetness. She is moaning and rocking back and forth on my face as my tongue licks up her sweet spillage. She mashes her cunt down on my face, and I lick faster, trying not to nip her with my teeth. She squeezes my face between her warm, soft thighs. Soon I know she is coming, so I suck harder. I feel warm juices running down the sides of my face, and she is rocking wildly in orgasm. "Shit," she says as she collapses forward, her pussy draining all over my face.

As the night passes, we continue sucking and fucking each other until we are thoroughly exhausted. Then we fall asleep on the wet sheets.—*L.M., Cleveland, Ohio*

GIRL USES DENTAL BRACES TO IMPROVE HER BLOW JOBS

Two weeks ago, I met a girl named Betty in a local bar. Although I'd never been attracted to girls who wear braces on their teeth, my experience with this one has altered my biased opinion.

After several rounds of beers, Betty and I decided to return to my apartment to enjoy some soft music and to mellow out on pot. After two joints and a few beers, our conversation turned to the topic of sex. Since Betty has one of the best asses I've ever seen, the thought of getting under her skirt made my pecker stand on end. She must have noticed the rise in my jeans, for she moved next to me, planted a feverish kiss on my lips and started caressing my balls tenderly.

The next five minutes passed in a blur. Clothes went flying. When I saw Betty's lovely body completely unclad, I damn near came instantly. Her tits were firm as melons, but soft to the touch, and her ass was everything I had expected. It was tight and compact, just the way I like an ass to be.

Betty took control of the situation. She told me to lie down on the floor and then started stroking my seven-inch hard-on. Just when I was about to cream, she applied the squeeze technique and said she knew some better places in which I could shoot my juicy load. She climbed adroitly on top of me, straddling my rod. Her cunt swallowed its entire length in one slow thrust. She bucked and balled for what seemed like hours. As I nibbled on her earlobes, I wet a finger and slid it up her ass until she was screaming with excitement. We both exploded into a climax that quaked my apartment floor.

After a few seconds of ecstasy, Betty slid off and said, "The best place for that dick of yours is in my mouth."

It didn't occur to me at first, but when she started licking the head, I remembered her braces. I looked at her and made an urgent request. "Be careful, please. It's the only one I have."

She just smiled and said, "Pain is the last thing I want to give you."

What followed was the best blow job I've ever received in my life. Betty's braces never even slowed her down. As she gobbled all seven inches and slid the entire length in and out, I felt no contact at all with the metal. Through the entire act, she held the base of my organ with one hand while her other hand gently rubbed my balls and my asshole.

Just as I was about to come deep in her throat, one of the rubber bands on her braces snapped. The pain coincided with my climax and made for absolutely the best orgasm I had ever felt.

Since that night, Betty and I have been balling regularly. She has learned to perfect her technique. Now she can flip one of the lower bands anytime she likes. And take it from me, she knows when and when not to flip her rubber bands. Whenever I see her now, she soon has me begging for one of her patented "flip jobs." Unless you've tried this interesting twist to oral sex, you haven't done it all.—*T.F., New York, New York*

MAN AND WIFE SATISFY EACH OTHER'S SEX FANTASY

W e are middle-aged, executive-type people, married for several years, and very open and uninhibited with each other regarding what we want sexually. Consequently, our sex is excellent.

However, we have been at loggerheads over the matter of anal sex. I had never had the pleasure of my wife's ass until late last night. Shirley had always considered the act somewhat repulsive and she'd worried about the pain involved. Her attitude, up until last night, had been "I love everything about sex, but I'll never be able to do that."

Well, three nights ago, we were discussing our sexual fantasies. I was a bit astonished when Shirley asked me about what techniques I use in masturbating. Frankly, I tried to change the subject as quickly as possible. I admitted that I masturbated occasionally, adding that how I did it was none of her business. She was annoyed to realize that she'd brought up a sore subject. As she continued to coax information out of me, she boldly stated that her favorite fantasy was one in which she would tantalize my cock to stiffness for three straight hours, and then have me masturbate to orgasm on her chest. "After that," she added, "I'd like to watch you suck all of your delicious juice off my tits."

That last suggestion really made me nervous. Beating off in front of her would be bad enough, but I told her that I would never eat my own come. But then, as an afterthought, I said, "That is, unless you give in to my favorite fantasy." She didn't need to be reminded of what that was, and the subject was dropped for the remainder of the evening.

When I returned home from work the following evening, she met me at the door in a red, full-length, transparent negligee. When I met her lips with mine, her hand went directly to my balls. She broke off the kiss and said, "My fantasy first!"

In no more than five minutes, I was completely nude, seated on the sofa with my legs spread. She was between them, planting kisses on the underside of my scrotum and tickling my ass with the long nail of her forefinger. I promptly got a huge erection, whereupon she took a cock ring from under the sofa cushion and fastened it tightly around the base of my penis. Then she inserted her finger into my ass and slid it slowly up my hole until it would go no farther. She looked into my eyes and said, "At the end of three hours, you're going to beg to come."

Those three hours were sexually the most frustrating I'd ever endured. One item she used on me was a rectal vibrator, which tickled my prostate and made my penis stiffer than it had ever been before. I got to the point where I was imploring her to let me do what she wanted before I went crazy with frustration. "I've got to come," I kept telling her. "Please, let me come."

She just looked up from where she was slavering kisses on the inside of my thigh and said, "Remember, if we do it my way tonight, this is what you get tomorrow." She then turned her back to me, bent at the waist, and proceeded to oil her ass cheeks, crack, and hole with my favorite lubricant for masturbation. (I had let that information out of the bag during our talk the previous evening.)

When the moment of truth arrived, I was so horny and my balls were so blue that I was nearly in tears. She lay on her back, and I knelt above her, my knees spread so that one was on either side of her. She poured oil into my hand and told me to oil my face, chest, abdomen and genitals. I stroked long and slowly. It was ecstasy. All the while, she was moaning about watching me, and repeating how she wanted to see my cock explode. It was a fantastic sexual experience, and when I finally did explode all over her breasts, I considered it a pleasure to slide my mouth into what I'd done, pleasing her nipples every time I passed them with my tongue.

Finally, she was satisfied.

Later, the next afternoon, I rushed home after work to find Shirley on her knees in front of our fireplace, with her chest resting on two pillows and her ass in the air, greased and naked.

It was my fantasy come true. I'd always fantasized about having sex with her just once without having to consider her needs or feelings—just raw sex for the pure joy of satisfying animal instincts.

I immediately stripped and positioned myself behind her. For several minutes, I let my cock graze along her heavily lubricated crack, until she finally cried, "Please, do it now!" The tightness that I felt around the crown of my cock as I entered her was like electricity. I slowly worked in and out of her, entering a fraction of an inch more on every forward stroke. Finally, I gave her my entire ten inches and gushed what seemed to be an endless stream of come. It was splendid.—*O.V., Bismarck, North Dakota*

GYMNASTIC WORKOUT TAKES A CUNT-STRETCHING TWIST

For the sake of keeping my thirty-two-year-old frame in shape, I enrolled in an evening gymnastics class at a high school in my neighborhood. The first class made me a bit nervous. There were nine women and only one other guy besides myself. The other guy dropped out of the class two weeks later.

The women were all very friendly toward me, but Mary and Lynn were the two students that I paired up with most of the time. Mary was twenty-four with a firm, lean gymnast's body. Lynn was nineteen with long legs and full tits. We all got along very well, as you will see.

One evening after class the three of us were talking. "How do you remain so limber?" Mary asked Lynn. Lynn said, "It's easy when you do yoga. It stretches all your muscles. I could teach you both yoga positions you would not believe."

Mary and I were curious, and we asked Lynn to show us a few stretches. She told us that the most interesting position would require a private demonstration, but that she would be happy to show it to us in the men's locker room. Since I was the only male in class, we knew that we wouldn't have to worry about anyone barging in on us.

As soon as we entered the room, Lynn peeled off her leotard. She wasn't wearing any underwear, and her naked body was an awesome and beautiful sight. She sat on the locker room floor with her back toward us. Then she assumed what I later learned was the yoga lotus position, crossing her legs in front of her and resting her feet on her thighs. After holding this position for a few minutes, she swung her legs over her head and placed her feet on the floor. Her pelvis was poised directly in front of her face, and she began to lick and tongue her pussy, pausing occasionally to glance at Mary and me through her legs. We couldn't believe that she was eating her own cunt! My eight-and-a-halfincher was beginning to swell as I watched her lap and suck her wet cunt. I pulled off my gym shorts and smeared my pre-ejaculatory jism over my cockhead. Mary took the hint and stripped quickly. I was delighted to see that her nipples were huge and almost covered her entire tits. Oh, my throbbing prick! Lynn was moaning loudly as she ate her cunt out from top to bottom. She flicked her tongue from side to side, alternately licking and sucking her swollen clit. Her cunt hair was soaked with juice and saliva, and the passionate sounds that she was making were getting Mary and me unbelievably horny.

Suddenly Mary knelt in front of me, took my cock halfway down her throat and began sucking me to high heaven. I came quickly, shooting most of my cream into Mary's mouth and depositing the rest all over her face as I pulled out. Lynn came out of her position and licked my come off of Mary's face. I remained hard while I watched them licking and finger-fucking each other. When Lynn started jacking me off, Mary lay on her back with her legs spread wide. Lynn positioned her head between Mary's legs and started eating her passionately. I slipped my prick into Lynn's cunt from the rear and slowly inserted one finger into her asshole. We established a rhythm and Mary came a few moments before Lynn and I orgasmed wildly and noisily together.

My classmates wanted to play some more, but I was drained. I suggested that we try some new positions at the next class. Mary said, "I'll practice at home so that I can eat myself the next time."

I suppose if I practiced I could learn to suck my cock, but why should I when I have two beautiful, lusty ladies like Lynn and Mary to suck me off? I am certainly looking forward to being part of this athletic sexual threesome for some time to come.— *J.H., Chicago, Illinois*

THE MAID MAKES HIM INSTEAD OF THE BED

I am a freshman at a large university in northwestern Ohio. I live in one of the dorms on campus and really enjoy college life. Every dorm has a woman who maintains the public facilities. Well, our dorm is lucky enough to have a twenty-six-year-old blond named Jackie. She's about five-feet-six and has the cutest ass I've ever seen. Every morning at seven o'clock Jackie vacuums the hall on my floor. I devised a plan to lure her into my room, and believe it or not, it worked!

I took a shower and at around seven o'clock I toweled myself off in my room with the door open. Next thing I knew, I heard a soft voice whisper, "Good morning." I turned around to see Jackie standing in the doorway. I returned her greeting and asked her if she'd like a cup of coffee. She said yes and came into the room. By now my erection had reached its full eight inches.

I saw her glance at my cock as she shut the door behind her. She said that she wanted a lot of cream with her coffee, and then she proceeded to remove her pants and blouse. I gazed lustily at her small but firm tits. She tore off her panties, revealing a nest of curly pubic hair.

Without saying a word, she knelt down and engulfed my cock with her hot, steamy mouth. She sucked, licked and stroked my cock until I was almost delirious. I shot a full load of come into her mouth and it began dripping down her chin. After she'd licked every drop of come off her face, she lay back on my bed and said, "Please eat my pussy." I knelt on the floor and licked and sucked her little love-hole, ramming my tongue in and out like a little jackhammer. Her hot juice flowed all over my face. She was moaning and groaning, and this made me lick all the harder.

She pulled me onto the bed, and I kissed her and fondled her nipples. Then she got on top of me and humped my rod with her back to me. Watching my cock slide in and out of her pussy made me incredibly hot. Between my gasps for air, I said, "Put it in your other hole." She lifted her sweet buttocks and squatted on my cock, taking it deep inside her asshole. I knew that I was in territory that had already been explored. She rode my prick wildly until I released a hot stream of come into her ass.

We both collapsed on my bed. She had come all over her little asshole. She said that she had to get back to work and dressed quickly. Before she left she gave me her undies as a memento.

As she walked out the door she said, "I'll see you tomorrow for coffee, and make sure we have enough cream." Then she winked and closed the door behind her. Now I look forward to our coffee breaks, and I give her all the cream she wants.—*Name and address withheld*

No Ticket for Reckless Driver as Diana Licks Two Long Arms of the Law

I am a twenty-two-year-old male who enjoys reading *Penthouse Letters,* but I have noticed that a lot of your letters are from small towns. I'm going to tell you about one of my experiences in the big city of Los Angeles.

It was always my belief that most women are prick-teasers. A few nights ago I found one who definitely isn't. I was leaving a disco in L.A. and walking to my car when I saw my best friend's girlfriend, Diana, standing there. She asked where I was going. I told her I was on my way home. She then asked if I would give her a ride to her place. "My pleasure," I told her, and I meant it because Diana is a super-looking lady.

As we were driving along the 405 Freeway in my 1965 Mustang, she told me that she and David had had a big fight and were no longer together. She also told me that she needed some sympathetic companionship. When Diana noticed me staring at her gorgeous tits, she started rubbing her hands over them and licking her lips.

My cock instantly hardened and sprang to its full eight-inch length. Seeing the huge bulge in my pants, Diana quickly unzipped them, whipped out my cock and started sucking it. I was so turned on that I wasn't watching the road and I caused another car to run into a fence alongside the freeway.

I wasn't even aware of what had happened. All I knew or cared about was that I was getting the best blow job I'd ever had. After I'd come all over her face, as Diana was licking up all my come, I noticed red lights flashing behind my car. The highway patrol pulled me over. Two officers walked up as I was trying to get my cock out of Diana's mouth. The officers were surprised but, I guess, too embarrassed to say anything about what Diana was doing. When I finally got my cock back into my pants, they told me that I'd been clocked at ninety miles an hour. They said they were going to write me up for speeding and reckless driving. Diana told them that if they would forget the charges against me, she would blow both of them. The officers agreed. Standing behind the passenger's side of my Mustang, so they couldn't be seen from passing cars, they pulled out their cocks and Diana quickly went to work, sucking each one off in turn. While she was doing them with her talented mouth, she was also stroking my cock. Both officers quickly came, after which they thanked Diana and took off in their patrol car.

As Diana and I drove off, she was still stroking my cock, but then she suddenly stopped what she was doing and began taking off her clothes. I pulled off the freeway and parked the car behind a shopping mall in Carson, where we spent the rest of the night sucking and fucking. When we woke up in the morning, both of us were naked, and five or six people were standing next to the car, looking in on us. I was so embarrassed that I hit the starter and took off at high speed.

Needless to say, that was the best night of sex that I've ever had. Now I know that Diana is not just another prick-teaser. She and David are back together, but every Thursday night she and I get together for more sex play.—*R.J., Long Beach, California*

ACTOR PLAYS HOTTEST SCENE IN HIS REPERTOIRE WITH THE REDHEAD OF HIS DREAMS

I'm an actor now residing in New York City. Every so often— though not often enough—I get work at one of the many regional theaters across the country. Not long ago I was with a summer repertory company in a large midwestern city. Since I was there for several months, I found an apartment that I could sublease on a month-to-month basis.

One morning as I was washing my car in the parking lot of my apartment building, a tall redhead pulled her car out of the garage and commenced washing it alongside mine. She was wearing a tight green sweater and a pair of faded blue jeans. I watched her as she leaned and stretched and rubbed and scrubbed. She, reminded me of a young Rhonda Fleming. A conversation was struck up, although I forget who started it. Her name was Leigh. She was twenty-seven, married, with one child. Hubby, a salesman, was away from home most of the time. Unfortunately, I was due at the theater for a costume fitting and had to leave, but I wanted her to know that I was interested in seeing her again.

"I'm home every morning," I told her. "Why not stop up for a cup of coffee one of these days when you have some time?"

"OK," she said. "Maybe I will."

But she didn't. During the next few weeks, I saw her on the street or in a store every so often and we'd say hello, but nothing seemed to be happening between us. Eventually I gave up on the whole thing and contented myself by fantasizing about her lovely breasts and shapely long legs.

One night when I didn't have to be at the theater, I was moping in my apartment with a bad case of terminal hominess. Only the usual crap was on TV, so I rolled a joint and was soon blissfully blown away. I unzipped my jeans—all I was wearing at the time—and slowly began to rub my hand up and down my hardening cock as images of Leigh's beautiful body played wantonly in my mind's eye. After about ten minutes I heard a soft knocking at my back door. I quickly stuffed my meat back into my jeans and padded barefoot through the dark kitchen. When I opened the door, there stood Leigh with a glass of scotch in her hand. She looked straight at me and said, "Are you busy?"

Well, I damn near choked. It was like a scene in one of Rhonda Fleming's movies. Trying to contain myself, I invited Leigh to come in. We sat on the floor in the living room and, perhaps too impetuously, I started to kiss her. She backed off. "I have to go check on my son," she said. "I'll be right back."

During the fifteen minutes before she returned, I barely managed to keep myself under control. I was waiting in the kitchen when I heard her coming back up the stairs. After I let her in, we stood there for a moment, wordless and very close to each other. She had obviously freshened her perfume. We kissed lightly and nuzzled one another for a while, and then I led her back into the living room to resume our kissing. She was tentative for a while, even shy, until my hand wandered to one of her firm, full breasts. Her breathing became uneven as I felt her nipple pressing against her tight sweater. Her lips then parted slightly and her tongue slid into my mouth. Immediately I slipped her sweater over her head and leaned back to look at her.

What a vision! Long red hair cascading over her shoulders,

huge green eyes glowing with nervous anticipation, and voluptuous breasts filling a low-cut lacy white bra.

As I kissed her again, I gently pressed her backward until she
was lying on the rug, and I slid her jeans down to reveal those
magnificent legs. Her white bikini panties quickly followed and
I saw that she was indeed an authentic redhead. Placing my head
between her creamy thighs, I started to lick her perfect pussy.
When I thrust my tongue into her juicy vagina, she moaned and
emitted high-pitched noises. "I never knew it felt so good," she
gushed. Was it possible that no one had ever done this to her before? While I was wondering about this, she arched her back,
pushed her pelvis into my face and came six ways at once.

When her orgasm was over, Leigh sat up and tried to collect
herself. Her eyes were flitting back and forth, trying desperately
to focus on something. I knelt behind her, removed her bra and
gently squeezed her breasts. She turned around and, as she did
so, I stood up. Her beautiful face was now only inches from my
hard, swollen cock, and she reached for it almost instinctively
with her hand. As she held it, she brought her lips closer and
closer to its head, looking up at me all the while. In a little-girl
voice she said, "I've never done this before, but I'd like to try."

Leigh touched her lips to the head of my cock and kissed it.
She then ran her tongue up and down the shaft. I placed one of
my hands on the back of her head and held my cock in the other.
"Open your mouth," I said. She complied. Once I'd placed my
cock between her lips, she needed no further help. She took as
much of it into her mouth as she could and sucked as hard as
she could. Soon she started to moan, pumping her mouth faster
and faster. The head of my cock was completely in her throat.
Both my hands were now holding her head and I slowed her
rhythm. Each time I pushed my cock slowly forward, I felt her
tongue twining around it. When I pulled it slowly back, she
sucked so hard that I thought my soul would leave my body.

After a few more delightful minutes of this, I stopped her head
with my hands and announced that I was about to come. Her

only response was a grunt and a nod of her head. She resumed sucking furiously. When I did come, I jammed my cock deeper down her throat. Her muffled moans and the convulsive contractions in her throat told me that she was also coming as I shot my load. Semen filled her throat and mouth and dribbled out of the corners of her mouth. She held my cock in her mouth, buried to the hilt, until I stopped shuddering. She then slid her lips slowly up and down the shaft until she had swallowed every last drop of my creamy come.

When it was over and we'd cleaned ourselves up, I begged Leigh to stay the night. Because of her young son, however, she had to leave. We did get together twice again after that night, but then I had to return to New York. With luck, maybe, the same repertory group will ask me back next summer.—*Name and address withheld*

Pursuit & Capture

Buttered Sex Is Better Sex— Especially in the Bathtub

I am deeply in love with Allison, my very beautiful and outgoing girlfriend. I consider us a perfect couple. We are both in our senior year in high school, and I am sure that we will get married someday. Our sex life is very open, and we talk about almost everything. Allison is thoughtful and beautiful, the kind of girl that any guy would give his right arm to go out with. Her body is, to be honest, the most perfect I have ever made love to. We are both very healthy.

Neither of us is into hard drugs or alcohol, although I smoke an occasional joint. I've tried to talk her into getting high with me for some time, but she has been brought up to think all drugs are bad. Finally, though, one day she broke down and promised that she would try it—"just as an experiment."

A few weeks later, when my parents left town on a business trip, I had almost forgotten Allison's promise. I called her up and told her to come over, because I had a surprise for her. Her parents were away, too, so she could stay the night. We talked, listened to music, and smoked pot well into the evening. I was becoming quite turned on, thinking of the possibilities. I was in one of my kinkier moods that night and a really far-out idea struck me. I grabbed her hand and led her upstairs into the bathroom. As we kissed, I removed her clothes. Then I ran into my room and grabbed a container of orgy butter that two of my friends had given me as a joke. I returned to Allison, who by that time was slowly masturbating.

I'll admit that I was pretty stoned, and so was she. We continued kissing for a while, and we stroked each other's body. Then I removed my clothes and started sucking on her nipples, which were poking out about half an inch. Grabbing a handful of orgy butter, I began to cover every inch of her body with a thick coat of the stuff. She looked so beautiful, standing there in the nude, shimmering in the light. I hungrily kissed her, sending my tongue down her throat, as I slipped my thumb deep inside her tight cunt.

She then applied the butter all over me in great globs. The feeling of that slippery stuff and her hands massaging my body brought me to a new high. I buttered the bottom of the bathtub before we slipped into it, giggling and moaning in pleasure. We fucked for about an hour before we both came.

After a short recovery, we slipped into the most sensual 69 position and I sucked her pussy until my tongue went numb. I could taste my come mixed with her pussy juices and the orgy butter. Just before I was about to come for a second time, I pulled my cock out of her mouth and shot about a gallon of hot sperm all over her tits and face. With my face still buried in her delicious pussy, I proceeded to massage my sperm into her stomach and tits.

After she had climaxed via my tongue, I asked her to roll over on her stomach. She knew what I was about to do, and she moaned as my thick cock eased its way into her ass. Gasping, she rolled on top of me, still keeping my cock up her ass, and started going into a hump-and-grind motion. She was pumping so fast that I couldn't even focus on her hips. All of a sudden, she started screaming at the top of her lungs and her whole body started shaking. She swung her head back and sunk her weight down on my whole cock, which was pumping hot sperm into her.

We lay there for a few minutes, getting our breath back, before we took a long shower, kissing and rubbing each other's body. We then dried each other off and went to bed, talking about all that had happened. Now we're planning to do something outrageous every month, and if anything really interesting happens, you'll be the first to know.—*D.N., San Francisco, California*

BUSINESSWOMAN GOES GOOFY OVER CANADIAN GUY

I've had some pretty exciting adventures, many worthy of writing to *Penthouse Letters* about, but most of them occurred a few years ago, when I was in my mid-twenties and unmarried. At thirty-one, however, after being married for five years, I felt old and out of the romance game. No one had made a serious pass at me in a couple of years, although I do have a slim figure, long blond hair, and a thirty-seven-inch bust.

But all that changed last spring, when I was in Los Angeles on a business trip and got involved in an unexpected, romantic and sexually exciting affair. After visiting several of my company's California offices for two weeks, and entertaining clients, I really had little energy left to enjoy myself—or so I thought.

One night, I decided to dress up and treat myself to a good dinner in L.A.'s posh marina area. As I waited for a free table, a man sat next to me at the bar and introduced himself as Gary. We talked until his table was announced. He took me to meet his friends, Larry and Tom. The three men talked me into joining them for dinner.

The four of us had a pleasant evening. I was especially interested in Tom, a Canadian who was being advised by Gary in the purchase of a new sailboat. Tom was handsome enough to be a male model—soft, thick, brown hair, a well-trimmed full beard, the most enchanting sea-blue eyes I'd ever seen, and a tall, slim, muscular body. He was only twenty-six.

Gary and Larry departed early, seeing that Tom and I had hit it off. After dinner, he and I had a drink and talked some more. Although Tom wanted to make a date for the next night, I politely declined. When I returned to my hotel, I couldn't help wondering if I had made a mistake by not inviting him to come with me.

The next evening, I went for a nightcap at a lounge where I had become a regular. I began drowning my loneliness, wondering if I would ever see Tom again. There was a possibility that I would see him, since I'd told him that I usually had an evening cocktail at this lounge, but it seemed like a long-shot hope. I was overwhelmed, therefore, when Tom walked in at a little before nine and handed me a lovely pink rose.

I told him how sweet he was, and how surprised and happy I was to see him again. After we'd had a drink together, Tom excused himself and said he would be right back. I thought he was going to the men's room, but he returned a few minutes later with another rose. Now I was altogether enchanted by this man.

Deciding to go and have a look at his new boat at the marina, we walked out to his fancy pickup. When I got in, I found twenty-two more roses on the seat. I was really blushing now. Tom explained that he had been prepared to bring the flowers into the lounge all night, one at a time, to show how he felt about me. By the time we arrived in the marina parking lot, we were both feeling pretty horny. Without even seeing his new boat, we turned around and drove back to my hotel.

In my room, we immediately began kissing passionately, and Tom soon started to undress me. The sight of my breasts caused him to gasp with admiration and desire. He caressed them and gently sucked my nipples, and I excitedly removed his shirt. He had a muscular chest and strong arms, and very little hair on his tanned body. Although I'd always preferred men with hairy chests, in Tom's case it didn't matter.

Tom kept saying that he loved me, that I had turned him on as no other woman ever had before. It didn't sound corny because he was so sincere. Since I would be leaving California the next morning, we both knew that after this one night together, we probably would never see each other again.

It felt great to be in his arms, but I had one worry as he rose to take off his pants. What if his cock was small and thin? (We had not even made it to the bed. We were on the floor together.) Under his pants he was wearing ugly print bikini shorts, and I anxiously waited to see what treat they held. When the shorts came off, the most beautiful cock I had ever seen was revealed—long, thick, too big to be believed. I couldn't contain my excitement as he slid down into a 69 position and we began to taste each other's treats. It was one of the high points of my entire life—and it only got better when he got on top of me to begin the most divine fucking I've ever known.

Tom's energy seemed endless, and his erection never wilted. As he pumped it into my eager pussy, I soon felt the start of a wonderful orgasm. Usually, I have one short-lived orgasm and my excitement fades, but as Tom kept thrusting his splendid cock deep inside me, my cunt responded with the longest, keenest orgasm of my life. When I thought it was subsiding at last, it began to build again to an even greater crescendo of pleasure. I moaned and gasped "thank you" over and over again.

Tom was the most satisfying and considerate lover a woman could hope for. In a hundred years, I don't think I could return the joy and gratification he gave me. When we were finally all fucked out, we moved to the bed for some sleep. As soon as we lay down, however, we began kissing and caressing again. His hands were all over my reawakening body, as if exploring it for the first time. Soon he was back on top of me, and we were fucking again with all our might.

The indescribable thrill of it was just as strong and wonderful as before. Tom called my name throughout, as I felt his throbbing cock fill my pussy with sweet, hot come. We were left exhausted and quickly fell asleep in each other's arms. When we awoke, we showered together, and I shampooed his beautiful hair.

I cannot describe how we sadly lingered over breakfast, dreading that final good-bye. Wherever he is, I'd like Tom to know that it was a night of perfect love that I'll never forget. I hope we meet again someday.—*Name and address withheld*

HE COMES TO NURSE'S AID;
THROWS HER CUNT A CURVE

Recently I was in New Orleans, and I felt like celebrating after closing a very lucrative business deal. As I showered and dressed, I thought about finding a good hooker. Suddenly, I remembered a young woman from our town who had left for a nursing job in New Orleans.

My recollections of Linda were extremely pleasant, since she is a striking beauty, with gray-green eyes and long, dark hair. Extremely shapely, and just a year older than my married daughter, she is a cock-raising combination. Last summer, in the country club swimming pool, I got a hefty erection watching her porpoise through the water with her beautiful ass stuck up in the air.

The thought of fucking Linda was far-out and far-fetched, so I decided that it would be nice just to see her, even if we only shared a bottle of wine and a friendly dinner. I checked the phone book. Sure enough, her name and number were listed. I felt the onset of a throbbing hard-on when she answered the phone in that sweet, sexy voice that I remembered so well. We chatted for a while, and she readily accepted my dinner invitation.

When I arrived at Linda's apartment, she looked breathtaking in a tight red dress with a slit that stopped just a few inches below hers. When we went out, I felt ten feet tall with such a fantastic dream woman on my arm.

We wined, dined and danced until almost midnight. After a few disco sets, we swayed cheek-to-cheek to a slow romantic number. Holding Linda's divine tits and thighs against me ignited the fire in my cock and balls that I'd always imagined it would. She glanced up at me in angelic perplexity, as if she was surprised to be causing the big bulge that her cunt was pressing against. I kissed her on the forehead, and she pressed even closer, not in a teasing manner, but as if to volunteer herself in a sublime offering.

Linda suggested that we go to her apartment. As we drove there, she nestled close and ran her hand up and down my straining manhood. We went directly to her bedroom, kissing and hastily undressing one another.

Seeing her naked, perfect body created the largest, stiffest hard-on I had experienced in years. She, in turn, stared with wide-eyed delight at my aching, arched organ. My cock is close to a foot long, and curves downward to a large, purple, flanged head.

Several years ago, in a Tokyo whorehouse, my girl called the madam in after she had washed and hardened me. The madam said it wasn't unusual for American men to have curved organs. However, she admitted that mine was unusually large. They both played with it and hefted it, and before the evening was over, I had also sampled the delights of the informative madam.

Linda and I fell onto the bed in a 69 position. Her warm, moist pinkness came alive to my tongue, while she managed to take most of my cock down her pretty throat in expert fashion.

I have found that my flared, flanged glans acts much like a French tickler, and the curvature of my shaft constantly tantalizes ladies with large, swollen clits, usually delighting them into a multi-orgasmic frenzy. I was impatient to give Linda's cunt a taste of my special tool.

Rolling over her, I jammed and jabbed the swollen head into her fiery, tight foxhole. With her moans urging me on, I slammed my curved cock into her straining, tender slit, jam-packing her gripping cunt. She began a multiorgasm as I pumped deeply and finally unloaded ball-draining gushes into the depths of her small, thrashing body. Later that night, she woke me, almost draining me again with her sweet mouth before I restrained her. I mounted her from the rear, then rolled over and twisted her around. She straddled me for another lingering love session that left my balls empty and her pussy full.

When I departed, early the next morning, she was smiling sweetly in her sleep. I smiled, too, as I reached for the door-knob, thinking that a session with this nurse was just what the doctor ordered.—*Name and address withheld*

HE PLAYS BALL BY DAY AND BALLS IT UP ALL NIGHT

I am a sophomore football player at a large California university. I was lucky enough to be recruited by dozens of colleges, and visiting six of them was very exciting. There's one visit I'll never forget and that's why I am writing this letter.

My friend, Barry, and I were both recruited by a certain West Coast university. We were greeted at the airport by one of the assistant coaches of the football team. He treated us like kings, and we visited the best restaurants and the wealthiest areas in the city.

On our tour of the town, we saw some of the most sensational ladies that I've ever observed. More than anything, I wanted to get my dick wet. At the end of the day, several other recruits suggested that we go out on the town. Barry and I eagerly agreed, thinking of the beauties we had seen earlier.

Later, while we were standing outside a disco, three dazzling chicks walked by. The one that caught my eye was quite a knock-out. Her skin was almost black, and she had a great pair of legs that she showed plenty of in her miniskirt. My dick got hard while I gazed longingly at her curved ass and a luscious set of melons that were about to pop out of her V-neck sweater.

We rushed into the disco, hot on the trail of these foxes. I went straight to the girl whose great body had caught my eye outside. She told me that her name was Sonya, and that she had graduated from the university a year ago. She was now doing PR work for a professional baseball team. When she found out that I was a football recruit, she was quite impressed. I am only five-foot-ten and one hundred eighty pounds. I told her that I hoped I wasn't too small for college football. Sonya looked down at my bulging crotch and said, "You look big enough to me." When she took out her car keys and looked toward the door, I gave my friends a signal to say that I would meet them back at the dorm.

When we got to Sonya's apartment, we snorted a few lines of snow and immediately undressed. Kissing passionately, we fell upon her water bed, and my hands roamed freely over her splendid body. I had never seen such big tits on such a small frame. Her nipples were the size of half-dollars, and my mouth eagerly welcomed them.

Sonya told me that she was going to take control. She ordered me to lie on my back without moving. After I obeyed, she started to lick my toes and feet. She ran her tongue up the sides of my legs, and turned her dripping cunt toward my face. We were doing a 69, and she was sucking my nine-inch member like it was going out of style. As I was lapping Sonya's cunt like a thirsty puppy, I shot a huge load all over her tits. Come ran down my balls and she licked off every drop.

After a short rest, all I wanted to do was fuck the hell out of her cunt. Within seconds, my dick became hard and swollen. Sonya got on top of it and began pumping slowly and rhythmically. The tempo soon got fast and furious as she started to come. She was moaning with pleasure. Her huge breasts were flopping in every direction. I grabbed both, and hung on for dear life as I shot off what seemed like a quart of hot juice.

After dropping two loads like those, most guys would be pretty drained. But, like most athletes, I have incredible stamina. Being an ass man at heart, I just had to get into Sonya's back door before I would be satisfied.

I found some Vaseline in her bathroom and lubricated her ass and my prick. We got on all fours. I grabbed her perfect, round ass and shoved my cock into it. To my surprise, she took it in to the hilt, and it fit like a glove. I grabbed her huge tits, and we started fucking like two wild animals. Just before I was about to come, Sonya reached around and stuck her finger in my ass. I shot another full load into her rear, and we collapsed on the bed.

This great fucking session helped me make my decision. I enrolled in school the next day, certain that I could score as well off the field as on it. I haven't been disappointed yet.—
Name and address withheld

SAD STORY TURNS SWEET: MARY-ROSE FINALLY GETS SATISFACTION

I first met Mary-Rose ten years ago. At that time, she was a cashier in a fast-food restaurant. Mary-Rose was the most luscious redhead I had ever seen; she reeked of sex. Her melon-size boobs and firm ass belong in a museum of natural wonders. When I first set eyes on her, my raging hard-on made it almost impossible for me to order a burger and fries. Before I could eat, I had to run to the men's room and jack off, dreaming of a more appetizing "fur burger." My sex life at that time was nonexistent, but my sex drive was at its peak. After three or four visits to that restaurant, all with the same result, I finally got up the courage to ask Mary-Rose for a date.

Our date was far from perfect, and, after dropping Mary-

Rose off, I turned once again to my trusty fist. A couple of weeks later, I called her and she asked me to stop by at a house where she was baby-sitting. When I arrived, her younger sister was with her and offered to keep an eye on things while Mary-Rose and I went out to my car for some privacy.

After some heavy petting, I told her how much I craved her crimson pussy. She told me that she never went all the way, but she released my throbbing cock and gave me my first and most memorable blow job. Afterward, she said she'd changed her mind and would let me make love to her, but, for the moment, she had to go back inside so her sister would not become too suspicious.

For two weeks I dreamed of nothing but that blow job and imagined what my first fuck would be like. The anticipation drove me to jack off four or five times a day. The big day finally arrived and Mary-Rose and I went to the house of a friend who had offered his water bed for my use. After a lot of fumbling, due to my inexperience as well as the sloshing of the water bed, we finally got a rhythm going and shifted into a 69 position—another first for me. I loved it and Mary-Rose went wild when I sucked her. Much to my shame, I could not obtain a full erection. My God, there she was right in front of me, begging to be fucked, and me with no rod! In desperation, I forced my semi-erect cock into the tightest, wettest pussy I have ever felt, and immediately shot my wad. I was so disappointed and embarrassed that I didn't call her again, even though she was very encouraging and understanding after my failure.

Over the next eight years, I traveled extensively, married, and continued to beat off to the memory of Mary-Rose, which never failed to give me a rock-hard boner. After a few years, I made several attempts to contact Mary-Rose, but without success. Then, a year ago, when I was at a party with my wife, who should walk up to me but Mary-Rose? My cock became engorged at the sight of her.

For months after that, our paths crossed continually, but nothing ever came of it except for a raging hard-on. Then one day we unexpectedly met at a bar. After talking, we ended up at her apartment and reenacted our first 69. She was again begging me to fuck her love box. This time I did. And on many more occasions as well.

She is still the most luscious nymph I've ever seen and I love to pound into her throbbing cunt as well as her gorgeous ass. What's even better is that she says she comes with nobody as well as she does with me. I hope to continue this relationship with Mary-Rose for many more years.—*Name and address withheld*

FRUSTRATED WIFE TAKES CO-WORKER LOVER MAKES HUBBY JERK OFF

I am a fairly attractive thirty-six-year-old waitress who gets propositioned quite often at work. Being a loyal wife, although not a satisfied one, I have always declined these invitations. However, after fighting with my husband for a week, I was extremely horny. When John, a handsome, twenty-six-year-old co-worker, offered me a ride home late one night, I accepted eagerly. On the way to my house he stopped the car in a deserted area, and we could both feel a sexual charge in the air. He put his arm around me, and I timidly let him fondle my breast. As we kissed, he slipped the zipper of my uniform down and reached inside to undo my bra. I started trembling as he grabbed my naked tits and began passionately sucking them. He ran his tongue all over my breasts, nipples and neck as his hand glided along my nylon-clad thighs. John pushed my skirt over my hips and let his hand slide up to my crotch. My panty hose were soaking wet, and I was embarrassed when the strong smell of my cunt juices started filling the car. I was so hot by this time that I began to hump against his hand. At that point, I think John knew he could do anything he wanted to me.

When he took my hand and guided it to his crotch, I was delighted to find nine inches of rock-hard cock (my husband's is only five inches). He opened his belt and zipper, and pulled his jeans down to his knees. When his shorts followed, I couldn't take my eyes off that super tool—his balls looked like small grapefruits! I nervously wrapped a fist around his giant shaft and jerked it up and down. John moaned his approval, and my hand worked faster and faster. I continued stroking him furiously, until he forced me to stop, saying he would shoot off if I kept doing it for another second. He pulled my legs up on the seat, forcing them wide apart. He leaned forward, finally placing his mouth directly over the large wet spot on my panty hose. As he ate my cunt right through the sheer nylon, I had a wonderful orgasm.

After I came, John pulled my head down to his lap and I took as much of his huge, stiff cock in my mouth as I could. I loved watching him pull and tug on his balls while I sucked him. Taking the hint, I also ran my hand between his legs, squeezing and pinching his love-sacks. Seconds later, he filled my eager mouth with his thick, gooey semen. Since the size of his load matched the size of his organs, I couldn't swallow fast enough, and his come ran down both sides of my mouth.

After resting for a while, John had me play with his cock again, until it stood up like a flagpole. He pulled my panty hose down to my ankles, and I got down on my hands and knees so he could fuck me doggie-style. When I was almost ready to come, he pulled out of my cunt and attacked my rear with his juicy cock. I screamed as he rammed his rod into my asshole, and fingered my cunt while he pumped a hot load deep into my cheeks. After he pulled out, I wet my fingers with his come and stroked my aching clit while I stared at his red, drained prick. After I came in a wave of violent spasms, I cleaned us both up with some Kleenex, and John drove me home. We arranged another date and passionately kissed good night.

I was still horny after I had undressed, so I masturbated in the bathroom while my husband slept. I guess the excitement of John's cock was too much, as I awoke and had to masturbate twice again during the night. After my husband dressed and left for work in the morning, I pulled my nightgown over my hips and stuck the handle of my hairbrush in my ass as I fingered myself silly. After coming, I stared at my swollen pussy and daydreamed about fucking John in a few hours. I was fully satisfied as I felt the warm, wet sheets under my ass that were soaked with my come.

That night, John picked me up after my shift and we drove to our secluded spot. It was another evening of fantastic sex as I eagerly took his meaty tool in every hole of my body. I was totally content after having about five orgasms.

When I returned home, I guess my husband didn't hear me come in. I entered the bedroom and found him lying totally nude, with the covers down around his ankles. His face was covered by the issue of *Penthouse Letters* he had been reading, and his hand was rapidly jerking on his stiff cock. He jumped when he heard me, and I said, "If you soil those sheets, I'll make you lick it up." He was so embarrassed that he was at a total loss for words. I continued scolding him in a harsh voice, and shouted, "So that's what you do while I'm out working myself to death!" I told him to finish himself off, but to do it in the bathroom. He begged me to fuck him, but I told him it was his own hand or nothing. I stood in the bathroom doorway and watched him sit on the toilet and jerk himself off. When he was done, I pretended to still be angry, saying, "Now get to bed, you little sneak." If he only knew.—*Name and address withheld*

KEVIN FUCKS SWEETIE TWO DOZEN TIMES AS RAIN PATTERS ON ROOF

I am a college student from central Illinois and have been dating Kevin for almost one year. We usually fuck seven times a week, but lately our sex life has taken an upward thrust. Last week, for example, our sex life more than tripled. In seven days we fucked twenty-four times. I don't have the time or space to write about the whole week, but I will tell you about one weekend.

It was a rainy evening, perfect for staying in, I thought to myself as I pulled into the drive. Not knowing what to expect, I opened the door with anticipation. Even though we have been going together for almost one year, my desire for Kevin has only increased. As I went inside, all I heard was the rain on the roof and the music on the stereo. I could see that Kevin was well prepared. I walked through the house to the bedroom, where I knew he would be. I stripped off my clothes all the way. Kevin was lying in bed, his beautiful eight and one-half inches throbbing with anticipation of what was to come.

At the sight of this, I could feel my already damp pussy become even wetter. I was ready to fuck right then, but I could see that he had other ideas. He poured me a glass of wine and had me lie on the bed and get comfortable. He started licking my ear and nibbling my neck, his hands dancing lightly over my breasts. He continued his journey downward, licking and nibbling all the way. Then on to my second-favorite thing in this world, being eaten. He ran his tongue up and down my pussy lips and then savagely attacked my clit, licking it up and down and side to side, exciting me to the verge of frenzy.

At this point, I grabbed his shoulders and pulled him upon me. Then I spread my legs and guided him into me. However, I decided to make him wait and asked him to lie on his back so that I could taste his gorgeous cock. I cupped his balls in one hand (a difficult task, since he has such lovely huge ones) and with my other one guided him into my mouth, knowing that as I did so, he would begin moaning with pleasure. Sure enough, I began hearing low moans, telling me I was doing the job right. Then I concentrated on flicking my tongue over his balls and down to his ass, sticking my tongue up his hole and driving him wild. Then I licked my way back up to the head, covering every inch of his cock with my tongue.

Kevin could take no more and abruptly flipped me onto my back, entering me with one hard thrust. As he began pumping furiously, he covered my neck and face with kisses. I wrapped my legs around him, and I could feel myself climbing to the heights of ecstasy that Kevin always brings me to. In two more fierce thrusts he joined me in the climax of a truly beautiful fuck. We lay there for a while catching our breath and pouring wine down our parched throats. We talked and smoked cigarettes. Soon Kevin started kissing me in such a way that I knew he was ready to fuck again, and so it went all weekend. The only time we were in our clothes was for a few hours when some friends dropped in unexpectedly. It had to be the most exciting weekend I have ever had.—*L.L., Jacksonville, Florida*

AH, SUCH WERE THE JOYS: BOY LOSES VIRGINITY

I have read letters in your magazine dealing with all sorts of sex, but rarely is there a narrative on that most memorable of moments: the loss of virginity, male or female. When I was a lad of seventeen in Europe forty years ago, the moral standards were far stricter than those of today. I had many girl-friends, but on only one memorable occasion had I been lucky enough to get further than cupping a breast through layers of fabric. I had my arm around a girl whom I had taken to the movies and was able to insinuate my hand into the rather capacious neckline of her dress. However, I barely managed to get my fingers onto her hard, little nipple before she withdrew my hand.

Most of us were still in school, so anything that cost money was a rarity. Our dates were usually spent in the local woods, necking frantically. The girl and I had been into the woods several times before, and we had reached the stage of my fondling her small but firm breasts. As she had a penchant for high-necked dresses, any attempt to advance in that direction would have been futile.

It was a warm summer evening and I had made a rather poor joke about girls' legs. She pushed me off her and in mock indignation demanded that I check her legs to see "if they aren't the best you've ever seen!" She was wearing a skirt of standard length—a little below the knee—and no stockings. I still am not sure if it was by accident or if she had decided to act the temptress, but when she pulled up her skirt for my appraisal I could see the crotch of her panties. That whiteness contrasting with the tan of her thighs is still crystal-clear in my memory.

I was thrilled at the sight and eased her back onto the grass, smothering her with kisses in hopes of sealing off any protest as I moved my right hand to her thighs. She closed her legs and moved a hand to stop me, but as I touched the fabric and relished the feeling of the stubble beneath, she relaxed her grip on my arm. Soon I felt her moisten and her kisses became more responsive.

At each fresh step along the way she moved as if to stop me, then she would relax and I would take advantage of my position. I slowly worked my fingers around the edge of the panties. Then I pulled at them until I could move the fabric aside to get freer access. Now with my right hand caressing her sexually and my left arm around her shoulders, I was faced with the young seducer's problem. How could I get my pants unfastened? Many kisses later I had freed my arm and moved it down to my fly. The fact that I too was soaking with excitement did nothing to help me free my penis.

I slid across until I was lying on top of her and gradually eased her legs apart with my knees. I was gripping my penis in my hand by this time and when I touched it against her vagina I was far too excited to take things gently anymore. In a frenzy I was in to the hilt and uncontrollably letting fly. The sensation was so exquisite that I could not have made any voluntary move, least of all withdrawn.

Both rather embarrassed, we rearranged our clothes and I took her home. It wasn't until the following evening, when we had reconciled ourselves to the fact that we had gone all the way, that I produced the contraception jelly I had been carrying hopefully for some months. She let me introduce it into her after she had removed her pants, and during the next couple of hours we enjoyed our newfound thrill seven or eight times. These days I don't have that kind of energy anymore, but I have learned a lot of tricks over the years!—*D. T., Toronto, Ont., Canada*

RESPIRATORY THERAPIST CURES HORNY INTERN WITH BLOW JOB AND MORE

I am a medical intern, on call every third night at the hospital. I'd begun to wonder if I would ever find time for sex during this busy year of training. Between my exhausting duties, which sometimes keep me up for thirty-six hours straight, and my need for sleep to recuperate, I'd begun to resign myself to my condition of unrelieved horniness. However, the other night I stumbled upon a way to combine business with pleasure.

Julia, a sandy-haired beauty, is a respiratory therapist at the hospital. She has a figure that will make any man breathe faster. She'd caught my eye long before we first jokingly discussed our fantasies. She had just completed her evening shift when I boldly suggested that she spend the night with me in the interns' call room. If she drove home, I explained, she would encounter dangerous road conditions after a heavy snowstorm that day. She blushed and grinned coyly, not taking me seriously at all.

During the next few days, however, the thought of this forbidden breach of professionalism kept recurring to me, and I began to see just how easily it might be accomplished. Julia and I continued to joke about the possibility until we each realized that the other was serious. It developed into a dare from which neither of us wanted to back down.

I felt a glow of excitement as I went about my duties on the night that Julia had agreed to bring her nightgown and toothbrush to work and to spend the night with me in the call room. I figured out how to escort her from our meeting place in the doctors' lounge to the interns' call room on the fifth floor with the least possibility of being discovered. We met in the doctor's lounge after I had tucked three wards of patients into bed and she had finished her ministrations to a wheezing asthmatic.

Half in disbelief, I walked Julia to her locker to get her nightie and toothbrush. My heart raced as I envisioned her buxom figure clad in a transparent negligee. To my joy, when she opened her locker, I saw a scanty black lace nightie hanging there. Aware that my fantasy would soon become reality, I had to fold my white coat over my green surgical pajamas to hide the growing bulge. In a trance of excitement and daring determination, we hurried through the dimly lit halls to my assigned call room, where I usually manage to get no more than two or three hours of light sleep. We arrived with pounding chests and heaved sighs of relief as we fell into each other's arms.

Julia modestly stepped into the closet to put on her nightie. I surveyed the narrow single bed where on other nights I had masturbated while reading *Penthouse Letters* before falling asleep at three or four in the morning. Next to the bed was the telephone, with its threat of interruption, which heightened my awareness of the present moment and of the sensual pleasures we were about to experience. I moved the bed away from the bare wall, for I knew that another intern slept on the other side.

When Julia emerged from the closet in her revealing nightie, I put my arms around her and led her to the bed, now lit up like a stage by a single lamp. I put her at ease by starting slowly to massage her soft shoulders while I sat astride her barely concealed hips. Lying on her stomach, she felt the hardness of my cock growing against the cheeks of her ass.

She rolled over on her back, trembling with excitement. With a wild look in her eyes, she drew me down next to her. We pressed our bodies together and I began to stroke her ample breasts through the nightie. The lace straps fell easily from her shoulders, exposing her magnificent chest, and I began licking and sucking her small, hard nipples. She deftly untied the drawstring on my surgical pajamas and positioned herself to suck my inflamed member. I stroked her wet pussy and thighs while she moved her mouth up and down my hot rod like a piston.

I was on the verge of an orgasm when she pulled herself away from my throbbing penis and snuggled at my side while we kissed, our tongues darting back and forth between our gaping mouths. I pushed her gently on her back and found her wet love box with my tongue after softly biting her inner thighs. Julia rocked her hips slowly, pressing her moist clit into my mouth while my tongue explored her wetness. I brought her to several shaking orgasms in succession with my educated tongue while she bit her lips and screamed into the pillow to muffle her passionate cries.

Then, when we were lying side by side again, she deftly grasped my penis and guided it to her swollen clitoris and used it to massage herself to a frenzy of excitement. I slid my fingers into her dripping pussy just before she erupted into another orgasm. I felt her vagina contract rhythmically. Unable to hold back any longer, I pushed her on her back and thrust my aching penis into her pulsating tunnel of love. For what seemed like hours of ecstasy, I thrust deep inside her tight vagina as she thrust her hips up to meet me with each stroke. We stiffened and rocked spasmodically as we came together, oblivious to the danger of discovery as we cried out and shook the bed.

Exhausted, we drifted off to sleep, hoping that no one who had overheard the ruckus had been bold enough to investigate the unfamiliar sounds. Several peaceful hours later, the phone rang and I received my first assignment of the day.

Later that morning, when I ran into the intern who is assigned to the room next to mine, I inquired as to how he had slept that night. He replied that he'd had a restful night of more than six hours of much-needed sleep. I only grinned and nodded as if to say "Me, too." If he only knew what a restful evening I had had!—*Name and address withheld*

Meets Her in Store; Fucks Her—And More!

I am a twenty-six-year-old single man who has had a very satisfactory sex life. It was also quite normal and routine until last Monday. I was out doing some shopping in the afternoon, browsing in a store here in Portland, when a vision of loveliness in a red dress appeared. She had long, perfectly shaped legs, firm upthrusting breasts, and brown hair that fell straight to her shoulders. She also had the most sensuous pair of lips I had ever laid eyes on. I also noticed that she was wearing a wedding ring. I was eyeing her magnificent body, which the dress revealed to perfection, trying to decide whether I should approach her in order to strike up a conversation. Then her husband appeared. I felt deeply let down as they went off together and took my hopes with them.

I then decided to get something to drink at the store's cafeteria. After getting a Coke, I was approaching a table when I saw the lovely woman with her husband sitting nearby. I decided to take a seat across from them so that I could at least enjoy looking. She was facing me, and her husband had his back to me. She was sitting with her legs crossed, exposing her marvelous thighs. I had been staring and wondering what it would be like to be between them when I looked up and saw her looking intently at me. She smiled and I smiled back, thinking that at least she knew I was admiring her body. Then she surprised and delighted me very much by reaching under the table and pulling her skirt up higher on her thighs. As she did this, she slowly crossed her legs to the other side, revealing her dark, luxuriant bush. Interpreting this as a definite come-on and feeling very horny, I looked at her and silently mouthed the words "I want you." I then held an imaginary telephone receiver to my ear and pointed to myself and then to her while mouthing "Can I call you?" She said something to her husband, who appeared to be utterly ignorant of what was happening right under his nose. Suddenly, he got up and took her cup to get some more coffee. She took a pencil and paper out of her purse and began to write something. When she had finished, she folded the paper and placed it under the napkin holder while she smiled seductively at me. Then she got up, took her coat and went to tell her husband that she didn't want any more coffee after all. As soon as they left, I went over to see her note. It said that her name was Lynne, and that she wanted to see me that very night at six o'clock. She'd also written down her address.

I knocked on her door precisely at the appointed time. The door opened, and there she stood in a very sheer green negligee that showed her body off well. Her breasts were crowned with the biggest nipples I had ever seen. Before I could say or do anything, she led me inside and unzipped my pants, releasing my throbbing cock. Her tongue and lips surrounded it, and the sensation was unbelievable. She licked and sucked it until I thought I couldn't stand the intensity of the pleasure. I soon had the most explosive orgasm I'd ever had.

We talked for a while, and she played with my cock, trying

to bring it back to life. She told me that her husband worked nights and wouldn't be home until after midnight. We then undressed each other, and I sank my tongue in her deliciously moist pussy. As I was eating her and she was writhing around the living-room floor in ecstasy, I was suddenly aware of a second pair of hands fondling me. I looked around and couldn't believe my eyes. Standing there was Lynne's identical twin! She said, "My name is Sue, but don't let me interrupt you." As I ate Lynne to the point of orgasm, Sue masturbated me with the touch of an expert.

To make a long story short, a lot of that night was spent sucking and fucking and generally having a very merry time. I did have to leave before Lynne's husband came home, however. It seems that these two thirty-year-old identical-twin sexpots do this quite often. They told me that one of them goes out, picks up an unsuspecting stranger and makes a date. Then she calls her sister and the two of them fuck the lucky stranger silly. I'm glad that I was one of their targets.—*Name and address withheld*

Serendipity

They're Caught in the Act by Her Stepfather, and He Loves the Show

I'm twenty years old and the girl I'm dating and very much in love with (I plan to marry her) has just turned eighteen. My most memorable sexual experience happened one night when Lisa's mother was out of town. Only Lisa, her stepfather and I were in the house. He was in his bedroom, and we were in the den, sitting on the sofa with a quilt over us. Lisa and I had been drinking tequila, and we were getting pretty loose. I was kissing her very deeply and playing with her beautiful little tits. Needless to say I got so horny that I had to have my lover's sweet pussy no matter what the consequences.

With her stepfather home, we couldn't head for Lisa's room without a hassle. So we decided to chance being caught in the act (she was also horny). Anyway, we thought that if her stepfather came out of the bedroom, we would hear him.

I put Lisa's legs over my shoulders and raised her ass high enough to pull her blue jeans down over her well-rounded buttocks. I left her jeans on right above her knees. I leaned over to taste the sweetness between her legs. I could spread her legs just far enough to squeeze my head in. I parted her lips and pulled at them, gently tugging with my teeth. Then I plunged my tongue into her hot, sweet cunt, retracting it only long enough to circle her clit and make her legs clamp down on my head.

All the while Lisa was massaging my dick through my jeans with her foot. After about five minutes, she pulled me up and begged me to ball her. She unzipped my pants and pulled them down, as I had done with her. She pushed me back on the sofa and eagerly tongued my balls, taking each one into her mouth and sucking it. Then she circled the head of my cock with her tongue and bobbed up and down furiously. I made her stop before I got off and turned her over on her stomach. She rested her head on the arm of the sofa and her beautiful bum stuck up in the air, exposing that sweet-smelling pussy that was now dripping delicious cunt juice. I mounted her doggie-style and slowly pushed my cock to the bottom of her warmness.

I pumped slowly at first, gradually building up speed while I leaned over to play with her tits. About three or four minutes later I could feel her building up to an orgasm. As I was about to shoot my wad in her, I heard the refrigerator door open in the kitchen, which adjoined the den. I glanced up and saw Lisa's stepfather looking right at us! I came harder than I can ever remember coming. As I shot off, I instinctively pulled my throbbing pecker out, which sprayed come everywhere! Of course, Lisa had started heading for cover, too, and we must have been quite a sight fighting over the quilt. But when I looked back up, her stepfather had gone. He had disappeared just as suddenly as he had appeared, apparently retiring to his room. He has never said a word to either of us about what he saw, but I'm positive he watched us balling our brains out. If he should read this and should realize who is writing it, all I can say is that I hope he enjoyed the experience. I certainly did!—*Name and address withheld*

Mademoiselle Teaches Businessman How to Talk Dirty With Class

I was in Paris last month, attending a business meeting. We do get some work done during the day, but these conferences are notorious for the good times that follow.

The second night of the convention, I was at a cocktail party where I struck up a conversation with a Frenchwoman from a large travel bureau in the south of France. I was immediately fascinated with her. She was in her early forties (forty-four, I later found out), and she had the kind of face that reaches its peak of beauty in middle age—very strong and self-confident. She had bright, gray eyes and thick jet-black hair, evenly streaked with strands of silver-gray, which she wore in a simple pageboy. Her attire consisted of a modest navy-blue dress that came just below the knee, but the movements of her body were graceful, and her walk was athletic. Best of all, she possessed an intelligent warmth that put me at ease. We wound up leaving the cocktail party and spending a thoroughly enjoyable "night on the town"—dinner, some wine, dancing and a walk through the still-romantic streets of Paris. Then she asked me if I'd like to come back to her hotel for more conversation.

By the time we got to her room, we were holding hands and pecking each other on the cheek. Once we were inside, she kissed me deeply, then backed off a few feet and said, "Let's get undressed." I was mesmerized.

As she pulled her dress and slip off, her large, pendulous breasts swayed and settled low on her chest. She had dense masses of black hair under her arms and an abundant growth between her legs. She smiled sweetly when I dropped my pants, revealing my erection.

She sat down on the side of the bed and cradled my head as I licked and kissed her moist pussy. Before she could come, I climbed up on the bed and sat on my haunches. She slid over to me, straddled my hips and slid my cock deep inside her. She leaned back on her hands, and my fingers played with her cunt until she was breathing heavily and breaking into beads of perspiration. When she came I could feel her vagina pulsing and gripping my rigid shaft. She quickly pushed me onto my back and rode my cock with long, slow movements of her hips. I soon came in powerful spurts.

We stayed up the rest of the night. She loved talking about sex. We would sit, face-to-face, and she would take my soft penis in her hand and talk about it and tell me how it made her feel when it was buried between her legs. We would soon be quietly masturbating each other, holding each other off as long as we could. Only when I could feel her lovely body tense and then go limp, would I let myself go, spending my seed all over and in between her fingers.

We finally fell asleep around dawn. But I woke up in a few hours to find this beautiful woman taking my cock in her mouth. I pulled her legs around so that her thighs straddled my ears, and she lowered her sweet pussy to my lips, burying them deep into all that thick come-matted hair. Her expert tongue caressed my prick until I was coming again, filling her mouth.

The rest of the week was heaven. She is the most sensual, loving woman I've ever known. She has an incredible imagination and refuses to quit after only one or two orgasms. She is constantly thinking of ways to excite me long after I thought I was through for the night (or the morning or the afternoon!). She is so comfortable with her sexuality that she enjoys an orgasm like no other woman I've ever fucked. And she is so loving that she derives an incredible amount of satisfaction from giving me pleasure.

She'll be in Denver next month on business, and I can already picture myself nestled between her soft, well-aged tits and plowing her warm cunt with the greatest pleasure.—*J.C., Denver, Colorado*

WAITRESS AND HANDSOME HARRY: A VERY SEXY SEDUCTION

While my husband was hunting deer, I was cleaning the house and accidentally found a copy of *Penthouse Letters*. As I paged through the letters and pictures, I was surprised how explicit things have become. However, I guess I'd rather have my husband curl up with your publication than have someone else offer him solace.

Since I would be alone for a while, I thought I'd share what has happened to me in seventeen years of married life.

About ten years ago, I made a mistake. I was working as a waitress at the Bavarian Inn, in Milwaukee, in order to supplement our income. Two women I worked with always went out for drinks after work. Up to that time, I had always preferred to go home to my husband and children.

I needed a change of routine. Hostile cooks, difficult customers, and a cranky boss had frayed my nerves. When the two women asked me to join them, I agreed. I hadn't eaten all day, and it was a long evening. We planned to get a drink and a sandwich someplace else. We stopped at a small bar in the suburbs. Kathy liked it on account of the higher class of the clientele.

It was very late when we arrived, and they were going to have to heat up the grill. We had a couple of drinks. One is my usual limit. Because I had two drinks this time, and no food, I was feeling light-headed.

Four fellows introduced themselves and sat down with us, and they turned out to be a jolly group.

Harry, an insurance salesman, chatted mostly with me. He must then have been about forty. I was twenty-seven at the time. He was quite different from the men I had seen all day.

Harry ordered us a round of drinks and asked me to dance. It was a bump-and-grind number. Kathy broke away from her partner and pretended to do a strip routine. She created a lot of attention when she actually began to disrobe, cheered on by the rest of our group. The next record was a slow one. Harry and I kept on dancing. He held me close, and we watched Kathy climb onto a table and continue her routine.

The drinks made me relaxed and horny. I planned to wake my husband for sex when I arrived home.

My thoughts and the stirring in my thighs were fueled by the festive atmosphere, the quantity of alcohol, desire for my husband, the handsome man I was dancing with, and an awareness of the pleasure in my loins.

As we danced, I realized he was hard. I could feel his erection against the flat of my belly. I was going to pull away but decided to wait until the end of the record. Sure, I was aroused and flattered that someone with such charm should find me attractive. When the dance ended, he held me for a moment, squeezed my right breast, and whispered, "Thank you." I flushed and told him that he was nice. He then escorted me back to the bar stool.

I sat facing the bar mirror and watching Kathy. My dance partner had his back to the mirror as he watched Kathy and occasionally stole a glance at me. Suddenly I realized his hand, which was previously resting on my knee, was gently stroking me just inside my knee. My skin tingled as I felt the hand move slowly up the inner side of my right leg. I felt hot flashes between my legs and was frozen with sexual tension and fear. He was close to my crotch when I squeezed my legs together to stop his hand. It didn't move; it just stayed there. Harry leaned over and whispered that I should look at Kathy. So I turned around. My legs parted as I pivoted on the stool, and I saw Kathy drop her bra and stand there with just panties on. A loud cheer went up, and I felt Harry extend his hand and cup my mound with his hand.

While everyone was watching Kathy, I could only think about what was happening to me. I looked down and saw Harry's arm between my legs and under my skirt. I looked at him, mouth open, unable to speak. He turned to me and smiled.

Again a loud cheer erupted. We both turned to see Kathy roll her panties down over her thighs, exposing her pubic hair, and step out of them. Then she started to dance again. Harry pushed toward me, his hand between my legs, separating them more. I felt his finger hook my panties, feel the pubic hair, and probe the folds of skin between my legs. I watched his hand under my skirt, and I gasped as he penetrated my vagina.

As I sit here writing, I can still feel his fingers and the excitement. He simply dominated me. Thoughts of my husband and of remaining faithful were overcome by the tension he was creating in me. I had been aroused before by men, but had always been able to control it.

When Harry suggested that we go out to his car, I said we mustn't go anywhere, believing he was going to take me to a motel. He assured me we'd stay and talk, away from the noise and my friends. I left, worried that they might see us leaving together and that I might have trouble explaining it at work, because I was always considered so straitlaced. But everyone was watching Kathy do her striptease.

Harry and I sat in his car, and he stroked my hair while we talked. He asked about my job, my sex life, my married life, and the dates I'd had. Since I was a virgin when I married, the heaviest petting I had ever done before with anyone but my husband was having my breast squeezed as Harry had done on the dance floor. He asked whether I would mind if he did it again. I hesitated and said things could get out of control. Then, instead of reaching for my breast, he unbuttoned my blouse, talking slowly, saying my nonpromiscuous lifestyle made me something special and different from my friends back in the bar.

Once my blouse was unbuttoned, he pushed it away from my chest and over my shoulders, exposing my bra. His hands were warm as he stroked my sides and my midriff. I was nervous and excited and told him he shouldn't touch me because I was afraid he would go further. When he reached behind me and unhooked my bra, I said, "Don't."

"Lift up your bra," he commanded. "Lift your bra up."

I leaned my head back on the headrest and with both hands lifted my bra. As I exposed my breasts, I realized the nipples were taut. I waited for him to touch me. I exposed myself totally, knowing he could see me clearly because of the lights in the parking lot.

Instead of touching me, he bent over and kissed my neck, whispering my name and saying that I was lovely. I felt I was drowning in a flood. I took both of his hands and placed them on my breasts. When he kissed me, I grasped him, seeking out his mouth, kissing him fully and deeply. I felt his hand take mine. I wanted to touch him. Instead, he placed my hands on the hem of my skirt and told me to lift it up. I did.

"Are you wet?" he asked.

"Yes," I told him. "Very wet."

He held me gently while I slid my head down against the door. Again he took my hands and hooked my panties with his thumbs. I arched my back and slid them off. He slipped off my shoes and nylons.

"Open your legs," he ordered. I wanted him, but I was nervous and shy. Still, I spread my legs and said, almost choking, "You can do anything you want to me."

He slid his palms under my thighs and cheeks and lifted them up. I thought he was going to place his mouth on me.

"Take me, all of me," I pleaded.

I was startled when he turned on the map light, exposing me to close inspection. I was so close to orgasm that fluid was running down my thighs. He placed his thumb and forefinger on the top button of my vagina, squeezing it so he could look deep into my cavern. I had never been so hot as I was then. When he inserted his finger into me, I exploded in the most violent orgasm I've ever known. It was so intense, I felt drained and exhausted when it was over. Within me, however, I still felt the need for more.

When he opened the door, the car light went on and I didn't even bother to cover up. I remember him unbuckling his trousers and sliding them down, and I saw his penis protruding between his shirttails. He reached over and pulled me closer to the open door. I offered no resistance or help as I saw him lean over and felt him slide up into me. I was as loose as a goose. Then I felt his weight on top of me: heavy, lighter, heavy, lighter. Then I felt him come hard, deep inside of me. "Oh, I can feel you come," I told him.

After a long while his weight and the car light forced us to adjust our postures and reluctantly get dressed. He kissed me again, and I told him I'd never forget him. I never have.

I slept soundly when I was home that night. I was glad everyone was asleep when I got there. The girls from work thought I'd left because Kathy started removing her garments on the dance floor. I never saw Harry again. I was tempted at times to visit his office. Maybe someday I will. I still think of him when my husband has been gone for a while, and when I masturbate, I relive that special evening.—*M.G., Milwaukee, Wisconsin*

Foxy Lady Phones Special Request to Horny DJ

I work an evening shift at a well-known album rock station in central New York State. Disc jockeys have always been thought to have the wildest sex escapades, but up until one night last week I was a bit skeptical of some of the stories that float around among my fellow DJs.

Of course, those who work the evening shift have an opportunity to spend those late hours keeping lonely, frustrated, and randy females company via radio. I had previously met many chicks, mostly through station promotional appearances, although a few acquaintances have been made through call-in phone conversations. I might add I also have the enviable option of enjoying the company of five excitingly different females at my discretion, individually, for some of the best sex and partying that could ever be imagined.

When a chick calls up and I sense she has more than a Stones request on her mind, I usually continue the conversation, anticipating what might develop. Once in particular a very sexy-sounding female called in for a request, which also happened to be one of my favorites. After a few minutes of small talk, she invited me over after work. Well, I have always turned down those "blind" rendezvous, opting rather to meet first, face-to-face, to avoid any embarrassment on either person's part. I instead invited her down to the station to get acquainted. She said she didn't have a car. I began to suspect something was up. She then laid her cards on the table, telling me she was twenty-five, slim, cute, the wife of an out-of-town businessman, and that she was just lonely for some male company to party with and was not into the bar scene.

I agreed and took down her directions. When my shift was over, I jumped in my car and smoked a couple of bowls on the way up (just in case she wasn't the treat I hoped she'd be), and within minutes I was knocking at her apartment door.

When the door opened, there stood a fox, wearing a sexy nightie and a beaming smile. I was pleasantly surprised, to say the least.

After casual greetings, we went into her living room to relax with a few bowls and some drinks, and we talked for a little while. Feeling quite relaxed, I asked her for a back rub. She obliged and really outdid herself. In the process I stripped down to my jeans.

I insisted that I return the favor, and before I laid one hand on her, her nightie was off, and I had a great look at her in front of me, wearing only a brief pair of panties.

What a body! Nice, pert tits, a slim waist, and a very cute ass; not a hint of fat on her five-foot-seven-inch frame at all. I proceeded to make her comfortable on her tummy, straddling her body and slowly massaging her neck and back and moving on down to her well-rounded ass. I had to laugh to myself, thinking that I must have done something right that day to deserve this.

Slowly I rolled her over and kissed her nipples, which immediately hardened. Her moans were rapid now as I moved my kisses down her belly to her thighs. I peeled her panties off and dived into her wet pussy. I must admit that the following fifteen minutes spent eating her were the best I had to date.

I sensed she agreed. She came maybe seven or eight times. I again began to kiss her all over, and eventually we swapped tongues passionately. My jeans made me feel uncomfortable, so I rose and took them off, with her ready assistance. As soon as my cock was exposed, she took it, fully erect now, and gently began to kiss it, working her tongue all around it, finally deep-throating me. I almost exploded.

Probably sensing this, she lay down in front of the TV, her legs spread wide. She then guided my hot cock to her pussy. As she wrapped her legs around me, I again laughed to myself, hardly able to believe this was really happening. When we both climaxed together, I lay exhausted on her, kissing her neck, and remained in her pussy, never going soft; I was ready for yet another good fuck.

This time I lay on my back and she rode me. I didn't leave her apartment until the morning, having experienced the most uninhibited and thoroughly exciting sexual pleasures of my twenty-three years.

After a few days thinking about it, I decided to write to you. Oh, what about my call-in date? Well, she phones in a request for her and her old man every day, and that voice still gets me hard just thinking about that cold night that turned red hot. Who knows, we may even get together again someday for a repeat performance. I can tell you that she gets all her requests played! I'd be interested if any female disc jockeys have had similar experiences, and would they mind sharing them?—*J.K., Albany, New York*

Long-Legged Blond Mixes It up With Lucky Salesman

I've read many letters that you've published, and one of my experiences is so special that I want to share it. If I didn't know better, I'd swear I dreamed this, because it was surely a dream come true.

It happened in a small town in North Dakota. I was there on a sales trip, staying in a motel. One afternoon, I went down to the lounge and sat at the bar. Since I wasn't paying attention to anything except the beer I was sipping, I barely noticed when someone sat on the stool next to me.

"I haven't watched 'My Three Sons' since I was a little girl," said the new arrival, referring to the show playing on the TV. I looked up and nearly fell off my stool. Sitting next to me was an incredibly beautiful girl. She had long blond hair and a body that was perfect, with large breasts, a small waist and very long legs. I could tell she was tall, but it wasn't until later that I learned she stood five feet ten inches.

I started talking with her and learned that she came from Montreal and was traveling to western Canada. She had a French accent, and I melted as she spoke. I couldn't help but stare at her magnificent breasts, and she must have noticed, because her nipples hardened under the skin-tight sweater that emphasized the shape and size of her bust to the maximum.

During dinner, I learned that she had just left her husband and was planning to return to her career as a model. She explained that she sometimes had difficulty finding modeling jobs because her breasts were so large. I asked if she wanted to come up to my room and smoke a joint after dinner, and she accepted.

As we smoked the Colombian I had rolled, our conversation centered around the effects of marijuana on sex. She explained how the drug increased the intensity of her orgasms, and how she really enjoyed sex after smoking. This sounded as much like an invitation as I've ever heard, so I suggested that we go to bed and enjoy the buzz together. At first, she hesitated, explaining that she was concerned about birth control. I had no rubbers with me, but I wasn't about to let this opportunity slip by. I assured her that I'd be careful not to come inside her, and this put her mind at ease.

I quickly stripped and lay on the bed, while she slowly took off her clothes. She wore no bra, and as she lifted her sweater, I was treated to the sight of the most magnificent breasts I had ever seen. They were shaped like large, firm melons, and their upturned nipples were about the size of a quarter and stood out hard and proud. She slid off her slacks and stood in front of me for a moment, wearing only her panties. She asked if I thought she was attractive enough to resume her modeling career, striking several poses as she spoke. With this sight in front of me, I could hardly speak, but the biggest hard-on of my life gave her my answer. She looked down at it, pulled off her bikini panties, and said, "I want some of that!"

She then joined me on the bed, and the next hour was pure ecstasy. She was able to express her desires like no other woman I've known. She showed me how to suck her nipples and caress her clitoris. Taking my hand, she showed me how to touch her in such a way as to give her the most satisfaction. When we kissed, our tongues wrestled. She tongued my chest and my navel, and licked my cock and balls, bringing me to the brink of orgasm several times. She seemed to sense when I was about to come, and each time she would ease up. She spread apart the lips of her vagina as I flipped her clitoris back and forth with my tongue, which caused her to moan loudly with pleasure. I stuck my tongue into her pussy as far as I could, and she began to writhe wildly on the bed. All of a sudden, she screamed, "I've got to feel it in me! Please, put it in me!"

I mounted her and slid my cock into her as deeply as I could. She let out an ear-piercing squeal of delight. For an instant, I was worried that the people in the next room would hear us.

But then I thought, "What the hell, let the poor bastards suffer." She had several orgasms, announcing each with a loud groan.

Finally, I pulled out of her just seconds before I was about to explode. As I lay back, she moved herself to a position where she was lying between my legs with her head above my crotch. She cupped my balls in her hands and kissed them. Then she inserted them into her mouth one at a time and gently sucked on them. After that, she spent some heavenly moments kissing the sensitive area just below them. I've never felt such overwhelming pleasure.

She then directed her attention to my cock. Sensing my urgency, she took its entire length into her mouth. Then she withdrew it until just the tip was in her mouth, and swirled her tongue around the circumcised knob. Pumping her head up and down, she kept increasing the suction until I finally erupted in her mouth. I've never had a stronger orgasm, or one that lasted as long. She swallowed as much as she could, but my come kept oozing from the corners of her mouth and all over her fingers. When she finally lifted her head, she smiled and then started to lick her fingers clean, and her face reflected the intense joy we had both just experienced.

Apparently, I dozed off for a few minutes, for when I opened my eyes, she was fully dressed and standing by the door. I asked what was wrong. She said that nothing was wrong, and that everything about the evening had been wonderful. She was leaving because she wanted to get an early start in the morning, and she was staying at another motel. With that, she blew me a kiss and left before I could protest. I lay on the bed for a while, trying to determine if it had all been a dream, when there was a knock on the door.

There she stood. She walked past me to the ashtray and picked up my gold-plated roach clip, saying, "I just want something to remember you by." She left without another word.

I was dumbstruck. I had lost my favorite roach clip, but I didn't care. I have stayed at that motel a number of times since then, and have visited the lounge each time. Sometimes, I even sit through a rerun of "My Three Sons," hoping that lightning may strike twice in the same place.—*Name and address withheld*

YOUNG MAN DEMONSTRATES THAT FOUR INCHES SUFFICE

I read every issue of *Penthouse Letters* and find it both interesting and sexually stimulating. It appears that many of the letters you publish deal with generously endowed men. One would almost believe that the less well-hung among us are missing a lot in life. My own cock, when fully erect, stands a brave four inches. I feel that most of these letters about men with gigantic dicks are a crock of shit. The only thing large about any one of these guys is his imagination.

As I stated earlier, four inches is not a hell of a lot. Nevertheless, I often find myself making it with girls equipped with enlarged parking zones, and none of them has ever complained. In my quest for sexual gratification, in fact, I have found the girl of my dreams—an oversexed sixteen-year-old named Cindy.

My affair with Cindy started about a month ago when she came to my house to see my sister, who wasn't home. I noticed her pretty brown eyes glancing more than casually at my crotch. Her long brown hair fell down around her breasts, which were developed well beyond her age. I guess the thing that turned me on most was the innocent look about this desirable young thing.

We sat and talked for about an hour when suddenly, out of the blue, the conversation took an unexpected turn by her saying, "I could satisfy you better than anyone ever has." The next thing I knew she was beside me, lustfully rubbing my crotch and kissing me up and down my stomach and chest. Before I could react, she unzipped my pants and started going down on my cock.

As her luscious tongue and lips gently caressed my penis, it quickly rose to its full four inches. Her gentle suction turned into a rough, rapid tongue and lip action. In moments, my balls exploded and I came all over her face. Losing no time, she undressed herself and me, and her innocent expression turned passionate. As she gently mounted my rock-hard cock, I could feel the warm juices of her cunt drowning my nuts. Her pussy was unbelievably tight! What surprised me was the tremendous number of orgasms she achieved as she rode me for the next two hours. She gave me such pleasure as I had never experienced before.

Cindy's frequent visits have since broadened my sexual horizons, which just goes to prove: "It's not how long your rope is, it's how you dangle your knot."—*Name and address withheld*

Is There Any Better Graduation Exercise?

As a recent graduate of a small, high-powered technical institute in Pasadena, at which the male (mostly nerd) to female (mostly dog) ratio is about ten to one, my list of sexual exploits is not particularly long or exotic. However, one incident, which occurred the night before my commencement, is worthy of your magazine.

Following the graduation dinner that evening, I was talking to some friends when a classmate, Angie, and her friend, Shelly, came over and invited me to share a bottle of champagne with them in Angie's dorm room. Not being one to turn down a good drink—or the possibility of tastier delights—I said I'd join them after I finished my conversation.

By the time I arrived at Angie's room, the two girls had already finished one bottle and were just opening the second. Several nerds had also joined the party; so I dropped into a comfortable chair and slowly drank champagne while we all talked and listened to music. Angie and Shelly repeatedly commented that I wasn't drinking fast enough, which made me wonder if something was up. I decided to test this hypothesis by drinking even more slowly.

Before long, Shelly proclaimed that as an incentive for me to drink more, she would kiss me every time I took a sip. Shelly is a pretty fine-looking lady, especially from the waist up, and I'm sure many guys around campus have fantasized about her; so I decided to take the offer. Several sips and kisses later, one of the nerds announced that he had noticed a correlation between the sip size and the length of the kiss, and he asked what I'd get if I drank a whole glass. Shelly replied that I'd get "a really good kiss." After I downed a full glass, Shelly and I fell back in a long, deep French kiss.

At this point, the action got too hot for the nerds and they all ran off, except for one who hung around, hoping to get in on the action. Shelly kindly gave him a few consolation kisses and sent him on his way. Then she went to find Angie, who had wandered off down the hall.

When they returned, they locked the door. Things started to happen rather quickly as the two girls literally attacked me. One ripped at my shirt while the other fumbled with my pants. Both had undressed with lightning speed. They were nude and my pants were around my ankles before I could suggest that we move from Angie's room to my off-campus apartment, which would be much more private.

We got dressed again and drove to my apartment. As soon as we were inside and the door was shut, the girls stripped and climbed into bed. They made love to each other while I undressed and got drinks. I've got to admit that I was pretty turned on from watching them and from listening to them moan about how much they loved each other. Eventually, I joined them and made it a threesome. It was the first threesome for both me and Angie. Shelly had previously been to bed with two guys at once, so she sort of directed the action.

The girls decided that I should lie back and let them do the work. Angie straddled my throbbing cock and rode us both to orgasm while Shelly worked on my upper body and rubbed her beautiful tits in my face. Later, Shelly lowered her hot, dripping pussy onto my face and I sucked and nibbled her into delirium. Her come flowed down over my face as she screamed her way to a powerful orgasm. While this was going on, Angie was busy sucking on my cock.

As the night progressed, we tried many other positions. I never did get to fuck Shelly, because she had forgotten her diaphragm and did not trust condoms, explaining that she had had a bad experience with them in the past. Nonetheless, it was a fantastic night. The three of us continued our lovemaking until early the next morning, when the girls left to shower and dress for commencement. I fell asleep and didn't wake up until late in the afternoon, well after the ceremony had ended.—*A.F., Pasadena, California*

"UNDERFUCKED" GIRL DOES SOME HEAVY CATCHING UP

Well, I never thought I would be writing you guys a letter. Like most readers, I've had my doubts about some of the letters you publish. However, after last night, I have no more doubts.

Having just moved to the central California coast from San Diego, I was looking forward to starting a new semester. However, I was not looking forward to not knowing anyone. My first class was music appreciation. When I arrived, I was a little surprised to see it so full. In fact, there were only two vacant seats in the class. I sat in one and put my motorcycle helmet in the other. About five minutes later, I heard a voice say, "Is that seat taken?" I looked up and damn near creamed my jeans. Not more than a foot away was a gorgeous blonde with nice, full tits and a body that would more than do justice to your fine magazine. Anyway, Nancy sat down, and we started talking. Conversation went from school to parents, drugs, and the like. When class was over, we both had a free hour, so I suggested a cup of coffee. She agreed, and we started walking over to the dining area. I am nuts about blondes, and Nancy even had blond *eyelashes*! I was going nuts while I was trying to imagine what her pussy looked like.

Maybe I should pause to describe myself. I'm five feet ten inches, weigh one hundred sixty pounds, and have dark brown hair and green eyes. Actually, I'm fairly average-looking. One thing the girls all say, however, is that my eyes are a turn-on, so I guess they are my best feature. I'm saying all this to show that I don't have a huge, muscular body like some of the men I've read of in *Penthouse Letters*.

Nancy and I sat and rapped about everything. When the conversation switched to sex, I found out that she had only had one boyfriend, and when they had finally fucked and Nancy lost her cherry, the dude had dropped her. She impressed me as open and honest, so I asked her what she did when she got horny. She smiled and asked me what I did. 'Nuff said, right? Anyway, Nancy jumped up and said she had to go to class. When she stood up, she knocked a book off the table. I bent down to get it and collided with those luscious tits as I came back up, for Nancy had bent over me. My view afforded me a great look at her tits, and I was happy to see that she made no effort to move. We just laughed, and then she split. As she walked away, I got real horny watching her. The sunlight coming through the doors gave me a great view of her legs through her dress.

Soon classes were over, and I was headed for the parking lot when I noticed Nancy at the pay telephone. I asked her if anything was wrong, and she said her car was fucked up. Being the gallant gentleman that I am, I offered her a lift on my bike, which she accepted. When she got on, her dress crept up to her thighs, and the sight of that gave me an instant hard-on. I caught Nancy looking at it, but she didn't say anything.

When we got to her apartment, she invited me up for a joint

and some lines. While I rolled a joint, Nancy went to the bathroom. When she came I out, we did the coke and lit the joint. Man, was I high! When we finished the joint, Nancy leaned against me and thanked me for the ride. I responded by putting my arm around her and kissing the back of her neck. She quickly turned around and gave me a deep French kiss, while one hand rested on my crotch. I cupped one of her tits with one hand and unzipped her dress with the other. I could feel her nipple harden under my touch. I quickly undressed and led Nancy back to the bedroom. We fell on her bed in an embrace. I kissed and nibbled her tits until they were at full attention. I was a little surprised to see that they remained perfectly upright and firm, with those delicious quarter-size nipples all erect. Nancy was moaning from the workout I was giving her and she begged me to fuck her, but I had a few other ideas in mind, first.

When I was through with her tits, I slowly kissed my way down her flat tummy to her panties. They were soaked, and there was a huge, dark stain on the blue silk. I jokingly said that she didn't get to the head in time. She said between gasps that it had been that way ever since she was on my bike. I kissed and licked the edge of her panties and slowly pulled them off. By now, Nancy was a wildcat. I blew on her pussy, very happy to see soft, blond pussy hair. It was the color of wheat, and was she wet! She said, "My God, are you going to put your *tongue* in there?" I guess her last boyfriend, when he got past the grope sessions, didn't do a whole lot with her besides fucking her that once. I smiled and shot my tongue deep inside, sucking on the lips. Nancy arched her back and screamed with pleasure when I nibbled her clit. She came in waves, and I flipped her over and went to work on her ass, watching that puckered little hole contract as I ran my tongue from her pussy right up her crack. She was almost delirious, having climaxed five or six times. I rolled her back over, and slowly entered her. I'm no John C. Holmes, but my six and one-half inches seemed like enough. One thing, when I'm high, I can fuck forever. For an underfucked chick like Nancy,

I thought, she sure was enjoying herself. After about fifteen minutes, I could tell she was starting to come again, so I began to really pump. Just as I started to shoot, Nancy started bucking and damn near threw me off the bed. Then she grabbed my ass and pulled my cock in even farther, until we were both spent. I lay down on top of her, and we kissed, then fell asleep, my prick still in her.

This morning was even better. Nancy's learning how to give head, and I am one patient teacher! One thing, though. I asked her what it was that had attracted her to me. She said my eyes really turned her on. Thank God for green eyes!—*Name and address withheld*

Sexy Blond's Response Warms the Cockles of Surveyor's Cock

The other day I was going door-to-door with a questionnaire issued by the company I work for. Since my girlfriend had long been out on the West Coast attending college, my mind was on sex. I got hotter and hotter each time a sexy woman invited me into her mid-Manhattan apartment after I requested her participation. Several times I was tempted to make advances, but I kept reminding myself that I had shown my ID card and I'd be risking being reported to the company.

It was near the end of a long, hot afternoon, and I knocked on yet another door, although I didn't know at the time that it would be the final one. I heard footsteps approaching the door, the peephole cover being lifted and the chain lock being removed. I thought it was unusual that the occupant didn't ask who I was, since I'd heard that there had been a lot of crime in that neighborhood recently. The door opened slowly, revealing a tall, sumptuous blonde. At first, only her seductive face showed, but as she looked me up and down a smile slowly came to her face and she drew the door back more. My cock almost popped out of my pants. She was wearing a short, black lace negligee with a plunging neckline. I almost went cross-eyed as I followed it to two huge and beautifully shaped tits. Her skin was snow-white, and the black lace made her look tantalizing. I was so fascinated with her gorgeous breasts that I almost didn't see her black garter belt and black stockings. I was ready to come in my pants when, without a word, she motioned me into her apartment. I gulped, walked in and sat down on the couch.

She locked the door, walked very slowly to the couch and sat down next to me. When she asked how she could help me, I nervously explained that I wanted to interview her. She said warmly, "Go right ahead." I began asking questions, which she answered with a brief yes or no.

After about the tenth question she began to run her hand through my hair very slowly. When I looked over at her, she was licking her lips. I simply had no choice. I put down the clipboard, dropped the pen and put my arms around her. She fell backward, pulling me on top of her. As we French-kissed I ran my hands up under her negligee and kneaded her beautiful breasts. She moaned with pleasure but pushed me off her and began to undress me. As she did, I ran my hands along her long, shapely legs. When I was completely naked, I took off her negligee but left the garter belt and stockings on. (Garter belts have always driven me wild.) We lay on our sides and kissed again as she stroked my throbbing cock and grabbed its head. Then she slid down to it, pushing me onto my back. She began to lick the insides of my thighs with her tongue, slowly working her way up to my balls. She flicked her tongue against one and then the other. Then she sucked one into her mouth, pulling the shaft up against her face. Next, she released my ball and lifted her face up, licking the shaft as she went. I was ready to explode all over her, but she refused to let me come yet. She licked all around the shaft of my dick while her hand played with my balls.

After a few enticing minutes of this, she slid up again and said, "Now you." I knew what she meant, so I slid down to take a look at her beautiful blond bush. I spread her legs and licked my way up her warm thighs as wetly as I could manage. When I got up to her cunt, I spread the lips wide with my thumbs while I cupped her tight ass with my other fingers. I quickly drove my tongue into her. Then I flicked it over her clit until she came in an explosive orgasm. Before she had time to recover I slid up on top of her, driving my aching cock into her wet pussy. She moaned loudly and wrapped her legs around my back, sliding her feet up and down my ass. Minutes later I came in a tremendous rush, and I set off another intense orgasm in her.

We continued to fuck, suck and lick each other merrily throughout the night. I didn't finish my quota of questionnaires that day, but I got the answer I wanted.—*Name and address withheld*

Aquatic Striptease Wins Him Floating Fuck With Wife's Friend

One hot Sunday afternoon I was swimming in my backyard pool while my wife, Amy, was in the house, chatting with her best friend, Denise. After a while I came in. When the women saw me in my tight trunks, Amy took off her shirt, revealing her stunning figure clad only in a bikini that showed most of her tits. I'm a breast man, so in no time at all my trunks showed quite a bulge.

Denise was quite impressed. She remarked, "You must be pretty well hung." Then she said to Amy, "Mind if I check him out?" Since my wife and I have always been proud of my meat, she agreed enthusiastically.

I instantly pulled my suit down under my cock and balls. Denise came over, fondled them and commented, "Mmmm, you've really got nice equipment." Then she went over and whispered softly in Amy's ear.

When she finished, Amy said, "Sure, go right ahead."

Denise then returned to me, put her hands on my chest and said, "Now you just stay right there and I'll be right back." With my cock hard enough to drill through a wall, I waited for Denise. Two minutes later, she came back, clad only in pink bikini underwear. "First," she said, "let's get rid of this bathing suit." Then she pulled my trunks off, blindfolded me and told me her plan: "We're going to go into the pool together, and the object of our game is for you, blindfolded, to remove my underwear. Once you've done that, we're gonna fuck right in the pool! Now how are you going to know where I am? Only one way; I will be holding your cock at all times!"

Then she led me, by the cock, outside in front of the pool. Amy followed, slapping me playfully on the ass, and chortled, "Good luck, stud!"

Denise reached around with her left hand, clutched my balls and said, "Oh, I'm sure he'll do just fine!"

Denise took her left hand off my cock but kept her right one wrapped tightly around it. Then she declared, "At the count of three, we'll jump in. Ready? One, two, three, jump!" The game really wasn't hard at all, and in no time I had stripped her bare. She removed the blindfold, and we grabbed each other and fucked wildly in the pool. It was so good that we easily could have won a pool-sex championship! Best of all, during our little game, these two beautiful dominatrices gave me nothing to fear, only breathless excitement and anticipation. That's what made it all the more fun. When I'm being dominated, I want love and I get it. That's why I love Amy so much. She knows how to lay it on me right, even in sharing me. That's a marriage that shouldn't be changed!—
P.H., Sacramento, California